Instrumentation for
Audiology and Hearing Science

THEORY AND PRACTICE

Instrumentation for Audiology and Hearing Science

THEORY AND PRACTICE

Shlomo Silman, PhD
Presidential Professor of Speech Communication Arts and Sciences
Brooklyn College, City University of New York
Brooklyn, New York
Doctor of Audiology Program, Graduate Center CUNY
Professor of Audiology
Professor of Speech and Hearing Sciences, PhD Program Graduate Center CUNY

Michele B. Emmer, PhD
Chair of the Department of Speech Communication Arts and Sciences
Professor of Speech and Hearing Sciences
Brooklyn College, City University of New York
Brooklyn, New York
Doctor of Audiology Program, Graduate Center CUNY
Professor of Audiology

PLURAL
PUBLISHING
INC.
SAN DIEGO
OXFORD
BRISBANE

MW

FSC
www.fsc.org

MIX

Paper from
responsible sources

FSC® C011935

5521 Ruffin Road
San Diego, CA 92123

e-mail: info@pluralpublishing.com
Web site: http://www.pluralpublishing.com

49 Bath Street
Abingdon, Oxfordshire OX14 1EA
United Kingdom

Typeset in 10.5/13 Palatino by Flanagan's Publishing Services, Inc.
Printed in the United States of America by McNaughton and Gunn

For permission to use material from this text, contact us by
Telephone: (866) 758-7251
Fax: (888) 758-7255
e-mail: permissions@pluralpublishing.com

*Every attempt has been made to contact the copyright holders for material originally printed in
another source. If any have been inadvertently overlooked, the publishers will gladly make the
necessary arrangements at the first opportunity.*

Library of Congress Cataloging-in-Publication Data

Silman, Shlomo.
  Instrumentation for audiology and hearing science : theory and practice / Shlomo Sil-
man and Michele B. Emmer.
      p. ; cm.
  Includes bibliographical references and index.
  ISBN-13: 978-1-59756-381-9 (alk. paper)
  ISBN-10: 1-59756-381-1 (alk. paper)
  1. Audiology—Instruments. I. Emmer, Michele B., 1951– II. Title.
  [DNLM: 1. Audiology—instrumentation. 2. Hearing Tests—instrumentation. WV 26]
  RF298.S55 2011
  617.8—dc23
                                                    2011024447

⌀/8/12

Contents

Foreword

This is a unique book. It fills a deep void in the audiologic literature for three reasons. First, it lays the foundation for our understanding of the physical principles underlying the auditory periphery as a complex of mechanical vibrating systems. Second, it lays the foundation for our understanding of the electric and electronic principles underlying much of audiologic instrumentation. Third, it shows us how these principles relate to the devices we all use in our day-to-day research and clinical activities. Authors Shlomo Silman and Michele B. Emmer have produced a volume that instructors can use to provide a much-needed basic understanding of the physical and electronic principles without which an understanding of current and future advances in diagnostic instrumentation and amplification cannot be fully grasped.

The approach is purposely gradual. The reader is allowed to ease into basic physical principles in a somewhat breezy, whimsical, and friendly manner. The first 5 chapters consider, in turn: (1) General Physics and Sound Energy; (2) Mechanical Impedance and Admittance; (3) Electrical Energy—Direct Current; (4) Electrical Energy—Alternating Current; and (5) Electrical Immittance, Filtering, and Power Reflectance. As these principles are mastered, the level of sophistication is slowly but firmly advanced. By the fifth chapter the reader will have overcome any initial apprehension and will be prepared to handle advanced concepts with relative ease.

Why is this basic scientific knowledge important to our profession? For three very important reasons. First and foremost, the peripheral auditory system is a complex mechanical vibrating system subject to all of the scientific principles governing such systems. If you are going to work with such a system it is best to understand how and why it works in the way that it does. Second, it is important that you know what you are actually measuring and why that is important to clinical evaluation. Third, virtually all test instrumentation is, in some way, powered by electricity, its action based on electronic principles. The design, calibration, and maintenance of such equipment requires a thorough understanding of the principles underlying the operation of such devices.

Chapters 6 through 10 are concerned with the application of these basic principles of physics and electronics in the design and operation of the many electronic devices used in the practice of audiology. Chapter 6 considers building communication systems; Chapter 7, devices to measure acoustic impedance and admittance; Chapter 8, digital technology and signal processing; Chapter 9, test equipment; and Chapter 10, calibration. These chapters relate to the use of almost every form of audiologic instrumentation. They are basic to an understanding of how such systems operate, how to combine components to produce new and unique systems, and how to ensure that they are operating in calibrated fashion. These considerations apply to virtually every active audiologist and hearing scientist.

Anyone engaged in audiologic research will find the entire book, but especially the last five chapters, particularly relevant to their needs. In the pursuit of new knowledge it is often necessary to create new instrumentation that moves beyond what is commercially available. Consider, for example, multifrequency tympanometry. During the early years of acoustic impedance/immittance testing in the clinic, tympanometry testing with commercially available equipment was almost entirely limited to 226 Hz. The value of testing at higher frequencies had to be demonstrated by research, principally on newborn babies. This required designing and calibrating ad hoc instrumentation for the problem at hand. And that required intimate knowledge of virtually all of the topics covered in this book.

Another example is the many clinical applications of otoacoustic emissions. Immediately after the first demonstration that such emissions could be recorded from the human ear, there was no commercially available instrumentation to measure them. It was only after a number of investigators assembled, from scratch, instrumentation to make such measurements and used them to gather data that the value of the results motivated the development of the excellent commercial devices we enjoy today.

Other examples include the delineation of acoustic reflex morphology, the binaural interaction component of the auditory evoked response, real-ear measurement of hearing aid response, dichotic tests of every stripe, and auditory event–related potentials evoked by human speech.

The lesson of history is that audiology cannot always rely on commercially available electronic equipment for progress. Those in a position to advance the profession by research must be in a position to design and fabricate test equipment not yet commercially available. That is why the material covered in this book is so important to all researchers, but especially newcomers to the field. It is a crucial part of the knowledge base of the profession, a set of basic principles underlying future progress.

This book is not only a boon to students but a valuable resource for instructors, hearing scientists, audiologic researchers, and clinicians. I heartily commend it to all groups.

James Jerger, PhD
Researcher

Reviewers

Mark Chertoff, PhD
Department of Hearing and Speech
University of Kansas Medical Center

L. Clarke Cox, PhD
Chief of Audiology, Boston Medical
   Center
Professor of Otolaryngology
Boston University School of Medicine

Helen Salus, PhD, AuD
Adjunct Assistant Professor,
   Communication Sciences
AuD, Hunter College CUNY

Brenda Lonsbury-Martin
Professor, Department of Otolaryngology
   —Head and Neck Surgery

Loma Linda University Medical Center
Senior Research Scientist, Research
   Service
VA Loma Linda Healthcare System
Loma Linda, California

Glen Martin, PhD
Senior Research Career Scientist
Loma Linda Healthcare System
Loma Linda, California

Aaron Roger Thornton
Professor of Hearing Science
Department of Clinical Neuroscience
University of Southampton, United
   Kingdom

Introduction

The theoretical principles underlying instrumentation in audiology and hearing sciences and their calibration and operation represent the foundations of the fields of audiology and hearing sciences. We believe that comprehensive understanding and knowledge of this instrumentation is central to the development of new technologies to overcome the limitations of current diagnostic, rehabilitative, and investigational research techniques; it also represents a significant influence on the respect held by professionals, clinicians, and scholars and educators in other fields for audiologists and hearing scientists. We also hold that knowledge and understanding of audiologic and hearing sciences instrumentation both facilitate and expand knowledge and understanding of the applications of this instrumentation.

Informed by our teaching, research, and clinical experiences, we attempted to introduce basic concepts and applications to readers who may have little formal training in mathematics, physics, electronics, computers, or engineering. We have not eliminated the mathematics, physics, or electronics underpinnings. Rather, we have attempted to provide explanations slowly and carefully in a manner that includes only the necessary formulae and basic scientific principles so that students and clinicians can appropriately use the instrumentation and make sound interpretations. Toward this goal, the text includes numerous illustrations and examples; an appendix that presents work done by past and current students that outlines pur-

pose, set-up, and use of instrumentation for calibration; and a companion DVD that concretely illustrates many of the basic concepts introduced in the text and procedures for instrumentation set-up and calibration. Because the research tools used by hearing scientists largely involve the same instrumentation used by audiologists for clinical and research purposes, we feel that this text could serve as a basic instrumentation text not only for AuD and PhD students, but also for hearing scientists and audiologists. Instructors of doctoral students in hearing sciences may also wish to supplement this text with materials on some other psychoacoustic instruments, such as the Coulbourn system. We intend for this text to serve as a basic reference for clinicians, educators, and researchers in audiology and hearing sciences, as well as a tool for understanding material presented in more advanced instrumentation texts. It also can function as a supplementary text for doctoral courses in amplification.

We have structured the text so that we present the basic concepts of general physics in Chapter 1, as these principles provide the foundations for understanding subsequent concepts in the other chapters. In Chapter 2, we address the fundamentals of mechanical impedance and admittance, thereby laying the groundwork for the discussion of basic electronics, including direct current (DC) and alternating current (AC) electrical energy in Chapters 3 and 4, respectively. In Chapter 5, building on the knowledge gained in Chapter 4, we present the basic elements of filtering in audiologic and hearing sciences instrumentation. Chapter 6 is concerned with the building of communication systems, and we describe microphones, amplifiers, and speakers, and their use in such systems. The first 5 chapters provide the basis for the discussion of the concepts and principles of acoustic admittance and power reflectance (wide-band admittance) in Chapter 7. We explain and describe the concepts of signal processing, digital technology, and fast Fourier transformation (FFT) in Chapter 8. The material in Chapter 8 serves as the underpinning for the presentation of the principles and function of instrumentation (e.g., audiometers, acoustic immittance devices, otoacoustic emissions devices, and auditory evoked potentials devices) in Chapter 9. In Chapter 9, we also describe and discuss the stimuli used in audiologic and hearing sciences instrumentation (e.g., pure tones, clicks, narrow-band and white noises, tone bursts). Chapter 10 addresses calibration of audiologic and hearing sciences instrumentation and the equipment for calibration (e.g., sound-level meter, 2-cc and 6-cc coupler, artificial mastoid, oscilloscope, real-time analyzer), and we discuss the related calibration standards of the American National Standards Institute (ANSI). We conclude with two appendixes: Appendix A includes selected student work on calibration and Appendix B explains digital circuitry. In order to maximize accuracy, breadth, and depth of materials presented, we submitted the chapters to a panel of nationally and internationally renowned scientists in the fields of audiology and hearing science for their review. We incorporated their constructive feedback and wish to thank them for their time, effort, and ideas.

We welcome feedback from our readers, which will inform us regarding the strengths of our text and guide us to areas where improvements and clarification may be needed.

Acknowledgments

SHLOMO SILMAN

There have been a myriad number of individuals who contributed to my professional career throughout the years. Please forgive me if I inadvertently omit someone. To my dear professor and mentor, Dr. Maurice Miller, who has continuously provided inspiration and support and who cochaired my PhD dissertation on middle-ear muscle reflexes with the distinguished Dr. Gerald Popelka. To Dr. Roy Sullivan, who instilled in me a great love of science and to this day continues to provide encouragement. To my friend and colleague Dr. Stanley Gelfand, who invited me to join the staff of the East Orange VA Medical Center and shared in a great part of my research career. To Dr. John Lutolf, whose smile lighted my days at the East Orange Medical Center. To my friend and colleague Dr. Barbara Weinstein, Executive Officer of the AuD Program—City University of New York, who shares great ideas with me. To Dr. Timothy Gura, who, as Chair, was instrumental in supporting me as Presidential Professor. To my good friend and colleague, Dr. Gail Gurland, who has been supportive of me since I first came to Brooklyn College. To my friends and colleagues in the Department of Speech Communication Arts and Sciences: Rochelle Cherry, Adrienne Rubinstein, Michael Bergen, Susan Bohne, and Lucille Nielson-Rosander. Last but not least, to Dr. Michele Emmer, my special friend and coinventor who has provided support and encouragement for many years, and who joined me in numerous research projects that have been successful, in large part, because of her intelligence and dedication.

MICHELE B. EMMER

It is a daunting task to acknowledge all who have brought me to this point in my professional career, so I offer my sincere apologies in advance to those whom I may forget. My former professors at Brooklyn College must be recognized as my first professional role models. I have the utmost respect for those who taught me so well. So many of us who were students in the Department of Communication Arts and Sciences have returned to its collegial atmosphere to teach and supervise, and have the honor of calling former professors "colleagues." Surely this is a testament to the caliber of the program and the respect with which we treat one another.

To Gail Gurland, whom I hold in highest regard, thank you for providing a paradigm of intellect, professional demeanor, and skill in the classroom. To Adrienne Rubinstein and Rochelle Cherry, thank you for the knowledge you have imparted. To Tim Gura, thank you for your exquisite mentoring, support, and humor as I continue to learn the ropes as Chair. To my colleagues: Beryl Adler, Isabelle Barriere, Michael Bergen (thank you for your composure, proficiency, and efficiency), dear Oliver Bloodstein, Roberta Chapey, Annsonia Garrick (administrative assistant extraordinaire), Susan Bohne, Baila Epstein, Tanni Haas, Susan Longtin,

Shuming Lu, John Lutolf, Klara Marton, Lucille Nielson-Rosander, Natalie Schaeffer, Cyndi Stein-Rubin (thank you for your kindness and friendship), Jason Thompson, and Barbara Weinstein, thank you for your continued support. To Carol Silverman, a member of my dissertation committee and someone I admire so greatly, you are my mentor and friend. And to Harry Levitt, who passed along so much knowledge, and was also a vital part of my dissertation committee.

Finally, and especially, to Shlomo Silman, who is a superlative professor, mentor, scientist, clinician, and friend.

JOINT ACKNOWLEDGMENTS

To our students who have provided us with endless inspiration — this text is for you! To our esteemed reviewers, we thank you for your indispensable comments and encouraging words. To Chinmay Nerurkar, in particular, for his intelligent suggestions, valuable comments, and continuous support. To Bradley Custer, for his important input. To Simon Henin, PhD student at the Graduate Center CUNY, who took time away from his studies to provide us with a state-of-the-art calibration of otoacoustic emissions. To Angelo Restivo, who was always ready and willing to help, in person and over the phone, we thank you. To Chuck Comitto, thank you for your help over many years. To Carlos Cruz, Brooklyn College, CUNY Library, for his skilled and amiable assistance. To Michelle Mozes, an amazing artist, and David Rozenblyum, an exceptional photographer and videographer, we thank you both! And finally, our sincere thanks to Delmar Cengage Learning, for transferring their copyright.

I dedicate this book to Dr. Carol Silverman, who has taken me under her wing and given me her love, care, and inspiration for many years during my professional career. I also dedicate this book to my son, Benny, his wife Cara, and little Lilah; to my sons Minash and Avi; and to Dr. Jerome and Dorothy Silverman and Dr. Alan Silverman, who embraced me within their family.

Shlomo Silman

This book is dedicated to my beloved family—my dear husband, Michael, who has always been my tower of strength; my adored children, Keith, Nolan, and Lisa, and Vincent (Zev) and Ashley; my cherished grandchildren, Brianna Rose, Katherine Maya, and Jacob Wyatt; and my parents, Sally and William Resnick, who still walk beside me. Everything is possible with your love and support.

Michele B. Emmer

1

General Physics and Introduction to Sound Energy

Figure 1–1. *Sir Isaac Newton.*

Dancing, singing, reading, crying, pushing, laughing, smiling, pushing, carrying. . . . For all, we need a fundamental element without which we cannot participate in these activities. What is this element? If you said "force" then you are correct. Force is the fundamental element that keeps us on the move. As we will see later, we also need force to generate sound, the basis of our profession. The unit of force is newton N named after Sir Isaac Newton (1642–1727) pictured in Figure 1–1.

If we move an object from one place to another, we have accomplished work. If for some reason the force was not great enough to move the object, it means that we did *not* do work, no matter how sweaty we became or how much force we actually used.

When you move a block from one place to another, you're doing work.

Mathematically, Force × Distance = Work. Therefore, $W = F \times D$. When a force of 1 newton moves an object a distance of 1 meter, the work is equal to $1 \, N/M$ equivalent to 1 joule. 1 joule = Force × Distance. There is no limit to the amount of work that we can do or the amount of energy that we can expend.

Adam and Eve are pushing blocks of equal weight from start to finish. In Figure 1–2 we see that Adam pushes his block from start to finish in 3 minutes using a force of 50 newtons while Eve, using the same force, pushes her block from start to finish in just 1 minute. Who is more powerful? If you said Eve, you are correct. Because it took Eve only 1 minute versus 3 minutes for Adam, we can state that Eve is more powerful than Adam. Power = Work/Time or Energy/Time. The unit of Power is the watt. 1 watt = 1 joule/second. Joule, the unit of work, is also the unit of energy. We can therefore state that work and energy are interchangeable.

Another example of work is that done by a weightlifter trying his best to lift a dumbbell as in Figure 1–3. He uses a force as great as 160 newtons and yet he is unable to lift the weight. Therefore, even with all his strength, he didn't do any work. His muscles, however, are working by contracting and stretching.

As mentioned above, theoretically, there is no limit to work or energy. For example, a space shuttle's power at takeoff (Figure 1–4) is billions of watts or billions of joules of energy converted from potential chemical energy to kinetic energy and heat energy each second.

Baby Jacob is busy pushing a ball (Figure 1–5). He's doing work. He pushes the ball along a path. The ball is very light, weighing only a few grams. Jacob

Figure 1–2. *Adam and Eve pushing blocks of equal weight.*

Figure 1–3. *Weightlifter.*

1,000 Dynes

100 cm

Figure 1–5. *Baby Jacob.*

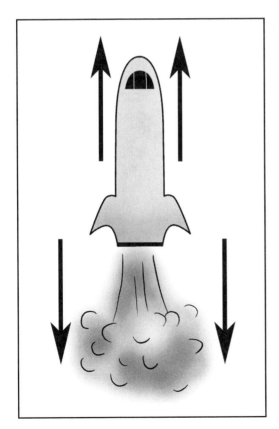

Figure 1–4. *Rocket.*

is struggling very hard but has succeeded in moving the ball only 100 cm. With the force Jacob is applying, and the distance he's pushing the ball, we no longer can use newton as the unit of force, but only a fraction of the newton, a dyne (1 newton of force = 100,000 dynes). In addition, he's moving the ball in cm, rather than meters. With his baby strength he was able to use 1000 dynes of force. This baby worked hard and used energy to do the work. 1000 dynes × 100 cm = 100,000 dynes/cm or 100,000 ergs. 1 dyne/cm of work or energy = 1 erg. The baby's power, therefore, is 100,000 ergs/100 seconds = 1000 ergs/sec.

We have been using the terms newton and force. It appears from the above discussion that force forms the core of all physical activity and the basis of Newton's three laws. Although Newton's Laws are studied in basic science courses in high school and college, they are worth reviewing. As you will see in several sections of this text, Newton's Laws relate in one way or another to our study of Audiology.

Newton's First Law states that every object continues in a state of rest or in uniform motion in a straight line unless a force disturbs the object. To illustrate this law, let us borrow from a well-known experiment. We have a cup covered by cardboard. A quarter lies on the cardboard (Figure 1–6). Pull the cardboard and the quarter will fall into the cup rather than following the cardboard. The quarter has preserved its inertia resisting a change in its position.

Why do we jerk forward in a car that has suddenly stopped moving? Again, the body is resisting a change in its position. In this case, we were already moving and therefore continued our motion. If you didn't have the good sense to wear a seatbelt, you continued through the windshield and then to a hospital (Figure 1–7). Inertia is the property that resists a change in position.

Figure 1–6. *Quarter on cardboard.*

Figure 1–7. *The unfortunate driver.*

Newton's Second Law describes the relationship among force, mass, and acceleration. We need a force to push a mass from its resting position. When the mass moves from its point of equilibrium (resting position) it accelerates. A force causes this acceleration. When a force accelerates a mass, friction between the mass and the ground reduces the net force. Friction is not restricted to a hard solid material pushed by a force against another solid material. In fact, friction exists in liquid and gas as well. For example, water molecules can collide with water molecules and air molecules can collide with air molecules thereby creating friction. In physics, fluid refers to both liquid and gas because both flow. The force of friction is always opposite that of the moving body, that is, resisting a motion, and can be expressed as $F_f = \mu N$ where μ is the static or kinetic coefficient of friction for a given set of materials, N is the normal force or (usually) weight pressing one object into another, F is force, and f is frictional force.

As we are dealing with mass in this section, we should note that there often is confusion regarding the concepts of mass and weight. Mass is a measurement of the amount of matter in an object and is usually quantified in *kg* on a balance scale (Figure 1–8A). We place weights in kg on one side of the scale and the matter to be quantified on the other. At this point the quantity of the matter is unknown. We add and subtract the unit of measurement, that is, the kg, until balance is achieved. The quantification in kg that achieved the balance is the quantification of the matter being measured. In another example, when we already know the quantity we want, for example, if you wish to purchase 5 kg of sugar, a 5-kg weight will be placed on one side of the balance, and sugar on the other. We add/subtract sugar until the scale is balanced. Such quantification does not change with height or location because the gravitational pull will work equally on both sides of the scale when the scale is balanced.

Weight is the measurement of the gravitational force that pulls a mass toward earth. For example, when we stand on a scale we are pulled to earth by the force of gravity (Figure 1–8B) and our weight is measured in pounds.

It is not correct to say that mass has no weight when it is measured on a scale. When a balance scale is unequal, gravity will act on both sides proportional to the

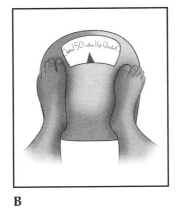

A   B   C

Figure 1–8. **A.** *Balance scale.* **B.** *Standard scale.* **C.** *Unequal balance.*

size of the mass (Figure 1–8C). One side will have more weight than the other.

Although mass will not change with height or location, weight *is* impacted by height or location. For example, Mrs. Thomas weighs 160 lb in California (Figure 1–9A). She takes a trip to the moon. Much to her delight, her weight is now 25.6 lb (Figure 1–9B). What a diet! Mrs. Thomas continued on her travels with a stop at Jupiter. To her horror she weighs 374.4 lb on Jupiter (Figure 1–9C). These weight discrepancies are because the force of gravity is different at each location. For example, on the moon, the gravitational force is 0.16 times earth's gravity. By contrast, Jupiter's gravity is 2.34 times the gravity on earth.

Newton's Third Law is also called the law of action and reaction. When an object *A* exerts a force on object *B*, the second object exerts the same force against object *A*. Let's consider the example of a car moving along a road (Figure 1–10). What is the actual force moving the car forward? Is it the road or the tires? Believe it or not, the road itself pushes the car.

The road exerts a horizontal force on the car. The tires push back on the road (the action) while the road provides the reaction by pushing the tires forward with an equal force!

Another example of action and reaction is as follows: A man is driving his car along the road when suddenly a bee hits the car's windshield. The bee is flattened against the windshield (Figure 1–11). Is it possible that the action of the car is actually equal to the action of the bee? In other words, is the force of the car (the action) equal to the force of the bee (reaction)? According to Newton's Third Law, the forces are equal. This doesn't seem possible. There must be something wrong with Newton's Third Law. Remember that Force = Mass × Acceleration. In this case, the car was unaffected by the motion of the bee. The car's acceleration decreased only minimally because the mass of the car is so much greater than the mass of the bee. But the deceleration of the bee was so extreme that it flattened. So, mathematically speaking, mass of the car × slight deceleration = mass of the poor bee

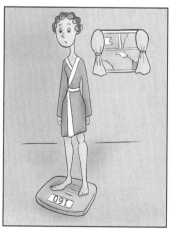

A. EARTH: 160 LBS   B. MOON: 25.6 LBS   C. JUPITER: 374.4 LBS

Figure 1–9. A, B, C. We see Mrs. Thomas weighing herself on earth, the moon, and Jupiter, respectively.

Figure 1–10. *Action/reaction.*

Figure 1–11. *Bee meets windshield.*

× colossal deceleration. So, according to Newton's Third Law, there is equal action and reaction.

We can find energy in myriad forms, such as sound, light, heat, motion, solar energy, atomic energy, and so forth. There are two main classes of energy: kinetic and potential. Kinetic energy is also known as the energy of motion, for example, moving cars, flying airplanes, and so forth. Radiant energy is an example of kinetic energy. Among the best known examples of radiant energy are visible light and the gamma ray generated by controlled or uncontrolled (such as the disaster in Chernobyl) nuclear explosion or by radiated atoms used in medicine to destroy cancer cells. Forms of radiant energy can be generated from radioactive material found in space. Solar energy, heat, and light are also radiant energy. Sound is an example of kinetic energy. Sound results from a force causing an object to vibrate. The sound energy is carried by molecules of air to an ear for which it is in an audible range of hearing. Otherwise, the pressure waves will be dissipated in the air as heat.

Potential energy is the energy of storage and is not used in motion. It can, however, be released as kinetic energy. An example is a compressed string or stretched rubber band. Another example of potential energy is gravitational energy. This kind of energy is stored in some object because of its vertical position in relation to the earth. A popular example is that of a rock sitting at the edge of a cliff. While stationary, the rock has potential energy. Once the rock falls off the edge of the cliff it has kinetic energy. The higher the elevation of the object, the stronger its potential energy, that is, the gravitational pull. Compressed gas also has potential, or stored, energy. Gas expands or compresses like a spring. Recall the story about Galileo who sought to disprove Aristotle's falling body hypothesis. As the story goes, Galileo dropped objects of differing weights from the Leaning Tower of Pisa (Figure 1–12). He compared the pattern of their falls. In contrast to Aristotle's theory, Galileo showed that a 10-pound stone did not fall any faster than a 1-pound stone, except for the small effect of frictional forces exerted by air molecules. He found that objects of various weights, when dropped at the same time from some height, fell together and hit the ground simultaneously.

Lightning is a result of the growing difference in electrical charges between the ground and the atmosphere. Electric potential increases between the ground and the atmosphere, that is, the negative charge on earth, and the positive charge in the atmosphere. When this potential difference grows beyond a certain threshold, the electrical resistance of the air breaks down and the electrons on earth will break away toward the positively charged atmosphere

Figure 1–12. Galileo atop the Leaning Tower of Pisa.

through the conducting medium of air. This lightning represents the movement of electrons from earth to sky and the flow of conventional electric current from the sky to earth through air (Figure 1–13).

The law of conservation of energy states that energy cannot be created or destroyed beyond what is already in a system but may be transferred from one place to another or changed from one form to another. For example, the atoms that form matter contain a large amount of energy. When the physical structure of the atoms is changed, their energy can be released in different forms. For example, sunrays, which reach earth as radiant energy, result from a disruption of atoms (Figure 1–14).

Although sound energy is only one type of energy, it is essential to our profession. Thus, we discuss sound throughout

Figure 1–13. *Lightning.*

Figure 1–14. *Radiant energy.*

this text. Sound energy is found in nature: when birds sing, wind rushes through the trees, thunder rumbles, waves crash against the rocks, and so forth. Sound can be made by humans and by animals: laughing, crying, talking, clapping hands, barking, meowing, sneezing, playing musical instruments, and so forth. Sound can also be generated through a variety of electronic techniques, as you will see in subsequent chapters.

We saw in previous sections that the efficiency of energy is determined by its power. We now discuss the power of sound and how it is generated. Power is defined as the rate of mechanical energy converted to sound energy, that is, energy/time. Power energy radiates equally in all directions from its primary source. Its geometric shape is spherical which means that all points that are equidistant from the source have equal power. The strength of a sound that a normal-hearing person can perceive depends on the ratio of the sound source to the total surface area of the sphere. This means that sound intensity = sound power/$4\pi r^2$, or the surface area of a sphere where r = distance from the source, that is, the radius, between the source and any point on a sphere. According to this formula, known as the inverse square law, as we double distance from a source, sound energy is reduced by a factor of four (Figure 1–15).

Let's consider a mathematical example of the inverse square law using the formula $4\pi r^2$. Suppose we have a point source generating a signal of 50 dB IL. Beginning

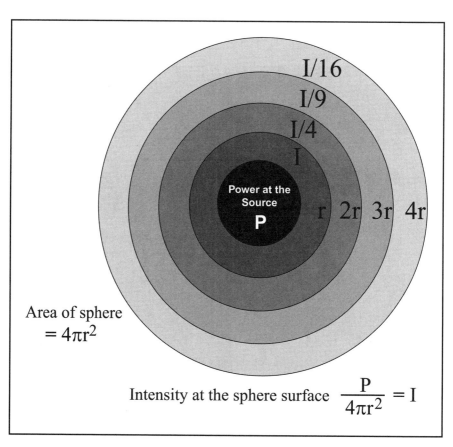

Figure 1–15. Inverse square law for sound.

at an arbitrary distance of 2 feet from the source of the sound, the area that is covered by 50 dB IL is calculated using the formula above. Thus, using 2 feet as our initial radius and $4\pi r^2$ to calculate the area of the sphere to be covered, we see that $4 \times (2)^2 = 16\pi$. Let's double our distance from the point source. We're now 4 feet away from the source. The initial intensity remains constant according to the Law of Conservation of Energy (energy cannot be created or destroyed beyond what is already in the system). Using 4 feet as our radius and $4\pi r^2$ to calculate our new area, we see that:

$4 \times (4)^2 = 64\pi$. The same amount of energy, 50 dB IL, must cover an area 4 times greater now that we have doubled our distance from the source. That is, according to the formula for the area of a sphere, the amount of energy per unit area decreases by a factor of 4. It's important to realize that the total energy of our new area of 64π will equal 50 dB IL just as it did when the total area was 16π. The actual reduction in terms of dB lost with each doubling is 6 dB. This number holds true for both IL and SPL.

Sound intensity from a sound source will obey the Inverse Square Law only if the path of the sound is unimpeded, that is, there are no barriers. We should note that the Inverse Square Law applies equally to light, gravity, an electric field, and radiation.

The most intense sound that is audible to a normal-hearing human before damage occurs is 100 trillion times greater than the softest sound a human can hear. Imagine telling your patient (Figure 1–16) that his hearing status is 17 trillion times greater than the softest sound a normal-hearing person can barely perceive, or describing the intensity of the music from his iPod as 16 trillion times greater than the softest sound he can hear! If we put the most intense sound in context, we see that little Jacob in Figure 1–5 is actually using much more force to move the ball than the force needed to reach a sound 100 trillion times greater than the softest sound the human can hear. Jacob is powerful!

Obviously, these numbers are meaningless as well as incomprehensible. We must find a way to compress the huge numbers into small and meaningful values that are straightforward and unambiguous. Let's play with some mathematical concepts. In the previous section we described power as related to physics. Now, we discuss power as related to mathematics, specifically, scientific notation. First, we construct a scale using scientific notation. We need a base to express power in scientific notation. Base 10 is the most commonly used, particularly when dealing with huge values. For example, the number 100 converted to scientific notation using base 10 is 10^2. Listing some other conversions we see that:

$1000 = 10^3$

$10,000 = 10^4$

$100,000 = 10^5$

$1,000,000 = 10^6$ and so forth

When we multiply power by power, we add. For example, $10^6 \times 10^3 = 10^9$ and $10^{12} \times 10^2 = 10^{14}$. The previous example used only positive values. What if we have an example using negative power? To multiply negative powers, we still add. For example, $10^{-6} \times 10^{-2} = 10^{-8}$, according to the mathematical law governing multiplication using negative numbers.

When we divide power by power, we subtract. Specifically, we subtract the

Figure 1–16. *Audiologist delivering results of a hearing test.*

value in power in the denominator from the power value in the numerator. For example, $10^{12}/10^2 = 10^{10}$. Of course, it becomes tricky when the denominator is larger than the numerator. For example, $10^4/10^8$ will yield a negative value, that is, 10^{-4}. What happens if both the power in the denominator and the power in the numerator are negative, for example, $10^{-2}/10^{-6}$? Our calculation follows the mathematical law governing division with negative numbers. For the example just mentioned $-2 - (-6) = -2 + 6 = +4$.

Figure 1–17 shows intensity and sound pressure scales (Figure 1–17). The numbers on the right side of the figure refer to intensity of sound in watts/cm². All of these numbers have a negative power sign representing a fraction of 1 watt/cm². The numbers on the left side of the figure represent sound pressure in dynes/cm² and µPa/cm².

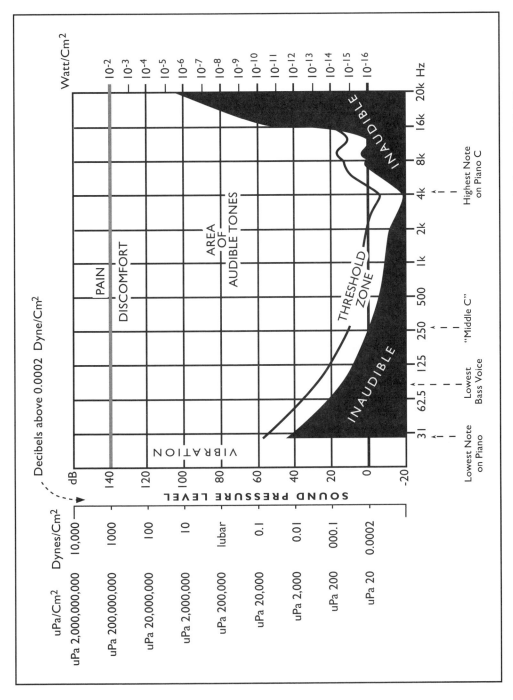

Figure 1–17. Intensity and sound pressure scales (adapted and modified from Davis and Silverman [1947]).

In order to construct an intensity scale, we must first have a reference point. The reference point for intensity (power/area) is 10^{-16} watts/cm^2, which is the lowest intensity a human can hear. All other intensity values will be compared to the reference point in the form of a ratio. The maximum intensity that a human can tolerate before there is damage to the hearing mechanism is 10^{-2} watt/cm^2. Recall that when we divide power by power we subtract. Therefore, dividing the ratio 10^{-2} (the maximum intensity a human can tolerate) over 10^{-16} (the reference) will equal 10^{14} watts/cm^2 re 10^{-16} watts/cm^2. In other words, the ratio of the most intense tolerable sound to the softest perceived sound is 100,000,000,000,000:1.

Exponent and logarithm are synonymous terms. Therefore, in the expression 10^{14}, 14 is simultaneously an exponent and a logarithm. In addition, exponent and logarithm are the same as bel (named after Alexander Graham Bell). For example, if a given ratio = 100,000, then log is 5 (equal to the number of zeros) and likewise we have 5 bels. When measuring hearing, we measure very small units. Therefore, we convert bel into 10 units; each unit is called a decibel (dB). Saying this differently, there are 10 dB in each bel. Therefore, dB = 10 log of the measured value over the reference value: measured value/reference value (10^{-16} watts/cm^2).

A further step is to establish an intensity level (IL) scale. The lowest value on the IL scale is the ratio of the softest sound a human can hear compared to the reference, which is also the softest sound a human can hear. In other words, 0 dB IL = 10^{-16} watts/cm^2/10^{-16} watts/cm^2 which gives us a ratio of 1:1. The log of 1 is 0. $10 \times 0 = 0$. Note that in the expression dB IL, dB of course refers to decibel, I is intensity, and L stands for level. L is always used to denote a conversion to decibel.

Let's continue with the dBIL scale as follows:

10 dB IL = 10 log 10/1 = 10 × 1 = 10

20 dB IL = 10 log 100/1 = 10 × 2 = 20, and so on until we reach 140 dB IL, the most intense sound the human can tolerate.

Acousticians, audiologists, and hearing scientists take advantage of the relationship between Power and Pressure, that is, Power = Pressure^2 or Pressure = √Power. As Power is measured at the source, and sound pressure can be measured anywhere by using a microphone and sound measuring device, it is easier to measure sound pressure rather than sound power. Sound pressure (SP) is measured using a sound-level meter (SLM), a device that will be discussed in detail in Chapter 10 on Instrumentation. As shown in Figure 1–7, on the left side, units of sound pressure are either dyne/cm^2 or µPa/cm^2. The softest sound the human can hear, expressed in dynes/cm^2, is 0.0002 dynes/cm^2. The reference in µPa (microPascal) is 20 µPascal/cm^2. Therefore, 0 dB SPL = 0.0002dynes/cm^2 or 20 µpascal/cm^2.

dB SPL = 10 log of a given pressure squared/reference pressure squared or 20 log of a given pressure/reference (recall that when we multiply using power, we add). Therefore, dB SPL = 20 log given pressure/reference pressure.

Let's establish a scale for dB SPL:

0 dB SPL = 20 log 1

20 dB SPL = 20 log 10

40 dB SPL = 20 log 100

60 dB SPL = 20 log 1000

80 dB SPL = 20 log 10,000

100 dB SPL = 20 log 100,000

120 dB SPL = 20 log 1,000,000

I'VE GOT IT!!

Thus far, we learned how to multiply and divide using dB. The addition and subtraction of dB is somewhat more complex. In order to add and subtract, we must convert to a ratio, then subtract or add, then reconvert to dB. However, there are some rules that govern addition and subtraction of dB without going through that multiple-step process. Tables 1–1 and 1–2 provide guidelines for adding and subtracting dB, respectively. You may need this in the future when you measure noise levels at multiple sites where you need to add and subtract dB.

We have learned about intensity and pressure, intensity level and sound pressure level. We also learned about the inverse square law as it relates to the intensity of sound and to other forms

Table 1–1. Addition of Decibels

Difference Between the Two Levels to Be Added (dB)	Add This Value to the Higher Noise Levels (dB)
0	3.0
1	2.5
2	2.1
3	1.8
4	1.5
5	1.2
6	1.0
7	0.8
8	0.6
9	0.5
10	0.4
11	0.3
12	0.3

Table 1–2. Subtraction of Decibels

Difference Between Two Levels (dB)	Value to Be Subtracted from Higher of the Two Levels (dB)
0	At least 10
1	6.9
2	4.3
3	3.0
4	2.2
5	1.7
6	1.3
7	1.0
8	0.7
9	0.6
10	0.5
11	0.4
12	0.3

of energy. We now continue with some mathematical practice with the dB. Recall that sound power is ideally measured at the source. Let us say that we need to double the intensity level at the source. How many dB must we add to the dB at the source to double the intensity? Let's begin with a simple example. To double the intensity level at the source we use the formula dB = 10 log 2/1. The numerator *2* refers to doubling and the denominator *1* refers to the reference you are doubling. 10 log 2/1 = 10 × 0.3 (the log of 2 is 0.3), which is equal to 3 dB (Table 1–3 lists abbreviated common logs). Now let's ask another question: how do we double sound-pressure level? If you can't figure this out on your own, here is the answer. Based on the relationship between power and pressure, that is, Power = Pressure^2 and Pressure √Power, we see that when we double the intensity dB level, sound pressure dB level is increased by 3 dB as well. Why is this the case? The reason is that sound pressure was already equated to intensity by squaring. That is, 20 log √2 = 20 log 1.414 = 3 dB. We can also ask why, when we double in IL, we increase the intensity level by 3 dB and when we double in SPL, we increase the SPL by 6 dB? We have already equated SPL and IL and now we're doubling the SPL. The rationale becomes clear by using our formulas:

dB IL = 10 log 2/1 = 10 × 0.3 = 3 dB

dB SPL = 20 log 2/1 = 20 × 0.3 = 6 dB

Let us now summarize the units used in this chapter and work on some examples. Recall that Jacob was using small units: cm, dynes, seconds. Adam and Eve and the unsuccessful weightlifter were using newton/meter, kg, and so forth. We therefore can divide the units of mea-surement used in physics into two major systems: cgs system (cm, gram, second) (Jacob's system) and mks (meter, kg, sec) system used by Adam and Eve and the weightlifter.

MEASUREMENT

Area

cgs: cm squared

mks: meter squared

Velocity

cgs: cm per second

mks: meters per second

Acceleration

cgs: cm per second squared

mks: meter per second squared

Force

cgs: dyne

mks: newton

Pressure

cgs: dyne per cm squared

mks: newton per meter squared

Work

cgs: cm × dyne (erg)

mks: newton × meter (joules)

Table 1–3. Abbreviated Table of Common Logarithms

No.	Mantissa	No. (cont.)	Mantissa	No. (cont.)	Mantissa
1.0	.00	4.0	.60	7.0	.85
1.1	.04	4.1	.61	7.1	.85
1.2	.08	4.2	.62	7.2	.86
1.3	.11	4.3	.63	7.3	.86
1.4	.15	4.4	.64	7.4	.87
1.5	.18	4.5	.65	7.5	.88
1.6	.20	4.6	.66	7.6	.88
1.7	.23	4.7	.67	7.7	.89
1.8	.26	4.8	.68	7.8	.89
1.9	.28	4.9	.69	7.9	.90
2.0	.30	5.0	.70	8.0	.90
2.1	.32	5.1	.71	8.1	.91
2.2	.34	5.2	.72	8.2	.91
2.3	.36	5.3	.72	8.3	.92
2.4	.38	5.4	.73	8.4	.92
2.5	.40	5.5	.74	8.5	.93
2.6	.41	5.6	.75	8.6	.93
2.7	.43	5.7	.76	8.7	.94
2.8	.45	5.8	.76	8.8	.94
2.9	.46	5.9	.77	8.9	.95
3.0	.48	6.0	.78	9.0	.95
3.1	.49	6.1	.79	9.1	.96
3.2	.51	6.2	.79	9.2	.96
3.3	.52	6.3	.80	9.3	.97
3.4	.53	6.4	.81	9.4	.97
3.5	.54	6.5	.81	9.5	.98
3.6	.56	6.6	.82	9.6	.98
3.7	.57	6.7	.83	9.7	.99
3.8	.58	6.8	.83	9.8	.99
3.9	.59	6.9	.84	9.9	1.00 (.996)

Source: Reprinted with permission from Durrant, J. D., & Lavrinic, J. H. (1995). *Bases of hearing science* (3rd ed.). Baltimore, MD: Williams and Wilkins.

Power

cgs: erg per second

mks: joules per second

Intensity

Intensity = Power/Area

Pressure = Force/Area

VALUES TO REMEMBER

1 N = 100,000 dynes or 10^5 dynes

1 joule = 10 million ergs or 10^7 ergs/sec

1 watt = 1 joule per second = 10^7 ergs/sec

0.0002 dynes/cm^2 = 20 µPa/cm^2

standard acceleration of gravity = 9.80 m/sec^2

speed of sound = 344 meters/sec (in air) at standard atmospheric conditions

speed of light in a vacuum = 2.9979 × 10^8 m/sec

radius of earth = 6.37 × 10^6 m

psi (pound per square inch)

force of 1 pascal = 1 newton/m^2

force of 1 pound (lb) = 4.448 N

With these values in mind, let us practice some mathematical examples.

1. Baby Jacob has grown up. He's now pushing a block using 50 dynes of force. He was able to move the block a distance of 25 cm. What is the work he performed (the energy he expended)?
2. John and his two friends were able to push a car a distance of 50 meters using 1500 newtons of force. What is the work they performed (the energy they expended).
3. Mrs. Jones was able to accomplish work in 10 seconds. Mrs. Smith accomplished the same work in 50 seconds. Who is more powerful?
4. 1000 dynes of force is focused on an area 100 cm square. What is the pressure per unit area? Answer: 10 dynes per unit area.
5. The speed of sound, expressed in feet/sec is _____.
6. What is the difference between power and intensity (provide an example)?
7. Acceleration is defined as _____.
8. A decibel represents a ratio of two values. What two values is the decibel comparing?
9. What is the mathematical relationship between power and pressure?
10. If a force is 100 dynes, and the mass is 3 kg, what is the acceleration?
11. (a) Given an initial distance of 5 feet from a sound source generating 40 dB SPL, calculate the area to be covered by the energy of this source.
    (b) Doubling the initial distance of 5 feet, calculate the new area to be covered by the same amount of sound pressure as well as the reduction in dB per unit area at our new distance.

Acknowledgment. Keith J. Emmer photographed Figure 1–14 in this chapter.

2

Concept of Mechanical Impedance and Admittance

Figure 2–1. *Georg Simon Ohm.*

CONCEPT OF IMMITTANCE

Although the concept of mechanical immittance (immittance refers to both impedance, which is the rejection of energy, and admittance, which is the acceptance of energy) does not directly relate to Audiology or Hearing Science, an understanding of its basic concept will facilitate the comprehension of more complex topics such as electrical energy (direct current and alternating current), filtering, acoustic admittance, and so forth. You will become aware of this fact as we proceed.

Let's consider mechanical impedance first. This discussion is based, in part, on the excellent work by Margolis (1981). The concept of mechanical impedance is illustrated by examining the interaction between a constant force applied to an object, in this case, a block, and the resultant velocity of the object. It is very important to note that in this chapter we encounter many of the concepts addressed in Chapter 1, including units of measurement, velocity and acceleration.

In Figure 2–2A, a small light box is being pushed by a baby using a sustained force, that is, a direct force having an amplitude that is unchanging over time (unlike an alternating force). A force of 1 dyne pushes the light box, which has a

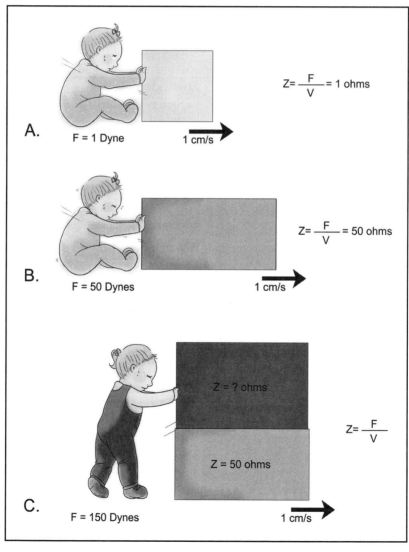

Figure 2–2. The relation between impedance Z, force F, and velocity V.

weight of 1 gram, over a surface having minimal friction. The velocity of the box is 1 cm/sec. We need a force of 1 dyne to move the 1-gram box a distance of 1 cm in 1 sec. The box presents an opposition to the applied force. The opposition is called mechanical impedance Z of 1 ohm. In order to calculate the mechanical imped-ance, the force applied to the object, for example, a box, is divided by the velocity of the object. The unit of ohm is named after Georg Simon Ohm (1789–1854), seen in Figure 2–1.

In Figure 2–2B, the baby is applying a greater force to push a heavier box. In this case, a force of 50 dynes is required to move the heavier box with a velocity of 1 cm/s. We can calculate the opposi-tion to the force (mechanical impedance Z) by dividing the force of 50 dynes by the velocity of 1 cm/sec. Thus, the mechani-cal impedance is equal to 50 dynes/cm/ sec or 50 ohms Ω. More force is needed to move the heavier box with a velocity of 1 cm/sec in Figure 2–2B than in Figure 2–2A because the heavier box in 2–2B presents more mechanical impedance than the one in the first figure.

In Figure 2–2C, we add another box atop the box in Figure 2–2B. More force (and a toddler) is now needed to move the two boxes than was needed to move the single box 1 cm/s because the opposition has increased. We can say that we need a force of 150 dynes to move the 2 blocks with a velocity of 1 cm/sec. We calculate the total mechanical impedance of this 2-box system as well as the mechanical impedance of the second box alone using the equation:

$$Z = F/V \qquad \text{(Eqn. 2.1)}$$

where Z is impedance, F is force, and V is velocity.

To calculate the total impedance of the 2-box system, we divide 150 dynes by 1 cm/sec giving us 150 ohms. What is the impedance of the second box that we added? If you answer that we must sub-tract the impedance of the first box (50 ohms) from the impedance of both boxes (150 ohms) you are correct. Our result is 100 ohms. 150 dynes was needed to move the two boxes with a velocity of 1 cm/s compared with 50 dynes to move the block in Figure 2–2B with the same veloc-ity. We see that an additional 100 dynes of force was needed to move the second block in Figure 2–2C.

We can ask if any of Newton's Laws is involved in the above examples. Yes! You can see that as the boxes become heavier, we need more force to push them in order to overcome the increased inertia (New-ton's First Law) according to the formula $A = F/M$ where A = acceleration, F = force, and M = mass. So, when mass increases, acceleration decreases (deceleration). In order to maintain a constant velocity, force must increase. Force must be increased to overcome not only increased weight but also an increase in frictional forces intro-duced by the increased weight. Therefore, the total force required to move a box from its resting position is dependent on its weight, friction, and acceleration.

ALTERNATING FORCE

When an alternating force (a force having an amplitude that changes over time) is applied to a system that has an object with mass, a spring fixed at one end, and a rough surface, the total mechanical imped-ance of the system cannot be obtained by simply adding the component imped-ances. In such a system $F(t) = A \sin (2\pi ft)$ where F = Force, t = time, A = amplitude, and f = frequency. That is, the force at a given moment in time = $A \sin (2\pi ft)$ at that moment in time.

In Figure 2–3, a mechanical force, Brianna, is alternately pushing and pulling on a spring fixed at one end to a tree. In Figure 2–3A, a mechanical force has just been applied to push a spring. The force, therefore, is at a minimum and the velocity of the spring is at a maximum since it has not yet been compressed. In Figure 2–3B, the mechanical force has pushed maximally on the spring. Although the force is at a maximum, the velocity of the spring is at a minimum because the spring is completely compressed. In Figure 2–3C, the mechanical force decreases until it reaches a minimum. The velocity of the spring increases until it reaches a maximum at the point at which the spring is completely uncompressed (the starting or resting position). In Figure 2–3D, the mechanical force is applied maximally in the opposite direction as it is now pulling rather than pushing on the spring. The velocity is at a minimum as the spring is maximally expanded. In Figure 2–3E, the mechanical force decreases until it reaches a minimum. The velocity increases until it reaches a maximum at the point at which the spring is no longer expanded.

Note that upon compression of the spring, kinetic energy is gradually converted to potential energy and this energy changes into a reaction to the force applied to the spring. There is also acceleration and deceleration involved in this interplay between potential and kinetic energy. Initially, force is minimum (acceleration is maximum) and at the point of conversion from potential to kinetic energy, velocity is minimum and deceleration is maximum.

The relationship just described, between a force applied to a spring and the

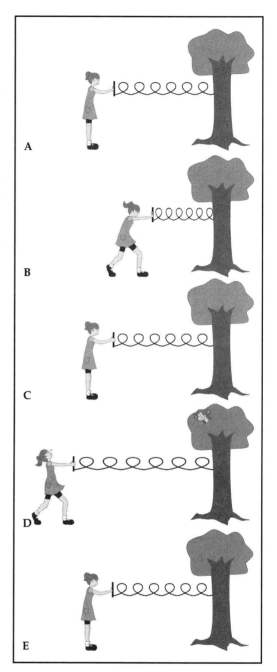

Figure 2–3. *An alternating force applied to a spring fixed at one end.*

resultant velocity of the spring, can also be understood in mathematical terms, as illustrated in Figure 2–4.

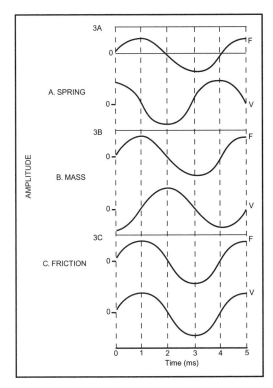

Figure 2–4. The relationship among a sinusoidal force F, velocity V, and time for a spring A, mass B, and friction C.

Figure 2–4A shows a sinusoidal force being applied to a spring, which alternates at a rate of 250 times per second (250 Hz). In this example, it takes 4 ms for the amplitude of the force to complete one cycle. At time *t* of 0 ms, the force is minimal (zero amplitude) and the velocity of the spring is maximal (in the positive direction), analogous to the situation in Figure 2–3A. At *t* = 1 ms, the force is maximal (in the positive direction) and the velocity of the spring is minimal, analogous to the situation in Figure 2–3B. At *t* = 2 ms, the force is minimal and the velocity of the spring is maximal (in the negative direction, analogous to the situation in Figure 2–3C). At *t* = 3 ms, the force is maximal (in the negative direction)

and the velocity of the spring is minimal, analogous to the situation in Figure 2–3D. At *t* = 4 ms, the force is minimal and the velocity of the spring is maximal (in the positive direction), analogous to the situation in Figure 2–3E. Clearly, the velocity of the spring reaches a maximum at 1 ms, 90° before the force applied to the spring reaches a maximum. Thus, velocity leads force by 90°.

In Figure 2–5, the relationship between an alternating force applied to an object having mass and the resultant velocity of the mass is described. In this figure, Tom is pushing and pulling on a heavy block.

In Figure 2–5A, the maximum push on the block has been exerted (force, inertia, and acceleration played a role). The block starts moving only after the maximum push is given because the block initially rejects the push as a result of its inertia. Thus, force is at a maximum and velocity is at a minimum. The mathematical analog of this situation is shown in Figure 2–4B at *t* = 1 ms. Between Figures 2–5A and 2–5B, the block moves faster (the velocity increases) and less pushing occurs (the force decreases). In Figure 2–5B, the block is moving at its fastest speed (velocity is maximal) and no more pushing is occurring (force is minimal). The mathematical analog of this situation is shown in Figure 2–4B at *t* = 2 ms. Between Figures 2–5B and 2–5C, Tom starts to pull rather than push the block in order to decrease the velocity (decelerate) of the block so it can be brought to a halt. Thus, the force increases, but in a different direction than shown in Figure 2–5A. In Figure 2–5C, the maximal pull has been exerted (force is maximal) and the block has been brought to a complete halt (velocity is minimal). The mathematical analog of this situation is shown in Figure 2–4B at *t* = 3 ms. Between Figures

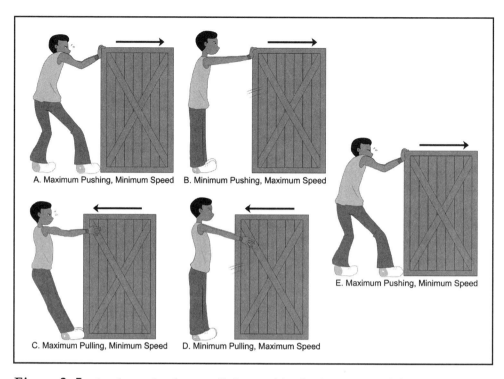

A. Maximum Pushing, Minimum Speed   B. Minimum Pushing, Maximum Speed

E. Maximum Pushing, Minimum Speed

C. Maximum Pulling, Minimum Speed   D. Minimum Pulling, Maximum Speed

Figure 2–5. *An alternating force applied to an object having mass, and the resultant velocity of the mass. The arrows represent the direction of the applied force.*

2–5C and 2–5D, the amount of pulling on the block decreases (the force decreases). As a result, the block begins moving faster in the opposite direction, that is, *toward* Tom rather than *away* from him (the velocity increases). In Figure 2–4D, there is no more pulling on the block (force is minimal) and the block is moving at its fastest speed (velocity is maximal). The mathematical analog of this situation is shown in Figure 2–4B at t = 4 ms. Between Figures 2–5D and 2–5E, Tom is now pushing rather than pulling on the block in order to slow down its speed and bring it to a stop. Thus, the force is increasing whereas the velocity is decreasing. In Figure 2–5E, Tom exerts the maximal push, thereby bringing the block to a complete stop. Thus, the force is maximal and the velocity is minimal. The mathematical analog

of this situation is shown in Figure 2–4B at t = 5 ms. It is apparent that at 1 ms, force leads velocity by 90°.

The relation between an alternating force and velocity of an object in a frictional system, which contains negligible mass or stiffness components, such as a light empty box, is illustrated in Figure 2–6. If an alternating force is applied to a springless object having negligible mass over a rough, frictional surface, the velocity of the object will attain maximum and minimum values at the same time that the force attains maximum and minimum values. Thus, the velocity of the object moving over a frictional surface is in phase with the applied force. (As the object is springless and has a negligible mass, it can be assumed that neither mass nor spring components modify this relation between

Figure 2–6. *Empty box with negligible mass and stiffness.*

force and velocity of the object over a frictional surface.)

As stated earlier, impedance $Z = F/V$ (Eqn. 2.1) and there are three impedance components. The impedance offered by mass is termed the mass reactance $+X_M$. The + sign indicates that force attains a maximum value before the velocity attains a maximum value when an alternating force is applied to an object having mass. That is, the force leads velocity by 90°. The impedance offered by a spring is stiffness reactance $-X_S$. The minus sign indicates that the force attains a maximum value after the velocity attains a maximum value when an alternating force is applied to a spring or an object having stiffness. Thus, the force lags velocity by 90°. The impedance resulting from friction is termed the resistance R. For each impedance component, $+X_M$, $-X_S$, or R, the impedance is equal to the force divided by the velocity.

If a system consists of an alternating force applied to several masses in series,

then the total impedance of the system is simply the sum of the mass reactance offered by each mass component, as the relation between force and velocity is the same for each of the mass reactance components, that is, force leads velocity by 90°. If a system consists of an alternating force applied to several springs in series, the total impedance of the system is simply the sum of the stiffness reactance offered by each spring, as the relation between force and velocity is the same for each of the stiffness reactance components, that is, velocity leads force by 90°. If a system consists of an alternating force applied to several frictional surfaces in series, the total impedance of this system is simply the sum of the resistance offered by each frictional surface, because the relation between force and velocity is the same for each of the resistance components, that is, velocity is in phase with the force. It's rare to find a system consisting of only one type of impedance component. If the three types of impedance components exist in a system (mass reactance offered by mass, stiffness reactance offered by a spring or an object having stiffness, and resistance offered by friction), then total impedance is not simply the sum of the impedance components, as the relation between force and velocity is different for each of the impedance components.

Figure 2–7 shows a mechanical system containing mass, spring, and friction. Thus, it contains all three types of impedance components: mass reactance, stiffness reactance, and resistance.

Recall that in Figure 2–4 velocity values reach a maximum at different times during the force cycle. That is, the maximum velocity occurs at $t = 0$ ms in the force cycle for the stiffness reactance, at $t = 1$ ms for the resistance component, and at $t = 2$ ms for the mass reactance. As the

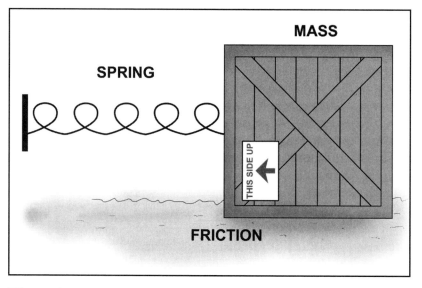

Figure 2–7. A mechanical system containing mass, spring, and friction components. A vectorial representation of the impedance components. $+X_M$ is the mass reactance, $-X_S$ is the stiffness reactance, R is the resistance, and F is the applied alternating force.

velocity maxima for the mass reactance, stiffness reactance, and resistance occur at different points along the force cycle, the maxima of the impedance occur at different points along the force cycle. Therefore, a vector system is required to obtain the sum of the impedance components (Figure 2–8):

$$Z = \sqrt{R^2 + X^2} \qquad \text{(Eqn. 2.2)}$$

In Figure 2–8, the placement of the resistance R component of impedance on the abscissa represents the fact that, for this component, the velocity is in phase with the force. The placement of the stiffness-reactance component $-X_S$ along the negative ordinate represents the fact that in the case of this component, the velocity leads the force by 90°. The placement of the mass-reactance component $+X_M$ along the positive ordinate represents the fact that in the case of this com-

ponent, the velocity lags the force by 90°. Note that the mass reactance $+X_M$ and the stiffness reactance $-X_S$ are out of phase by 180°. Therefore, to obtain the net reactance X, the stiffness reactance is added to the mass reactance. If the system has more stiffness than mass reactance, the net reactance of X will be negative. If the system has more mass than stiffness reactance, the net reactance of X will be positive. The vector that is perpendicular to the resistance is also called an imaginary line. As we don't want to confuse you, we won't elaborate on the imaginary line at this time. You will see this concept again in Chapter 5 when we discuss alternating current and impedance. Of course, should you wish to satisfy your curiosity, feel free to jump to Chapter 5 at any time. Readers who have come across the imaginary line in a mathematics course will have seen the symbol i used to represent the imaginary number. Why then do we use $+j$ or $-j$ in

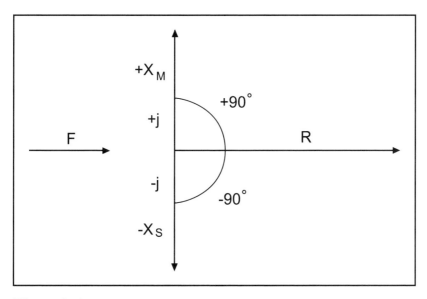

Figure 2–8. *A vectorial representation of the impedance components. +X$_M$ is the mass reactance, –X$_S$ is the stiffness reactance, R is the resistance, and F is the applied alternating force.*

this chapter when describing impedance? You will see the answer in Chapter 5.

Figure 2–9 shows the vectors for impedance, resistance, and the net reactance. The resultant impedance is the vector sum of the resistance and net reactance:

$$Z^2 = R^2 + (-X^2) \qquad \text{(Eqn. 2.3)}$$

The magnitude of the impedance vector (the diagonal line in Figure 2–9) can be calculated using the Pythagorean theorem, which states that the hypotenuse squared equals the sum of the squares of the other two sides of a right triangle. Thus,

$$Z^2 = R^2 + X^2 \qquad \text{(Eqn. 2.4)}$$

and

$$Z = \sqrt{R^2 + X^2} \qquad \text{(Eqn. 2.5)}$$

The phase angle of the impedance vector is calculated using the formula:

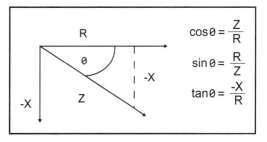

Figure 2–9. *The vectors for the total impedance Z, resistance R, and the net reactance –X. The phase angle ø is also shown in the figure. The formula for calculating the total impedance from the resistance and the net reactance is shown in Eqn. 2.3.*

$$\cos ø = R/Z \qquad \text{(Eqn. 2.6)}$$

or

$$\tan ø = X/R \qquad \text{(Eqn. 2.7)}$$

or

$$\sin ø = X/Z \qquad \text{(Eqn. 2.8)}$$

where tan is *tangent* and ø is phase angle.

We expand on the concept of phase angle in Chapter 4 where it will be more appropriate and at which time it will be easier for the reader to understand the concepts.

We now calculate the mechanical impedance of a system consisting only of stiffness reactance and resistance in which the velocity and force are known. The velocity of the spring is 5 cm/s and the force required to produce this velocity is 50 dynes. The velocity of the friction is 10 cm/s and the force required to produce this velocity is 50 dynes. The impedance offered by the spring $-X_S$ is force divided by velocity (50/5) or 10 ohms. This stiffness reactance is the net reactance X as there is no mass reactance. The impedance offered by the friction R is force divided by velocity (50/5) or 5 ohms. To obtain the complex impedance of the system the Pythagorean theorem is employed, so $Z^2 = 5^2 + 10^2$ so $Z = \sqrt{25 + 100}$ and $Z = 5\sqrt{25}$, which means $Z = (5 \times 2.29)$ ohms, or 11.45 ohms.

In all the previous examples, the alternating force driving the mechanical system was a 250-Hz force. The mechanical impedance of a system also varies as the frequency of the applied force varies. The relationship between mechanical stiffness reactance, stiffness, and frequency is illustrated by the formula:

$$-X_S = S/(2\,\pi f) \qquad \text{(Eqn. 2.9)}$$

where S is stiffness and f is frequency. According to this formula, the stiffer the spring the larger the mechanical stiffness reactance; the higher the frequency the smaller the stiffness reactance. Thus, the stiffness reactance can be increased by increasing the stiffness or by decreasing the frequency; it can be decreased by decreasing the stiffness or increasing the

frequency. If there is no stiffness reactance at one frequency, one cannot conclude that there is no stiffness reactance in the system; it may be present at other frequencies. In calculating stiffness reactance, we may use compliance (elasticity) rather than stiffness reactance. This is important to point out because alternating current and electrical Z use compliance rather than stiffness. Therefore the formula for $-X_S$ (stiffness reactance) is written as $-X_C = 1/2\pi fc$ where $-X_C$ refers to compliance reactance.

The mass reactance also changes with frequency. The relation among mechanical mass reactance, mass, and frequency is illustrated in the formula:

$$+X_M = 2\pi\, fM \qquad \text{(Eqn. 2.10)}$$

According to this formula, the mass reactance increases as the mass or frequency increases; it decreases as the mass or frequency decreases. Because mechanical mass reactance decreases whereas mechanical stiffness reactance increases as frequency decreases, and vice versa, there is a frequency at which the stiffness and mass reactance are equal. At this frequency, there is no mass or stiffness reactance. This frequency is known as the resonant frequency, which can be calculated with the formula:

$$fo = (1/2\pi)\,(S/M) \qquad \text{(Eqn. 2.11)}$$

where fo is the resonant frequency, S is stiffness, and M is mass. If there is no mass reactance at one frequency, one cannot conclude there is no mass reactance in the system; it may be present at other frequencies. Resistance, unlike mass or stiffness reactance, does not change with frequency. That is, resistance is independent of frequency.

As $-X_S = S/(2pf)$ (Eqn. 2.9), the total impedance of a system that has a net reactance, or stiffness reactance, can also be written as:

$$Z^2 = R^2 + [S/(2pf)]^2 \qquad \text{(Eqn. 2.12)}$$

As $+X_M = 2pfM$ (Eqn. 2.10), the total impedance of a system that has a net reactance, or mass reactance, can be written as:

$$Z^2 = R^2 + (2pfM)^2 \qquad \text{(Eqn. 2.13)}$$

MECHANICAL ADMITTANCE

The ability of the system to transfer energy can also be expressed in terms of its acceptance rather than rejection of energy. If the force applied to System A is the same as that applied to System B and if the resultant velocity of System A is greater than that of system B, then System A has more admittance (less impedance) than System B. As mechanical admittance is the reciprocal of mechanical impedance, it can be calculated using the formula:

$$Y = V/F \qquad \text{(Eqn. 2.14)}$$

where Y is mechanical admittance, V is velocity, and F is force. The unit of admittance is mho (the reciprocal of ohms). Note that the relation between velocity and force for admittance is the reverse of that for impedance since admittance is the reciprocal of impedance. The ease with which energy flows into a mass is called mass susceptance $-B_M$. The ease with which energy flows into a spring or an object having stiffness is called stiffness susceptance $+B_S$. The ease with which energy flows into friction is called conductance G.

The relation among the admittance vectors is shown in Figure 2–10.

Note that the stiffness susceptance is on the positive ordinate rather than the negative ordinate and the mass susceptance is on the negative ordinate rather than the positive ordinate. In this graph, the net reactance, B, obtained by adding the negative mass susceptance to the positive stiffness susceptance, happens to be stiffness susceptance. The admittance vector is calculated using the Pythagorean theorem.

Admittance is calculated from the formula:

$$Y^2 = R^2 + G^2 \qquad \text{(Eqn. 2.15)}$$

The unit of admittance, mass susceptance, stiffness susceptance, and resistance is mho (1000 mmhos). The relations among stiffness susceptance, stiffness, and frequency, and among mass susceptance, mass, and frequency are given by formulas:

$$+B_S = (2\pi f /S) \qquad \text{(Eqn. 2.16)}$$

and

$$-B_M = 1/(2\pi f M) \qquad \text{(Eqn. 2.17)}$$

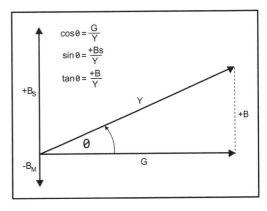

Figure 2–10. Relationships among conductance (G), stiffness susceptance (+B_S), and mass susceptance (−B_M)

According to Eqn. 2.16, the stiffness susceptance increases as the frequency increases or as the stiffness decreases; it decreases as the frequency decreases or as the stiffness increases. According to Eqn. 2.17, the mass susceptance increases as the frequency or mass decreases; it decreases as the frequency or mass increases. If there is no mass or stiffness susceptance at one frequency it cannot be concluded that there is no mass or stiffness susceptance at other frequencies.

REFERENCE

Margolis, R. H. (1981). Fundamentals of acoustic immittance. Appendix A. In G. R. Popelka (Ed.), *Hearing assessment with the acoustic reflex* (pp. 117–143). New York, NY: Grune & Stratton.

3

Electrical Energy—
Direct Current

Figure 3–1. *Hearing test with the tuba.*

As mentioned in Chapter 1, electricity is both potential and kinetic energy. In ancient times, people believed that electricity was magic. Greek philosophers observed that when amber, a fossilized tree resin, was rubbed with cloth, it attracted straw. They recorded the first references to electrical effects such as static electricity and lightning more than 2,500 years ago. Although electrical phenomena of lightning and static electricity have been known to man since antiquity, it was not until the 17th and 18th centuries that studies and advances in electrical science emerged, and it was not until the 19th century that industrial and residential applications emerged. Many commonly used products rely on the movement of electrons.

The versatility of electricity as a source of energy has enabled applications to lighting in the home and in business, communications, computing, transport, and so forth. Audiology and hearing science are no exception. Few topics in audiology and hearing science can be discussed without understanding the basis of electrical energy. Imagine an audiologist or otolaryngologist evaluating hearing without electricity. What would be left? Clapping hands? Speaking softly or loudly? Beating a drum? How about our personal favorite: the tuba (Figure 3–1)?

In the 20th century, a considerable number of children with hearing impairment were misdiagnosed as mentally retarded because of inadequate diagnostic instrumentation, leading to placement of many of these children in institutions. Eventually, many were appropriately identified as having severe to profound hearing impairment rather than mental retardation. But these later diagnoses led to prolonged lack of auditory stimulation over a period of years, and that, together with placement in an environment where their co-inhabitants were mentally retarded, ultimately resulted in severe language, educational, and cognitive deficits. This underscores the need for audiology students to study electricity.

Electricity is a general term that encompasses a variety of phenomena resulting from the presence and flow of electrical charge. An understanding of how electricity is formed is needed before understanding other aspects of this form of energy. Matter is anything that has mass and occupies space. Matter surrounds us. Our lives depend on matter. Matter exists in a gaseous, liquid, or solid state.

The air we breathe, the water we drink, and all kinds of metals are examples of matter. We are familiar with the word *element*. Elements form the basis of matter. All matter is composed of mixtures and chemical combinations of one or more of the elements. Examples of elements include sodium, gold, oxygen, hydrogen, nitrogen, and iron.

Any material composed of two or more elements that have combined chemically in a particular order is called a compound. Water, salt, and sugar, are compounds. All compounds in our environment are formed by the chemical combination of two or more of the 94 elements found in nature. These elements can be combined in various ways to form millions of different compounds. A molecule represents the smallest particle of a compound that has the chemical characteristics of that compound. A molecule is composed of atoms of two or more elements. For example, water molecules consist of two atoms of hydrogen and one atom of oxygen (Figure 3–2). Thus, the smallest particle of water that is still water is a molecule. Further breakdown of water molecules ultimately yields atoms of hydrogen and oxygen. Thus, the mole-

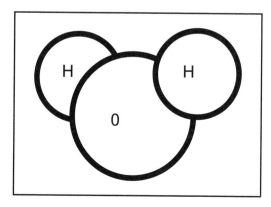

Figure 3–2. *A water molecule.*

cule is the smallest particle of a compound whereas the atom is the smallest particle of an element. Another example of a compound is common table salt. A salt molecule consists of one atom each of sodium and chlorine. Further breakdown of a salt molecule ultimately yields the atoms of sodium and chlorine. Just as a compound is made up of molecules, an element is made up of atoms.

An atom is the smallest distinguishable particle into which an element can be divided without losing the chemical properties of that element. Atoms are very small with a radius on the order of 10^{-10} meters. They cannot be observed without using extremely powerful microscopes. As there are only 94 natural elements, there are only 94 different types of atoms found in nature. Atoms differ from each other according to their constituent number of protons, electrons, and neutrons. These three basic building blocks of atoms are called *subatomic particles*. Protons and neutrons form the center, or nucleus, of the atom. Although current theories describe electron movement in terms of probability distributions, the classic description of electron movement posits their revolution around the nucleus somewhat parallel to the revolution of planets around the sun (Figure 3–3).

The nucleus of a hydrogen atom (H^+) contains a single proton and one electron (e^-) and revolves around the nucleus. For all other atoms, the nucleus contains both protons and neutrons. The nucleus of oxygen (O^{8+}) contains eight neutrons and eight protons clustering together and eight electrons (e^-) revolve around the nucleus in orbits like planets revolving around a sun. Atoms normally have equal numbers of electrons and protons. A hydrogen atom has one proton and one electron and a copper atom has 29 protons and 29 electrons.

Electricity begins at the level of the atom. It is a property of electrons and protons that causes them to behave in certain predictable ways. Each of these subatomic particles has a tiny electrical charge. Electrical charge is a fundamental, conserved

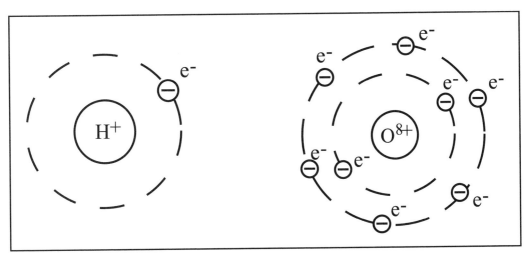

Figure 3–3. *On the left is a planetary model of a hydrogen atom and on the right a planetary model of an oxygen atom.*

property of some subatomic particles, which determines their electromagnetic interaction. The International System of Units (SI) unit of electrical charge is coulomb. One coulomb is defined as the amount of electric charge transported in one second by a steady current of one ampere. A proton has a positive charge with a magnitude of 1.602×10^{-19} coulombs. An electron, on the other hand, has an equivalent charge to that of the proton, but the charge is negative rather than positive. Therefore, the charge on an electron is -1.602×10^{-19} coulombs. Unlike electrons and protons that have electrical charges, a third subatomic particle, a neutron, found in the atom does not. Negatively charged electrons are held in revolution around the nucleus by the attraction of the positively charged protons in the nucleus of the atom and by the repulsion of other electrons revolving around the nucleus.

COULOMB'S LAW

Two particles with the same charge (e.g., both have positive charges or both have negative charges) have a repulsive electrostatic force that propels the particles away from each other. Two particles with opposing charges (e.g., one particle has a positive charge and one particle has a negative charge) have an attracting electrostatic force that propels the particles towards each other. According to Coulomb's law, which describes the behavior of charged particles, the magnitude of the electrostatic force between two point electric charges is directly related to the product of the magnitudes of each of the charges and is inversely related to the square of the total distance between the two charges.

In a stable atom or molecule, the number of positive charges is equivalent to the number of negative charges so the charges cancel each other out leaving the atom or the molecule without any net charge. An ion is an atom or a molecule with a net negative charge that is more or less than the net electrical charge. An ion consisting of a single atom with a net positive or negative charge is called a monatomic ion whereas a polyatomic ion consists of more than one atom yielding a net positive or negative charge. Monatomic ions are formed when an atom loses one or more electrons from its outermost shell or "orbit" (electrons in this outermost shell are called *valence* electrons) or gains one or more electrons into its valence shell. This process by which atoms gain or lose electrons from the valence shell yielding an atom with a net electrical charge is called *ionization*. The electrons in the inner orbits (shells) are tightly bound to the atom by the force of the positively charged nucleus so ionization generally does not involve these electrons.

We return to the hydrogen atom. When the hydrogen atom loses its valence electron (e^-), it gets ionized, leaving behind a positively charged hydrogen ion (H^+). A positive ion is also called a *cation* (Figure 3–4).

As electrons have negative charges, an atom that gains an extra electron becomes a negative ion, which is termed an *anion*. An oxygen atom, for example, that gains an extra electron (e^-) during ionization becomes a negatively charged oxygen ion (O^-) or anion (Figure 3–5).

One way to produce free electrons and positive ions is to rub a glass rod with a silk cloth. Although both the glass rod and silk cloth are electrically neutral (no net charge) objects, rubbing the glass rod causes the glass rod to transfer many electrons to the silk cloth, resulting in a positively charged glass rod and nega-

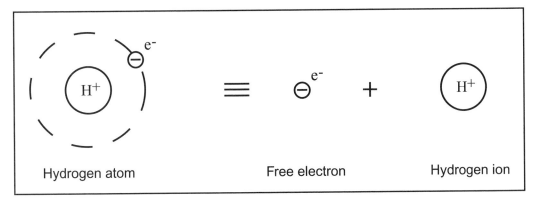

Figure 3–4. *Ionization of a hydrogen atom, resulting in a hydrogen cation.*

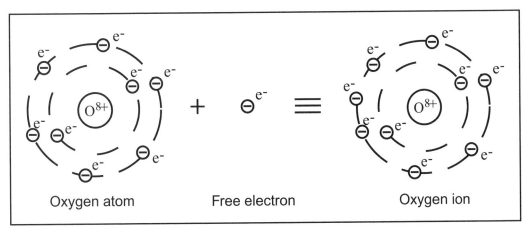

Figure 3–5. *Transformation of an oxygen atom into an oxygen anion by the process of ionization. On the left is an oxygen atom with 6 electrons. During ionization, it gains an electron and becomes an anion with 7 electrons in its valence shell (see the right side of the figure).*

tively charged silk cloth. If the positively charged glass rod touches a neutral body (without any electrical charge), then electrons are drawn from the neutral body by the positive charge on the glass rod. Thus, the electrons from the neutral body neutralize the charge on the rod. Because the neutral body gave up electrons to the positively charged rod, the neutral body now becomes positively charged. This is called charging by contact.

Objects also can be charged by induction without actually touching each other.

Electrostatic induction is the redistribution of charges in an object due to the influence of nearby electrical charges. Figure 3–6 illustrates a positively charged object A and an electrically neutral object B.

When object A is brought in close proximity to object B, it exerts an electrostatic force of attraction on the electrons in object B as explained by Coulomb's law. The electrons in object B therefore flow toward the side-facing object A thereby making it negatively charged. At the same time, the opposite side of object B farthest

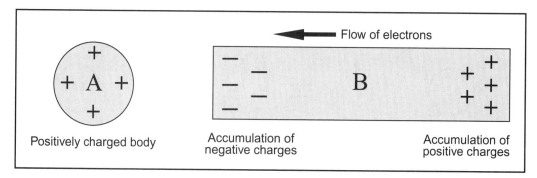

Figure 3–6. *Charging by induction.*

from object *A* becomes positively charged because of a deficiency of electrons there. Thus, negative charges are induced on one side of object *B* due to the electrostatic force exerted by the positively charged object *A*. This phenomenon is called induction. We should note that redistribution of charges occurs from the motion of negative charges, electrons, as only these particles are free to move in the object. All the positive charges, protons, are bound to the nuclei of atoms and, therefore, cannot move from one side to the other in the object. In the aforementioned example, the electrons move toward the side nearest the positively charged object *A*, leaving a positive unbalanced charge on the right side of *B*. Object *B* as a whole still is electrically neutral as it has not lost or gained any electrons, only a redistribution of electrons across the object has occurred. Once object *A* is no longer in proximity to *B*, the electrons in object *B* will redistribute such that no charge is induced at either of its ends.

An important part of Coulomb's law is an equation that allows us to determine the force of attraction or repulsion between the interacting charged bodies. The equation states that:

$$F = k_e \frac{q_1 \times q_2}{d^2} \qquad \text{(Eqn. 3.1)}$$

where *F* (unit is newton) = the force of electrostatic attraction between unlike charges or the force of repulsion between like charges, q_1 = the electrical charge on one body (unit is coulomb), q_2 = the charge on the second body, *d* = the distance between the two bodies (unit is meters), and k_e = 8.987 × 10⁹ Newton meters² coulombs⁻² (Coulomb's force constant) or 8.987 × 10⁹ NmC⁻². In Coulomb's law, *F* gives the magnitude of electrostatic force on charge q_1 from the presence of charge q_2 at a distance *d* from q_1. According to Equation 3.1, the magnitude of *F* will increase as the magnitude of either of the charges increases and will decrease exponentially with an index of 2 as the distance between charges increases.

Force in electronics (voltage), like the force (dynes) in mechanics (see Chapters 1 and 2) is a vector quantity and therefore has direction as well as magnitude; its direction can be determined using the vector form of Coulomb's law. The vector form takes into consideration the direction vectors of both the charges of the two point bodies along with their magnitudes. If the charges q_1 and q_2 have the same polarity, then the electrostatic force, *F*, between the two point charges is repulsive whereas if the charges q_1 and q_2 are opposite in polarity, then the electrostatic force, *F*, between the two point charges is attractive.

CURRENT, VOLTAGE, AND RESISTANCE

Electric current refers to an orderly flow of electric charge through a medium in a particular direction. This is analogous to the velocity in a mechanical system described in Chapter 2. The flow of charge can result from electrons in a conductor such as a metal wire, ions in an electrolyte, or both electrons and ions in plasma. A conducting material such as metal wire, for example, copper or aluminum, has an abundance of free electrons. The electrons in the valence shells of these metal atoms keep jumping from one atom to another in a random fashion in all directions due to thermal energy (see Chapter 1). Given the random motion of electrons, the electrical current due to electrons flowing in any particular direction is canceled by an equal current due to the same number of electrons flowing in the opposite direction inside the conducting metal. The net current through any part of the conductor in the absence of a driving force is zero. Subjecting a wire to a driving force at either of its ends causes the free electrons in the wire to start flowing in the direction of the force. This orderly flow of electrons constitutes the flow of current through the metal wire. The SI unit of current is amperes A and the device used to measure current in a circuit is called an ammeter.

Connection of a battery across the two ends of a metal wire leads to generation of an electric field upon the free electrons in the wire. The negative terminal of a battery has excess electrons whereas the positive terminal has a deficiency of electrons. Upon connection of these battery terminals using a wire, the wire's free electrons are forced to move, under the influence of the electrical field, through the wire from the negative terminal of the battery to the positive terminal of the battery.

Other electrons that are released by chemical reactions within the battery replace electrons that leave the negative battery terminal. Thus, a battery can maintain a continuous flow of electrons through a metal wire connecting the terminals until the deficiency of electrons at the positive terminal is eliminated by the excess of electrons on the negative terminal leading to neutralization of the electrical field driving force as when, for example, a battery no longer produces chemical reactions to replace the electrons leaving the negative battery terminal. If this happens in your car you need a boost or a new battery.

The flow of electrons through the wire between the terminals is electrical current (defined as flow of electrons/unit of time), which travels from a negative charged terminal to a positive charged terminal. The definition of electrical current is an analog to velocity in a mechanical system. Velocity is defined as distance/time. Although it is now understood that electrons flow toward positive charges, by convention, the direction of the flow of current is considered opposite to the direction of the flow of electrons, consistent with older theories whereby positive charges were thought to be flowing toward the negative electron charges. Conventional current can be defined as the rate of flow of charge through a point in the conductor. You will see in some of the schematic drawings of direct-current circuits in this text that the direction of the current is opposite that of the direction of the electrons. In reality, current flow is in the same direction as electron flow, that is, from negative to positive. Perhaps you have come to the conclusion that it's foolish to schematize current flow in this unrealistic manner as current is electron flow/unit of time. However, we felt it necessary to conform to the traditional concept used in the majority of textbooks on electricity.

To this day, electrical engineers debate whether to keep the traditional drawings. You might conceptualize the following to clear up the concept: the negative terminal is losing electrons while the positive terminal is gaining electrons. The formula for calculating the magnitude of current (*I*) is as follows:

$$I = Q/t \qquad \text{(Eqn. 3.2)}$$

where *I* = electric current (unit is amperes), *Q* = electrical charge (unit is coulombs) transferred through a point in the conductor, and *t* = time (unit is seconds).

As current flow is conventionally specified, based on older theories, to be in the direction opposite that of electron flow, it is accepted that current flows from a higher electrical potential to a lower electrical potential. Electrical potential at a given point in a circuit can be defined as the difference in electrical charge between that point and the ground reference in that circuit.

OHM'S LAW

As previously mentioned, electricity refers to the flow of electrons. Electrons possess energy, which has the potential to do electrical work. When there is a difference between electrical potentials at two points, we say that a potential difference exists. This potential difference is what we commonly refer to as the voltage (force in a mechanical system). The SI unit of voltage is volt. When a conductor is used to connect two points at different potentials, current flows from the point of higher potential to the point of lower potential. Ohm's law specifies the relations among the voltage, current flowing through the circuit, and the resistance offered by the circuit to the current flow (Eqn. 3.3). Ohm's law states that the magnitude of electrical current flowing through a conductor is directly proportional to the potential difference or the voltage between the two points across which a potential difference exists, and is inversely proportional to the resistance between these two points. In Figure 3–7, a potential difference of *V* volts exists between points A and B because of the battery connected between them. The circuit contains a resistor (*R*) and the current flows from the positive terminal of the battery through the resistor and finally into the negative terminal of the battery. The relations among *V*, *I*, and *R* are given by Ohm's law (Eqn. 3.3).

$$I = V/R \text{ or } V = I \times R \qquad \text{(Eqn. 3.3)}$$

where *V* = voltage across points A and B in volts, *I* = current through the circuit in amperes, and *R* = resistance between points A and B in ohms (Ω). Such a circuit provides power, which is released through the resister. Power is defined as the rate of the release of electrical energy. The units for electrical power are *watts* (W). This unit of measurement is analogous to the unit of power in a mechanical system (see Chapter 1). Watt is also expressed as

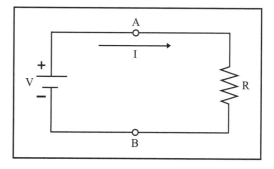

Figure 3–7. *Circuit with current (I), voltage (V), and resistance (R) and Ohm's law.*

joules per second (J/sec). We are referring to power when we describe the strength of a light bulb; for example, a 100-watt bulb emits 100 J/sec or 100 watts. Power emitted from the resister (Figure 3–8) is quantified as the voltage drop at the resistor times the current of the circuit. We can therefore calculate Ohm's law for the circuit in its entirety and Ohm's law at the point of the resistor. The result will be the same in both cases, for the following reason: in 1845, Gustav Kirchhoff described 2 important laws of electricity; these are just as important as Ohm's law. Collectively, the laws are called the *Law of Conservation of Electrical Energy*. These laws are analogous to the *Laws of Conservation of Mechanical Energy*. The first of Kirchhoff's laws is the *Voltage Law* and the second is the *Law of Electrical Current*. The Voltage Law states that the voltage drop in an electrical circuit is equal to the supplied voltage. In other words, the voltage remaining in the circuit after the drop is 0. The Law of Electrical Current states that at any electrical junction of a circuit, the sum of the current entering the junction is equal to the magnitude of the current leaving the junction. In other words, the sum of the current at the junction is 0.

Don't let Figure 3–7 frighten you. Figure 3–8 is a much more familiar and realistic schematic drawing of a DC circuit. Here we show you how electrons flow from the negative direction to the positive terminal.

Voltage, also called electromotive force or more commonly EMF, is similar to force in a mechanical system. Recall the relations among mechanical impedance, force, and velocity $Z_M = F/V$ or $F = Z/V$. Just as force in a mechanical system is the analog of voltage in an electrical system, velocity in a mechanical system is the analog of current in an electrical system. The EMF is a force that causes electron flow in a certain direction inside a conductor.

The larger the difference in electrical potential between two points (potential difference) the stronger the voltage or

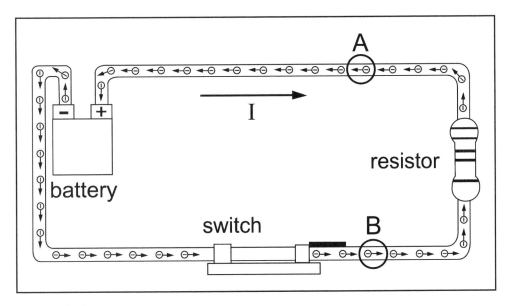

Figure 3–8. *Electrical circuit for direct current.*

force. This is the same rule that governs the gravitational law in physics (see Chapter 1). An inactive voltage can be referred to as potential voltage. An unconnected battery represents an example of inactive voltage as a difference in electrical potential exists between the two battery terminals but the voltage is simply stored in the two terminals (see Chapter 1). When the battery terminals are connected by a wire, the electrons move toward the positive terminal and, as specified by convention, the current flows from the positive to negative terminal. This is analogous to converting potential energy into kinetic energy in a mechanical system (see Chapter 1).

Resistance (R) in an electrical system is the analog of resistance resulting from friction in a mechanical system. Its function in an electrical system is to resist the current flow, that is, to slow current flow by converting the electrical energy into various forms of energy such as heat, light, or sound. When a current of one ampere flows through a resistance due to a potential difference of one volt applied across it, the value of the resistance is one ohm. The resistance of an object depends on its physical dimensions and its resistivity (ρ). The resistivity or specific resistance of any material is characteristic to that material. It is a measure of how strongly a material resists the flow of current through it. Thus, a material with high resistivity will strongly resist the flow of current through it whereas a material with low resistivity will allow current to pass through it more readily. The SI unit of resistivity is ohm-meter (Ωm). The specific resistance of iron, for example, is 10^{-7} Ωm. Conductors have low resistivity.

Consider an example of biasing (supplying a voltage) of a light bulb (Figure 3–9), which contains a coiled filament, made of a thin tungsten wire that acts as the resistance. Connecting a battery of V

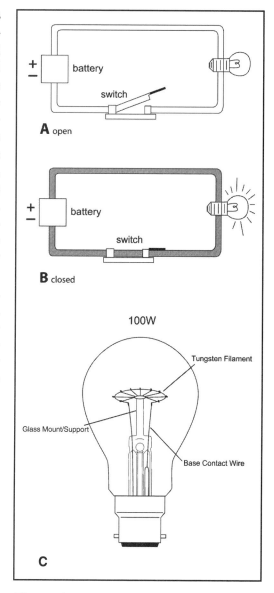

Figure 3–9. *Biasing of a light bulb. **A** is a circuit with an open switch (no light) and **B** shows a circuit where the switch is closed (the bulb is lit). **C** is an enlarged version of a bulb.*

volts in series with the tungsten filament of the light bulb is called biasing of the light bulb.

A filament is made of a thin-coiled wire with a long length l and a very small cross-sectional area A. The specific resistance of tungsten is high as compared to that of most metals. Thus, the filament of the bulb has a large resistance value. When we connect a potential difference of V volts across the bulb, a current of I amperes flows through the tungsten filament causing a voltage drop of V volts across the filament resistance R (like converting energy into heat by heating up the resistor). The filament offers high resistance to the flow of electrons through it. These electrons use their energy to do work against the resistance to keep flowing through the circuit. The work done by the electrons heats up the filament to a very high temperature and causes it to glow and emit light. Thus, the resistance here is used to convert electrical energy into usable light energy.

Let us conduct a small and simple experiment to illustrate the above concept using elements easily purchased at any hardware store. The components include: 6-volt battery; 3-ampere bulb; a base for the bulb, and a wire with two terminals at each end (Figure 3–10).

At home, a typical 100-watt bulb connected to a 120-volt supply has a resistance of 9.5 ohms, which is not a large value. The actual resistance of the filament is temperature dependent. The value of the cold resistance of tungsten-filament lamps is about 1/15th of the value of the hot-filament resistance when the lamp is operating. The resistance of the same bulb during operation is 144 Ω.

Electrical energy can be converted to other forms of energy, including sound

Figure 3–10. Connection between 6-volt battery and bulb will generate light.

energy. Let's consider an old-fashioned basic electric bell (Figure 3–11). The bell consists of a gong, armature, two parallel magnets housed within metal coils, hammer, battery, switch, contact system, and spring.

Figure 3–11A shows the doorbell with the switch off. Figure 3–11B shows the doorbell with the switch closed. In this situation, electrons will flow from the negative side of the battery through the switch, contact system, coils, and back to the positive side of the battery. The flow of electrons will create a magnetic field that attracts the armature pulling it downward. This in turn pulls the hammer down and you hear the bell. The current path breaks when the coils energize and pull the armature down. Therefore, contact is lost with the breaker system that has been supplying the electrical energy. The armature is then released. The process begins again.

We conduct another simple experi-ment with the 6-volt battery used in the first experiment. Replace the bulb with a small bell (Figure 3–12). You will hear the ding-dong.

As resistivity is a physical property of all electrical materials and resistance is a parameter that is integral to electri-cal circuits, resistors employed in circuits are composed of various compounds and films (a component important to the con-struction of resistors) as well as resistance wire made of a high-resistivity alloy, such as nichrome (80% nickel and 20% chro-mium). Commercial resistors are charac-terized by parameters like their resistivity, tolerance, power rating, and maximum working voltage. Other characteristics include temperature coefficient, noise, and inductance. The resistors are color coded so that the user can easily read these parameters. The color-coding is shown in Figure 3–13. In other words, resistors commonly have 4 color bands.

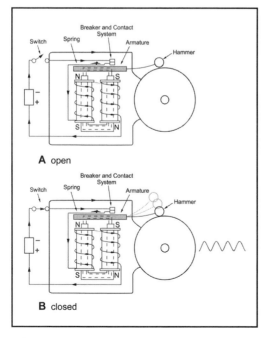

Figure 3–11. *Operation of a simple doorbell.*

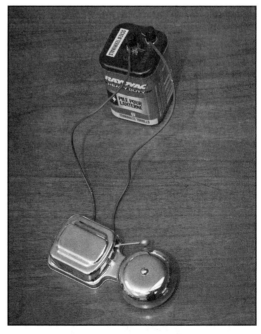

Figure 3–12. *A simple electric doorbell.*

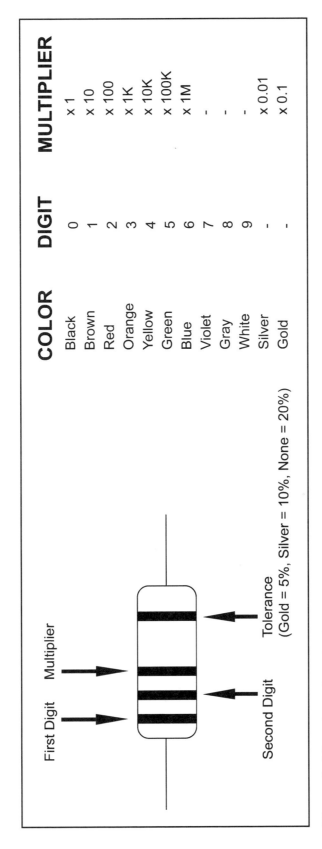

COLOR	DIGIT	MULTIPLIER
Black	0	x 1
Brown	1	x 10
Red	2	x 100
Orange	3	x 1K
Yellow	4	x 10K
Green	5	x 100K
Blue	6	x 1M
Violet	7	-
Gray	8	-
White	9	-
Silver	-	x 0.01
Gold	-	x 0.1

First Digit   Multiplier

Second Digit

Tolerance
(Gold = 5%, Silver = 10%, None = 20%)

Figure 3–13. Color-coding of resistors.

43

A single digit is associated with the color of the first band and a second single digit is also associated with the color of the second band. The color of the 3rd band specifies the multiplier (number of zeros to be added to the first two digits associated with the first two color bands). The color of the 4th band specifies the tolerance of the resistor (e.g., 5% tolerance for gold and 10% tolerance for silver). Suppose a resistor has the following color bands, in sequence, from left to right: green, blue, orange, and silver. The green band codes for the first digit (the number 5). The blue band codes for the second digit (the

number 6). The orange band codes for a multiplier of 1,000, so 56 (digits 1 and 2) is multiplied by 1000 to yield a resistor of 56,000 Ω. The fourth color band of silver indicates that this resistor of 56,000 Ω is a 10% tolerance resistor.

Before moving along to resistors in series and parallel, let us conduct a small experiment in which both Ohm's law and Kirchhoff's law are highlighted. Refer back to the light bulb where we had a 6-volt battery and a little bulb. Recall from Ohm's law that we need to have voltage, current, and resistance in a circuit. In Figure 3–14A, we measured the voltage

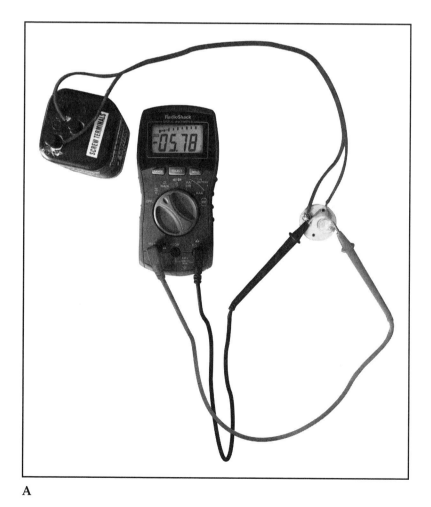

A

Figure 3–14. A. *Voltage measurement.* continues

across the bulb using a digital multimeter. This device measures voltage, current, and resistance. Kirchhoff's law states that the sum of voltage drops across a circuit are equal to the supplied voltage. In this case, where we have only one component, we expect the voltage drop to be equal to the supplied voltage. In order to measure the voltage delivered by the battery, you connect the positive end of the voltmeter (one component of the multimeter) to the positive side of the battery and the nega-tive end of the voltmeter to the negative side of the battery and you read the volt-meter. In this case, with the 6-volt battery and one component, the reading is 6 volts. The results are consistent with Kirchhoff's law. If we add another component to this circuit, the voltage drop across both com-ponents will be equal to the supplied voltage.

For the second step of the first experi-ment we measure the current along the wire (Figure 3–14B). Two tiny slits are

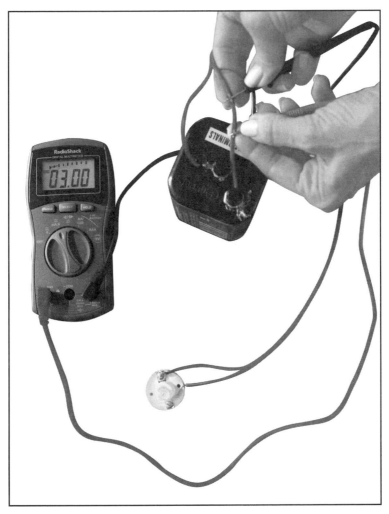

B

Figure 3–14. continued **B.** *Current measurement.*

made through the insulation along the wire leading to the positive terminal of the battery in order to expose the wire. Select ammeter on the device to measure current. The positive end of the ammeter touches one exposed slit and the negative end of the ammeter touches the other. In this case the reading was 3 amperes.

In our experiment, V = 6 volts and I = 3 amperes. Therefore, we can calculate R (resistance) using Ohm's law, $R = V/I$. In this case, R = 6/3, that is, 2 Ω. This calculation is analogous to the Impedance, Z, in the mechanical system described in Chapter 2. Voltage is analogous to the steady force in dynes. Current is analogous to velocity in the mechanical system. Resistance is analogous to the friction component in mechanical impedance Z_M.

Now, let us calculate power (W) of the bulb: $W = I \times V$ (3 × 6) = 18 W.

SERIES RESISTANCE AND PARALLEL RESISTANCE

The way in which two or more resistors are connected influences the equivalent resistance of the combination of resistors and the performance of the circuit as a whole. Resistors in a circuit can be connected in series or in parallel. Resistors are connected in series when they are connected one after another, forming a chain; imagine a chain of soldiers standing in a single line. When resistors

are connected in parallel, it is similar to two lines of soldiers parallel to each other. The resistances add up arithmetically in value, thereby increasing the equivalent resistance of the total resistor combination (Figure 3–15 and Equation 3.4). The equivalent resistance R_{eq} (in ohms) of resistors $R_1, R_2 \ldots R_n$ connected in series is the sum of all the individual resistances:

$$R_{eq} = R_1 + R_2 + \ldots + R_n \quad \text{(Eqn. 3.4)}$$

The total equivalent resistance of the circuit increases when we connect resistors in series. The voltage drop across the total equivalent resistance is the sum of all the individual voltage drops across each of the resistors, but the same current flows through every resistance connected in series. The individual voltage drop can be calculated using the voltage divider rule. If the total voltage drop across all the resistances connected in series is V volts, then the voltage drop across any individual resistor is shown in Equation 3.5:

$$V_k = V \times \frac{R_k}{\sum_1^n R_t} \quad \text{(Eqn. 3.5)}$$

where V_k is the voltage drop (in volts) across an individual resistor (R_k). Let's assume we have a circuit with three resistors as follows: R_1 = 2000 ohms, R_2 = 3500 ohms, and R_3 = 4500 ohms, and the total voltage drop across all resistors is 18 volts, then the individual voltage drop (V_1) across

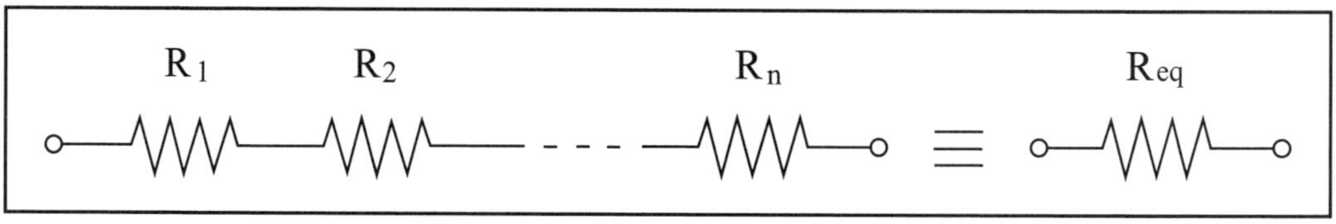

Figure 3–15. *A combination of resistors in series (R₁ to Rₙ). R_eq is the total resistance across the individual resistors.*

R_1 = [(2000)/(2000 + 3500 + 4500)] × 18 = 3.6 volts, the individual voltage drop (V_2) across R_2 = [(3500)/(2000 + 3500 + 4500)] × 18 = 6.3 volts, and the individual voltage drop (V_3) across R_3 = [(4500)/(2000 + 3500 + 4500)] × 18 = 8.1 volts.

A common example of an in-series connection is the fuse box connected to our home appliances. The fuse box contains a resistive fuse wire, which is connected in series to our total group of electric appliances, which has a total resistance. The same current that flows through the fuse wire flows through the group of appliances connected in series with fuse wire. The voltage drop across the fuse wire differs from the voltage drop across the group of appliances. If the fuse wire burns out due to a voltage spike then the series circuit is broken and all the appliances connected to the fuse box stop operating. So the voltage spike causes the circuit to open, that is, the circuit stops conducting current when any of the resistances in an in-series connection develops an electrical problem; all of the resistances must be working for the circuit to be complete.

If we connect several resistors across two points they are connected in parallel (Figure 3–16). The reciprocal of the total equivalent resistance (R_{eq}) represents the sum of the reciprocals of each individual resistance (unit is ohms) and is less than the smallest individual resistance (see Equation 3.6). This type of connection is also called a shunt as the equivalent value of the total

$$1/R_{eq} = 1/R_1 + 1/R_2 + \ldots + 1/R_n$$
(Eqn. 3.6)

resistance also gets shunted (a decrease in total resistance). In a parallel circuit, the current is divided across the multiple resistor paths. If resistors are connected in

parallel, then the current will divide such that some current will flow through each resistor. So if R_1 stops working, some current will still flow through the remaining resistors. In contrast, if the resistors were connected in series, then the current would flow through a single path through all of the resistors, and if one resistor stopped working, the current would not flow through the other resistors. With a series circuit, the total equivalent resistance is the sum of the individual resistances so a larger total equivalent resistance means less current flow leading to lower battery drainage. With a parallel circuit, the reciprocal of the total equivalent resistance is the sum of the reciprocals of the individual resistances so more parallel resistors mean a smaller total equivalent resistance, higher current flow, and higher battery drainage.

As previously mentioned, the total equivalent resistance of the combination of resistors in a parallel circuit decreases when we connect the resistances in shunt (in parallel). The voltage drop across each of the resistances is the same in a parallel circuit. However, the total current flowing through all the resistances in a parallel circuit is the sum of the currents flowing through each of the individual resistors. If the total current flowing through all the resistors is I, then the current flowing through a particular resistor (R_k) is I_k (in amperes), which can be calculated using Equation 3.7:

$$I_k = I \times \frac{R_T}{R_k + R_T} \qquad \text{(Eqn. 3.7)}$$

where R_T is the parallel combination of all the resistances except R_k.

So, if the total current flowing through all the resistors is 50 amperes, and the circuit has 3 resistors in parallel (R_1 is 100 Ω,

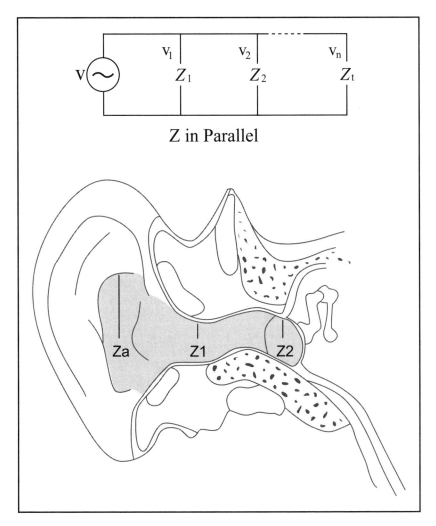

Figure 3–16. *A parallel circuit. You may be interested to know that the eardrum and the entrance to the ear canal are resistors in parallel. We elaborate in Chapter 7.*

R_2 is 200 Ω, and R_3 is 300 Ω), then the current flowing through R_2 can be calculated as follows:

$I_2 = 50 \times$ (parallel combination of the 100 and 300 Ω resistors)/ (200 W + the parallel combination of the 100 and 300 Ω resistors); and
$I_2 = 50 \times$ (reciprocal of $1/100 + 1/300$)/

(200 + reciprocal of $1/100 + 1/300$); and $I_2 = 50 \times (1/0.013)/(200 + 1/0.013)$ $= 50 \times 75/275 = 50 \times 0.2727 =$ 13.64 amperes.

An example of a parallel circuit is the connection of our household appliances or audiological equipment in our labs and clinics. All the appliances and audiological instrumentation are connected to the same voltage mains. The current flowing through each appliance may vary depending on its resistance. If one of the household appliances, or one piece of audiological equipment, (e.g., audiometer or OAEs), develops an electrical problem, the other appliances and equipment remain unaffected and keep working. If the household appliances, or audiological equipment were connected in series, when one appliance or one piece of equipment develops an electrical problem, all of the other appliances or equipment stop working.

Some electrical systems need both series and parallel circuits. As just mentioned, all household appliances and scientific equipment are connected in parallel with each other so that if one household appliance or piece of equipment develops an electrical problem, the other equipment will keep working. But their parallel combination is connected in series to a fuse box to ensure that our expensive appliances and equipment are not damaged due to voltage spikes in the fuse box.

DIRECT CURRENT CIRCUIT

Now that we have studied the basic building blocks of an electric circuit let us try to understand a basic direct current (DC) circuit and some terminology related to it. An electrical circuit allows a single, unidirectional path for the electrons to follow. It is a simple looping electrical network that provides electriciy from one terminal of the power source to the other terminal of the power source. It consists of components like wires, resistors, switches, voltage sources, current sources, and some other

components like inductors, capacitors, diodes, transistors, and so forth (inductors and capacitors are described in Chapter 4 and diodes and transistors are described in Chapter 6) that are more functional in alternating current (AC) circuits (AC circuits are described in Chapter 4). Resistors may be in the form of resistive devices like a light bulb or in the form of an attenuator (variable resistor). Measuring devices such as an ammeter, voltmeter, or wattmeter (used for measuring power), can be connected in a circuit. Figure 3–17 shows symbols of some of the commonly used electrical components in circuits.

One can connect a switch in series with the circuit loop to switch the circuit operation on or off (see Figure 3–9). When we open a switch we get an open circuit. A circuit is open if the current has no return path to the power source. The operation of a device connected in the circuit is terminated (switched off) if the circuit is open. Closing the switch completes the electric loop and allows the current to flow through a return path to the power source. Thus, in the closed switch mode, all the devices connected in this circuit are in operation. In a circuit, a ground is a point of reference voltage. Voltage, as we know from the discussion earlier in this chapter, represents the difference in potential between two points (negative terminal versus positive terminal or negative terminal versus ground). The process for measuring voltage and current is described above (see Figure 3–14A and Figure 3–14B).

Safety is the most important consideration while handling any electrical circuit or component. Electrical shocks can cause burns and can be fatal. Live wires should never be touched with bare hands and necessary precautions must be taken in cases

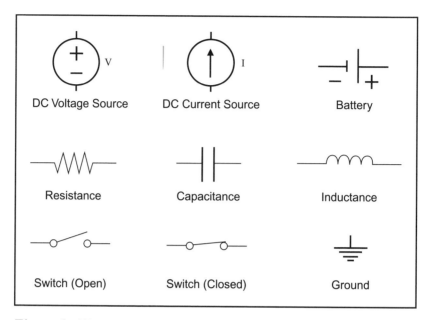

Figure 3–17. *Electrical components and their schematic symbols in electric circuit diagrams. Subsequent voltage measurements for that circuit are based on that same reference point. This circuit reference point, called a ground, is considered to have zero voltage. A ground that is not connected to the earth is said to be a floating ground.*

where handling of live wires is required. Electricity mains should be switched off before making repairs or examining electric components and devices. It is important to put on insulating rubber gloves before handling or repairing circuits or cables carrying high voltage. Every electrical device must be grounded to avoid unexpected electric shocks due to contact with an ungrounded device (Figure 3–18). In electronic circuit theory, a *ground* is usually considered an infinite source or sink for electric charge, which can absorb an unlimited amount of current without changing its potential.

Grounding is the process of connecting the appliance body to the physical ground or earth to avoid a buildup of electric potential that can damage the circuit and insulation because of high voltages. Grounding limits the buildup of static electricity when handling flammable substances and repairing circuits. Most appliances come with a third pin on the power connector to ground the device. This pin is connected to the earth through a wire and prevents electric shock in case of an insulation failure. Thus, it is always advisable to use a 3-pin connector with all electrical devices.

Figure 3–18. *Electric shock due to contact with an ungrounded television.*

4

Electrical Energy— Alternating Current

INTRODUCTION

This chapter focuses on information directly related to Audiology and Hearing Science. Although these concepts may be somewhat difficult, the knowledge acquired in Chapter 2 on mechanical impedance should be helpful.

The power source of choice for most of our small appliances (e.g., mobile phones, lamps, portable media players) is direct current (DC) and some of our audiologic devices (e.g., sound-level meters, otoscopes, hearing aids). But this is not the only kind of electricity in use. Some sources of power such as rotary electromechanical generators produce voltages that switch polarity (between negative and positive) periodically over time. The voltage and the associated current alternate between positive and negative polarity, increasing from zero to a maximum peak in the positive direction, decreasing to zero and then increasing to a maximum peak in the opposite (negative) direction, and then returning to zero. This kind of electrical current is called alternating current (AC), similar to the pure tone about

which you learned in Acoustics. The pure tone alternates between positive and negative peaks, as does the alternating current. We receive AC current in our homes. It is used in some appliances such as light bulbs that can operate on AC as well as DC and many audiologic devices such as audiometers, acoustic admittance meters, and instrumentation used to measure auditory evoked potentials. Many appliances that run on DC can operate on AC if a rectifier is used to convert AC to DC. The main power supply in our homes is AC.

In AC circuits, the polarity of the flow of electric charge changes periodically, so AC and voltage in an AC circuit can be characterized by the four parameters of a sinusoidal wave: wavelength, time period, frequency, and amplitude. Recall from a course in Acoustics that distance between two maxima points or two minima points on a waveform is called one wavelength (λ). The time required for one wavelength of alternating current or one cycle of a sinusoidal acoustic wave to pass through a point is called the time period (T), which is measured in seconds. The frequency (f) of alternating current is the number of cycles the current waveform completes in one second and is the inverse of the time period (Eqn. 4.1). Frequency is measured in cycles/seconds or more commonly in hertz (Hz).

$$f = 1/T \; Hz \qquad \text{(Eqn. 4.1)}$$

In a good conductor, the current travels almost at the speed of light and hence the relation between frequency and wavelength may be given as $c = f\lambda$, where c is the speed of light and λ is wavelength.

The magnitude of the amplitude of an ideal DC voltage is fixed. The magnitude of an AC voltage signal, however, varies with time. One way to specify the amplitude of AC voltage is by measuring the peak amplitude of the voltage sine waveform. This peak amplitude does not describe the effective capacity of the AC to perform work so it cannot be compared with the magnitude of a DC voltage. Therefore, we use an effective value to describe the amplitude of an AC volt-

age signal, which is defined as the amplitude of a DC voltage signal that would perform the same amount of work as this AC signal. This value is called the root mean square (RMS) value of the AC voltage signal. The RMS value can be obtained by multiplying the peak amplitude of the AC voltage signal by a factor of 0.707. Alternatively, the peak amplitude of the AC voltage signal can be obtained by multiplying the RMS value by a factor of 1.414. The amplitude of an AC signal is best described by its RMS value.

The waveform (amplitude as a function of time) of an alternating current is described in Figure 4–1. The current starts at time $T = 0$ seconds from zero amperes and rises to a positive maximum amplitude of $+A$ amperes at time $t = T/4$ seconds. The current then starts to fall to zero amperes at time $t = T/2$ seconds. This marks the completion of half of the cycle. The current continues to fall reaching negative maximum of $-A$ amperes at $t = 3T/4$ seconds before rising up again and reach-

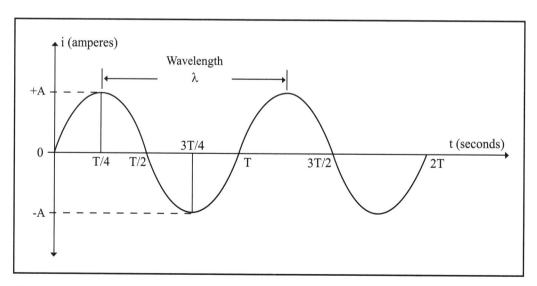

Figure 4–1. *Waveform of a sinusoidal alternating current. The alternating current signal i is a sine function of time and can be represented as i(t).*

ing zero amperes again at $t = T$ seconds. The cycle is completed in T seconds so T is the time period of the AC waveform. The signal from time $t = 0$ seconds to $t = T$ seconds represents one wavelength of the alternating current. Each completion of T seconds represents a repeat of the signal so the signal is periodic. As specified by Equation 4.1, the frequency of this AC waveform is the reciprocal of the time period T. The RMS value of the current is 0.707 A (amperes). The current (in amperes) at any specific instant in time can be derived using Equation 4.2:

$$i(t) = A \sin 2\pi ft \; amperes \qquad \text{(Eqn. 4.2)}$$

where i is current at time (t), A is amplitude of the current at $\sin 2\pi f$ (frequency) at time t.

In our homes, the power supplied to the power mains is a 120 volt AC sinusoidal waveform with a frequency of 60 Hz. This standard is used mainly in North America and is governed by the International Electrotechnical Commission (IEC). The time period of this AC voltage supply at 60 Hz is given by the reciprocal of the 60 Hz frequency, which is $1/60 = 0.0167$ seconds. The RMS value of the mains voltage is 120 volts. The peak value of this voltage is nearly 170 volts (i.e., 1.414×120). In homes in Europe, the power supplied to the power mains is a 240 volt AC with a frequency of 50 Hz. Some countries (e.g., Japan) use a mixture of 50 Hz and 60 Hz frequencies for the power supply.

PHASOR REPRESENTATION OF AC

A phasor or a phase vector is a rotating vector. It is a representation of a sinusoidal signal in terms of its amplitude (A), phase (θ), and angular velocity (ω) (Figure 4–2). The amplitude of the sinusoidal waveform can be thought of as the projection of the rotating vector or phasor. The absolute value (modulus) of the phasor represents the amplitude A of the current or signal. The phase θ gives the angle that the phasor makes with the horizontal axis beginning at time $t = 0$.

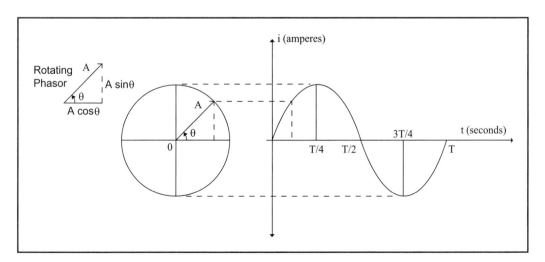

Figure 4–2. Phasor representation of AC.

Although we comprehend an AC signal as a sinusoidal waveform, it can also have shapes (e.g., triangular wave, square wave, saw-tooth waveform) that are generated by certain types of digital oscillators and have applications in the digital logic design industry. The square wave is the most widely used in fields such as communications, digital design, signal processing, and audio processing. Square waves play an important role in technologies for generating pure-tone signals in modern audiometers (see further information in Chapter 9). These applications underscore the need for a basic understanding of a square wave.

SQUARE WAVE

A square wave is a periodic mathematical function that alternates instantaneously between two levels, ideally for the same amount of time. It can be defined as a signal that has amplitude $+A$ units for $t = T/2$ seconds and $-A$ units for the next $t = T/2$ seconds (Figure 4–3). This constitutes one cycle or one wavelength of the signal. As the signal is periodic, this amplitude variation sequence repeats every $t = T$ seconds. Thus, the period of a square-wave signal is T seconds. Note that t is the time variable whereas T is the constant value of this time variable.

The percentage of time period during which a signal's amplitude has a positive value represents the duty cycle. In the square wave shown in Figure 4–3, the amplitude is positive for exactly half the cycle or time period. Therefore, the signal has a 50% duty cycle. If a signal's amplitude is positive across only one-fourth of its cycle, then the signal has a 25% duty cycle (Figure 4–4). Note that the signal amplitude is positive only for one-fourth of its cycle from $t = 0$ to $t = T/4$ seconds. Pulses with low duty cycles often are used as triggering pulses for digital logic circuits.

Square waves are typically encountered in electronics, communications, and digital signal processing (DSP) to represent voltage pulses, binary logic diagrams, and so forth. High-frequency square waves are used as clock signals at precisely timed intervals in digital switching circuits (e.g., computer chips in digital hearing aids and audiometers) to provide synchronization.

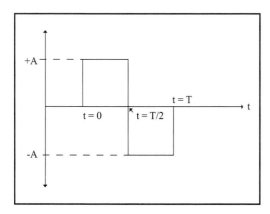

Figure 4–3. *Waveform showing one cycle of a square wave.*

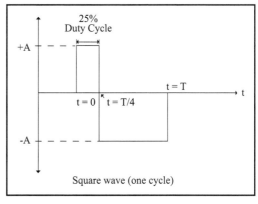

Figure 4–4. *Square wave with a 25% duty cycle.*

Analysis of a Square Wave

Unlike a sine wave, a square wave has more than one frequency component. Subjecting a square wave to Fourier analysis can resolve the signal into its components (see Chapter 8 section on fast Fourier transform). The components are pure sine waves of different frequencies that mix in different proportions to give a square-wave signal. Consider the analogy of refining crude petroleum oil. During the refining process, different components such as kerosene, diesel, gasoline, and wax are separated by fractional distillation and filtering so they can be used for different purposes. Similarly, if we can determine which sine-wave components are present in the square wave signal, and the proportions of these components in the sine-wave signal, then we can represent the signal mathematically. These basic components and their proportions are given by a mathematical algorithm called fast Fourier transform (FFT). Using the Fourier transform, we can represent a square wave as a weighted arithmetic sum of its component signals. The square wave signal is a sum of all the odd sinusoids such that the odd multiples of the frequency of the signal are added in decreasing proportions. If we add all these odd harmonics in the right proportions, the signal converges to a square wave. It is analogous to mixing three primary colors—red, green, and blue—to create a desired secondary color.

Figure 4–5 shows the approximation of a square wave obtained by adding weighted sine waves. The figure illustrates that the signal waveform more closely approaches the shape of a square wave as more odd harmonics are added together. An ideal square wave with an infinite number of odd harmonic frequencies would require an infinite bandwidth, which is not possible. The admixture of the first three or four odd harmonics yields a good approximation of a square wave for many applications.

A simple way to construct a square wave is by using switching circuits. Consider the simple assembly in Figure 4–6. The output is connected to a switch that alternates between +5 volts and −5 volts. When the switch is at point A, the output is a DC voltage of +5 volts. Flicking the switch to point B will instantly change the output to −5 volts. Continually flicking this switch back and forth at regular intervals of *T* seconds will result in continual alternation of the output between +5 and −5 volts, such that the waveform resembles that of a square wave with frequency equivalent to $1/T$. If this switching action is simulated with a circuit, then a square wave can be generated. There are various ways to generate square waves. One of these methods is used in the construction of the oscillator in some audiometers. We revisit this issue in Chapter 9. By that time, you will have learned various aspects of electronics such as filtering and electrical impedance.

POWER TRANSMISSION

Electric power transmission refers to transmission of electricity from the generating stations into our homes. In the 19th century, Thomas Edison's DC transmission was the standard for power transmission. Based on Nikola Tesla's concept and application of AC electrical transmission, beginning in the late 1800s, AC transmission superseded DC transmission of electricity from power plants as AC power generators were easier to construct and much more efficient than DC power generators. Because electrical transmission

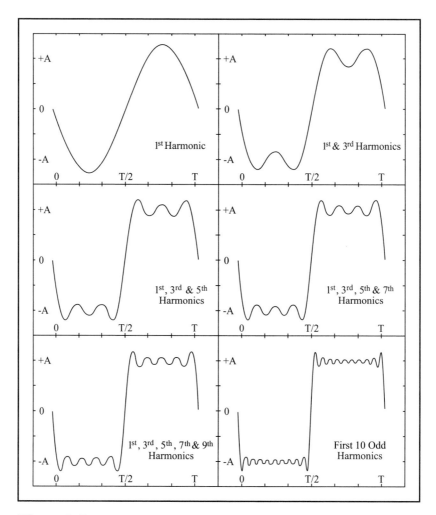

Figure 4–5. *Waveforms resulting from the addition of odd harmonics, from a single harmonic component in the left cell of the top row to 10 harmonic components in the right cell of the bottom row.*

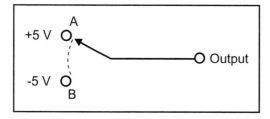

Figure 4–6. *Switching circuit for constructing a square wave.*

over long distances leads to power losses by heat dissipation resulting from the resistance of the transmitting wires, the voltage carried by the transmission lines must be boosted. With DC electrical transmission, this boost was accomplished using complex and expensive spinning rotary converters (a hybrid of an AC motor and a DC generator) at regular points along the transmission line. Based on Nikola Tesla's demonstration that electronic transformers, devices that transfer an alternating current from one circuit to one or more other circuits, usually with a change in voltage (step-up transformer for increased voltage or step-down transformer for decreased voltage), these simple, relatively inexpensive, and efficient transformers could be used to accomplish the necessary voltage boost in AC electrical transmission. Lacking moving parts, these transformers required minimal maintenance. The advantages of these electronic transformers contributed to the replacement of DC power transmission by AC power transmission.

Today's AC power generators are three-phase alternators. An alternator is an electromechanical device that converts mechanical energy into electrical energy. It consists of a rotating magnet called a rotor that spins inside a coil of wires wound around a cylindrical iron core called a stator (Figure 4–7). When the magnetic field changes due to the rotation of the magnet with respect to the wires on the stator, alternating current is induced in the coiled wires.

A three-phase alternator has three coils of wires wound such that each generates independent voltages of the same amplitude but differing in phase from each other by 120°. Thus, their pha-

sors are always 120° apart. Three-phase power generation systems have considerable economical and technical advantages over one-phase or two-phase power generator systems with the same voltage. The three phases are transmitted together on the power lines. Heavy duty motors and some large loads are powered by all three phases simultaneously. Our homes, however, receive a single-phase power supply for household appliances.

Recent technologic advances have improved the feasibility of conversion of AC power transmission to high voltage DC for transmission of large amounts of power over very long distances. For example, high voltage DC power transmission is used for submarine power transmission since high voltage AC power transmission can be associated with insulation damage due to adverse electromagnetic interactions between the current and metal casing of the cable.

AC CIRCUIT COMPONENTS

Resistive AC circuit

Earlier in this chapter, we described a simple resistive DC circuit consisting of a resistor R connected to a DC source of power, a battery, and current flow in a single direction. Let us connect the same resistor R to an AC source of voltage and see the resultant current flow (Figure 4–8). The circle containing a sine wave in Figure 4–8B illustrates an AC voltage source (designated by v rather than V as in the DC circuit in Figure 4–8A).

In electronics, by convention, DC parameters are labeled using upper-case letters whereas AC parameters are labeled using lower-case letters. When we connect the voltage source v in the AC circuit, a current i flows through it. Whereas, in a

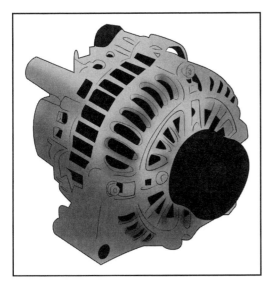

Figure 4–7. Alternator.

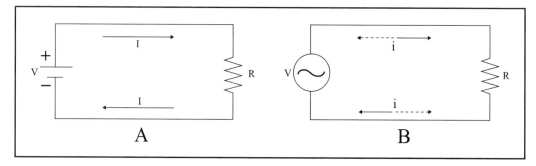

Figure 4–8. *Current flow in a simple resistive DC circuit is shown in A and a simple AC circuit is shown in B. In B the solid arrows show the direction of current flow in one direction during one-half of the cycle and the dotted lines show the direction of current flow in the opposite direction during the other half of the cycle.*

DC current the current *I* flows in a single direction, in an AC current, the current *i* changes its flow direction periodically, depending on the frequency of the voltage source. In an AC circuit, the current *i* flows in one direction for one-half the cycle then flows in the opposite direction for the remaining half of the cycle. Thus, current *i* flows to and fro through the resistor *R*, which resists the flow of this current through a voltage drop given by Ohm's law. Thus, Ohm's law also applies to alternating currents.

In some applications whereby the function of the resistance is to dissipate electrical energy in the form of heat or light, the direction of current flow through the resistance is unimportant. For example, an alternating current flowing through a light bulb meets high resistance from the bulb's tungsten filament regardless of the direction of current flow, and heat dissipation with current flow in either direction still causes the bulb to emit light. As previously mentioned in Chapter 2, because resistors do not store energy, the voltage and current are in phase in an AC circuit. Capacitors and inductors represent electrical components that can store rather than dissipate electrical energy. Recall

from Chapter 2 that in a mechanical system, the spring and mass components store energy and are analogs to the capacitors and inductors.

Capacitors and Inductors

Recall that, in the domain of mechanics, energy is constantly being converted between its potential and kinetic forms or becomes lost in some other form of energy such as heat. Dissipation of energy by a resistor into heat in an electrical circuit is analogous to dissipation of energy by friction into heat in a mechanical system. In a mechanical system, the energy of an oscillating object changes continually between its potential and kinetic forms; springs and masses are storehouses of potential energy. Inductors and capacitors respectively, represent the electrical analogs of masses and springs. As discussed in Chapter 7, in the outer and middle ear, the muscles, tympanic membrane springiness, and air molecules in the ear canal space and tympanic cavity represent springs or capacitors; the masses of the ossicles, tympanic membrane, and air within the mastoid cavity represent masses or inductors; and the collisions of the air molecules in the outer and middle ear represent the resistance or friction.

Capacitance is the measure of the ability of an object to store an electric charge similar to the spring's ability to store mechanical (potential) energy (Figure 4–9). Subjecting two conducting plates separated by nonconducting (dielectric) insulating material to a potential difference using a voltage source will cause the plates to start charging to the applied potential. As dielectric material resists electric current flow through it, the negatively charged electrons in the current aggregate on the conducting plate that is connected to the negative terminal of the voltage source, leading to the development of a potential on the other conducting plate (connected to the positive terminal) that is equivalent in magnitude but is positively rather than negatively charged.

A potential difference starts building up between the conducting plates until it reaches the applied potential from the battery and a certain charge is stored in an electric field generated around the two conducting plates. This charge has the capacity for electrical work so it is analogous to potential energy in a mechanical system. If a charge of Q coulombs is stored in the electric field generated by these conducting plates separated by a potential difference of v volts, then the capacitance of this two-plate assembly is C coulombs per volt (Eqn. 4.3).

$$c = \frac{Q}{V} \text{ Farads} \qquad \text{(Eqn. 4.3)}$$

The unit of capacitance is also called farad. Capacitance also can be defined as the ratio of the charge on one conducting plate to the potential difference between the two plates. If these two charged plates are connected to a resistor then they will act like a battery, supplying electrical energy in the form of current to the resistor until they discharge completely. In summary, this setup of two conducting plates separated by a dielectric material forms a capacitor.

A capacitor is a passive component used to insert capacitance into a circuit. A passive component is one that does not require power for its operation. Imagine a river that branches into many directions. The branches don't actively change the flow. Rather, they are passive and the water flows through each of these branches. A narrow passage will always be narrow; the wide passage will always be wide. They can't narrow or widen themselves. As you will see later, an inductor is also a passive component. Resisters, as discussed in Chapters 2 and 3, are also passive components.

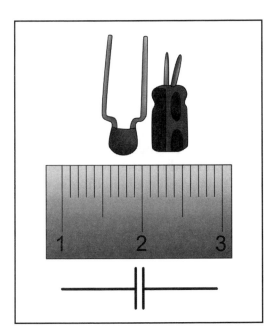

Figure 4–9. Capacitors shown on top and the electronic symbol for a capacitor is shown on the bottom.

A capacitor stores electrical energy in the form of an electric field. A simple two-plate capacitor can be constructed using two parallel conducting metal plates separated by a dielectric substance such as air, paper, glass, plastic, mica, or ceramic. The lead wires from each plate are connected to create a circuit. An ideal capacitor stores the charge accumulated on it without dissipating any energy in the form of a counter-EMF (electromotive force) to resist charging by the connected source. Counter-EMF may not be a term with which you are familiar. If EMF refers to the flow of electricity, then counter-EMF refers to the rejection (much like impedance) to the flow of electricity. Counter-EMF is called the capacitive reactance in a circuit with capacitors. The unit of capacitive reactance is ohms, as it is in mechanical impedance. A capacitor, however, also has some resistance due to the resistivity of the conducting plates and the lead wires. When a capacitor is connected in an AC circuit, its conducting plates charge and discharge continuously because of the polarity-changing nature of alternating current. As shown in Eqn. 4.4, the capacitive reactance offered by a capacitor C connected in an AC circuit is X_C (the unit is ohms), the value of which is inversely related to the frequency f of the current or voltage source:

$$X_C = 1/2\pi f C \qquad \text{(Eqn. 4.4)}$$

where X_C = capacitive reactance in ohms, f = frequency of the alternating current in Hz, and C = capacitance of the capacitor in the circuit in farads. Capacitive reactance is analogous to stiffness reactance in a mechanical system (Chapter 2).

In a purely capacitive circuit, the phase of the current is 90° or $\pi/4$ radians ahead of the phase of the voltage due to the counter-EMF generated by the capac-itor, so the voltage lags the current by 90° or $\pi/4$ radians. This concept reminds us of the relationship between applied force and velocity in a spring that is in a mechanical system. Recall that in a spring, velocity leads force by 90°. According to Ohm's law, capacitive reactance can be considered to be the ratio of voltage to current, both of which have phase. In a purely capacitive circuit, the capacitive reactance has a phase of −90° or $-\pi/4$ radians and is plotted on the negative side of the imaginary axis.

Capacitors have application to almost every electronic device or appliance we use today such as cell phones, music players, computers, airplane flight control circuits, and satellite transmission circuits; they also have wide applications to devices used in Audiology and Hearing Science such as acoustic immittance devices (see Chapter 9 for further discussion), audiometers, narrow-band noise filters (see Chapters 5, 9, and 10 for further discussion), and pure-tone oscillators in audiometers (see Chapter 9 for further discussion). Capacitors represent the most commonly used component in electrical circuits after resistors. They are sturdy, easy, and inexpensive to manufacture in various shapes and sizes. The motor in a ceiling fan requires a capacitor to assist initiation of fan rotation. Televisions and radios contain capacitors in their tuning circuits to tune in to the broadcasting frequencies. Capacitors are fabricated on microchips and memory elements that can process and store data.

Series Capacitance and Parallel Capacitance

We offer our apologies to the reader for the large number of formulas that follow. These will prove helpful as you progress in this text.

Consider capacitors $C_1, C_2 \ldots, C_n$ connected in series with an AC voltage source v (Figure 4–10). As the only path for the flow of current passes through each of the capacitors, one by one, the same current i passes through all the capacitors. The capacitive reactance creates a voltage drop across each of the capacitors. According to Kirchhoff's law, the sum of these voltage drops across all the capacitors is equal to the supplied voltage v. Let the equivalent capacitance be C_{eq} (eq is the same as total) with a voltage drop of V_{eq} across it, as shown in Figure 4–10. Then, as shown in Eqn. 4.5:

$$V = V_{eq} = V_1 + V_2 + \cdots + V_n \quad \text{(Eqn. 4.5)}$$

In accordance with Ohm's law, v (representing the total voltage drop in the circuit which equals the applied voltage) equals current i multiplied by the capacitive reactance Xc, so V_{eq} and Xc_{eq} can be calculated as follows using Eqns. 4.6 or 4.7:

$$V = iX_{Ceq} = iX_{C1} + iX_{C2} + \cdots + iX_{Cn} \quad \text{(Eqn. 4.6)}$$

or

$$X_{Ceq} = V/i \quad \text{(Eqn. 4.7)}$$

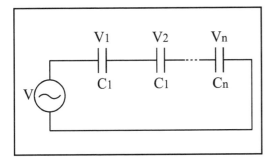

Figure 4–10. *Capacitors connected in series. V_{eq} is the total voltage drop across all the capacitors and C_{eq} is the total capacitance across all the capacitors.*

Eqn. 4.7 is similar to saying that compliance reactance = force/velocity as mentioned in Chapter 2. In Eqn. 4.7, voltage has replaced force, and current has replaced velocity.

Let us connect the same capacitors in parallel across an AC source i (Figure 4–11). It is important to understand the concept of parallel capacitance because it is directly related to the impedance characteristics of the outer and middle ear which are considered a parallel system. As all the capacitors are connected to the same two terminals of the current source, the voltage drop across all the capacitors is v. By Kirchhoff's law, the sum of the currents flowing through all the capacitors equals the current supplied by the current source (see Eqn. 4.9). The total current or equivalent current i_{eq} flows through the total equivalent capacitance C_{eq} as follows:

$$i = i_{eq} = i_1 + i_2 + \cdots + i_n \quad \text{(Eqn. 4.8)}$$

Using Ohm's law,

$$i = v/X_{Ceq} = v/X_{C1} + v/X_{C2} + \cdots + v/X_{Cn} \quad \text{(Eqn. 4.9)}$$

In our previous discussion of mechanical impedance (Chapter 2), the impedance offered by a spring can be referred to either as stiffness reactance or compliance reactance. Therefore, impedance is measured in terms of stiffness reactance or compliance reactance. In electronics, however, we measure only compliance reactance. Therefore, the formula for compliance reactance is:

$$X_C = 1/2\pi fC \quad \text{(Eqn. 4.10)}$$

The equation indicates that compliance reactance is inversely related to frequency. This is very important to remember when we discuss filtering and electrical impedance in Chapter 5.

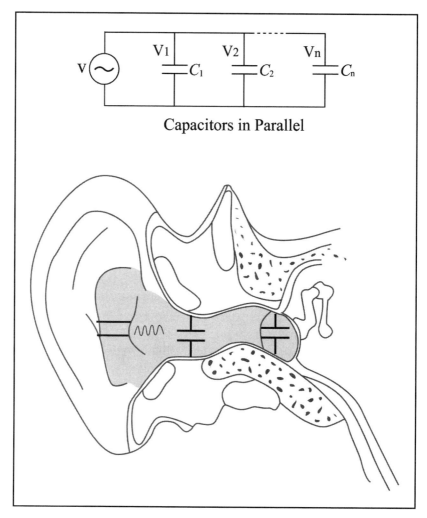

Figure 4–11. *Capacitors connected in parallel.*

Equivalent capacitance of capacitors connected in parallel is equal to the simple sum of the individual capacitances:

$$X_{Ceq} = X_{C1} + X_{C2} + \cdots + X_{Cn} \quad \text{(Eqn. 4.11)}$$

Inductance (Figure 4–12) is the property of a conductor whereby any change in the flow of AC generates an EMF that resists the change in flow of the AC through the conductor. When a changing current *i* passes through a conductor, it produces a electromagnetic field with magnetic flux Φ. The unit of magnetic flux is webers (volt-seconds). Lenz's law states that this flux works on the conductor to oppose any change in the flux that leads to a back EMF. This back EMF, in turn, resists the change in the current flowing through the conductor. The ratio of the magnetic flux generated around a conductor to the changing current passing through it is called self-inductance, commonly referred to as the inductance of the conductor. Inductance is represented by the letter *L* in the circuit and its

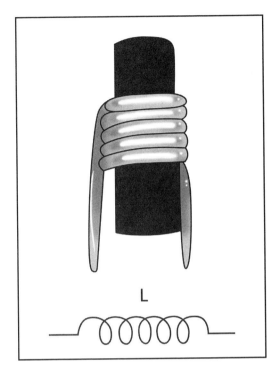

L

Figure 4–12. Sample inductor is shown on top and the electrical symbol for an inductor is shown on the bottom.

unit of measurement is henry (H). Henry is equivalent to the mass in mechanical impedance. This property of inductance is only exhibited by a conductor carrying changing alternating current and does not apply to DC circuits. Even a wire in a circuit carrying alternating current will have inductance; this kind of stray inductance is negligible.

Inductance is added in to a circuit by using a component called an inductor. An inductor is a passive device that stores energy in the form of a magnetic field when a changing current passes through it. It is made by coiling a wire in loops, thereby strengthening the magnetic field around it allowing the inductor to store more energy. An ideal inductor only has a particular inductance and does not radiate or dissipate any energy. A real induc-

tor will have a small resistance due to the resistivity of the coiled wire and some capacitance between two coils along with the inductance. As the inductor resists the change in flow of current passing through it without dissipating any power, it is said to have an inductive reactance. Reactance is the opposition to the alternating current due to a buildup of electric or magnetic fields in the circuit. This reactance is given as X_L and has a unit ohms (Ω). The reactance of an inductor depends on the frequency (f) of the current passing through it.

The back EMF is the source of opposition to the flow of current in an inductive circuit. This back EMF increases to a certain point until the polarity of the alternating current changes and the energy stored in the magnetic field around the inductor is dissipated back into the circuit in the form of current. Thus, there is no loss of energy in an ideal inductor. The magnitude of the back EMF generated increases with the increase in frequency thereby creating more opposition to the flow of current through it. As a direct current is constant and has no frequency, an inductor in a DC circuit will not provide any reactance. The inductor will only act as a resistive coil in a DC circuit. Thus, the inductor, like a capacitor, is also an AC component.

In a purely inductive circuit the phase of the voltage is 90° or $\pi/4$ radians ahead of the phase of the current due to the opposition of the inductance to the flow of current. Therefore, the voltage leads the current or the current lags the voltage by 90° or $\pi/4$ radians. This situation is analogous to the relationship between force and velocity in a mass loaded system where force leads velocity by 90° or $\pi/4$ radians. Observe that voltage lags current in a capacitor by 90° and in inductance voltage leads current by 90°. In other words, the current in a capacitor and the current in an inductor are 180° out of phase. This concept is similar to the relationship between force in the spring and the force in the mass discussed in Chapter 2. As we progress in this text, you will see that this relationship between current in the capacitor and current in the inductor will play an essential role in filtering as well as the construction of oscillators.

Inductors have other practical applications in our day-to-day lives. The electric motor inside mounted and ceiling fans inside our houses has inductor coils wound around magnets. When a current is passed through the coils it generates a magnetic field that spins the motor and the fan attached to it. Inductors are used in tuning circuits inside our radio and television sets. In industry inductors are used for inductive heating and melting of metals. The object to be heated is kept at the center of the inductor coil and alternating current is passed through the coil. The changing magnetic field that is due to the inductor generates small but strong current loops called eddy currents in the metallic object that opposes this magnetic field. This opposition to the magnetic field generates heat and melts the object. Inductive coils are placed around the metal wheels of trains to help them slow down. When the brakes are applied, an alternating current is set flowing through the inductive coils. The magnetic field generated induces eddy currents in the rotating wheels. The interaction between the magnetic field and the eddy currents leads to a braking action and slows down the train.

Series Inductance and Parallel Inductance

Consider inductors $L_1, L_2 \ldots, L_n$ connected in series with an AC voltage source v

(Figure 4–13). The same current i flows through all the inductors. By Kirchhoff's law, the sum of all the voltage drops v_i across the inductors L_i is equal to the total voltage v applied across the series inductances. Let the equivalent inductance be L_{eq} and the voltage drop across it v_{eq}. Then,

$$v = v_{eq} = v_1 + v_2 + - - - + v_n \quad \text{(Eqn. 4.12)}$$

Using Ohm's law, which states that voltage = current times reactance (in this case inductance reactance), we can calculate the voltage in the circuit as follows:

$$v = iX_{Leq} = iX_{L1} + iX_{L2} + - - - + iX_{Ln}$$
$$\text{(Eqn. 4.13)}$$

Therefore,

$$X_{Leq} = X_{L1} + X_{L2} + - - - + X_{Ln} \quad \text{(Eqn. 4.14)}$$

The relationship between frequency, inductors, and inductance reactance is written as:

$$X_L = 2\pi f L \quad \text{(Eqn. 4.15)}$$

Inductance reactance will increase as frequency increases and as the value of the inductors increases. This is similar to the formula used in mechanical impedance where $+X = f \times M$. In a mechanical system, the mass reactance is similar to inductance reactance in electricity.

Now consider the same inductors L_1, $L_2 \ldots, L_n$ connected in parallel across one

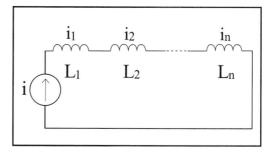

Figure 4–13. *Inductors in series.*

alternating current source i (Figure 4–14). Can we find a similar parallel inductor in the auditory system? As all the inductors are connected between the same two points in the circuit (i.e., the two terminals of the alternating source), the voltage drop v across all the inductors will be equal. By Kirchhoff's law again, the sum of all the currents i_i flowing through the inductors L_i, respectively, will be equal to the current i from the alternating current source. Let L_{eq} represent the total effective inductance in this case with the current i_{eq} flowing through it. Then,

$$i = i_{eq} = i_1 + i_2 + - - - + i_n \qquad \text{(Eqn. 4.16)}$$

By Ohm's law,

$$i = v/X_{Leq} = v/X_{L1} + v/X_{L2} + - - - + v/X_{Ln}$$
$$\text{(Eqn. 4.17)}$$

We calculate inductance reactance as follows:

$$1/X_{Leq} = 1/X_{L1} + 1/X_{L2} + - - - + 1/X_{Ln}$$
$$\text{(Eqn. 4.18)}$$

Inductance reactance is directly related to frequency and to the value of the conductors

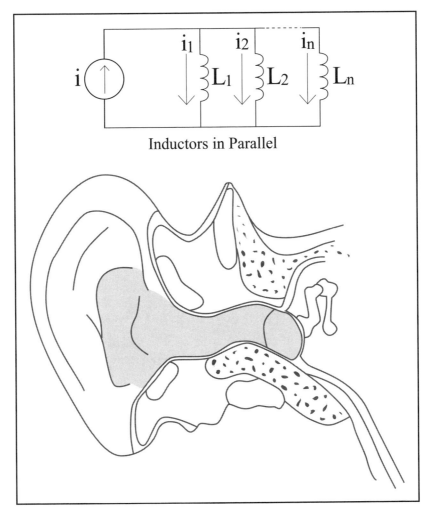

Inductors in Parallel

Figure 4–14. Inductors in parallel.

as follows: $X_L = 2\pi f$ (L is the unit of inductance expressed in henrys).

You will encounter this equation in Chapter 5 as it relates to filtering, and in Chapter 7 as it relates to acoustic impedance.

Thus, when inductors are connected in parallel, the inverse of the total equivalent inductance is equal to the simple sum of the inverses of the individual inductances.

5

Filtering and
Electrical Impedance

IMPEDANCE AND ADMITTANCE

Impedance is a measure of the opposition to the flow of alternating current through a circuit similar to the mechanical impedance that measures the velocity of a mechanical system driven by an alternating force (Chapter 2). In the current chapter we extend the concept of impedance to AC circuits. As we have seen in Chapter 4, capacitors and inductors oppose the flow of current in an AC circuit; their reactance depends on the frequency of the flowing current. Hence, we can say capacitors and inductors impede the free flow of electrons when connected in an AC circuit. There can be multiple combinations of resistances, capacitances, and inductances (similar to stiffness reactance, mass reactance, and resistance mentioned in Chapter 2) in a typical circuit. Keep in mind that these elements are found in the outer and middle ear as well, as shown in Chapters 3 and 4. Impedance is the opposition provided by inductors, capacitors, and resistors to the flow of current in the circuit connected to a source of voltage.

You should be familiar with this concept from Chapters 2, 3, and 4.

Consider a circuit with an alternating voltage source v volts with a frequency f Hz powering a series combination of a resistor R ohms, a capacitor C farads, and an inductor L henrys (Figure 5–1). A current i amperes flows through the circuit generating a voltage drop v_R across R, v_C across C, and v_L across L.

The impedance Z of this circuit can be represented as a phase quantity or as a vector of a real quantity, that is, resistance and an imaginary quantity, that

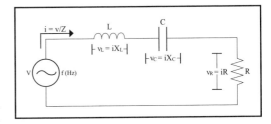

Figure 5–1. RLC series impedance where R is resistance, L is inductance, and C is capacitance. The RLC circuit is analogous to a resistor, spring, and mass, respectively, in a mechanical impedance system.

is, reactance (Figure 5–2). The resistance accounts for the energy loss in the circuit and is plotted on the positive side of the real axis $Re\ (Z)$. The reactance does not cause any loss of energy from the circuit and thus is considered an imaginary part of the impedance. This is the answer to the question posed in Chapter 2, that is, why do we use $+j$ and $-j$ as the imaginary components for impedance? The inductive reactance X_L is considered positive and is plotted on the positive side of the imaginary axis whereas the capacitive reactance X_C is considered negative and is plotted on the negative side of the imaginary axis represented by the downward-pointing arrow. The net reactance X is obtained by subtracting the capacitive reactance from the inductive reactance (i.e., $(X_L–X_C)$ Ω). The circuit is inductive if $X > 0$ and capacitive if $X < 0$. For a purely resistive circuit the net reactance $X = 0$ (the system is in resonance).

When Z is obtained using a vector quantity, we use the following formulas:

$$Z = \sqrt{R^2 + X^2} \qquad \text{(Eqn. 5.1)}$$

As $X_t = X_L - X_C$, then

$$Z = \sqrt{R^2 + (X_C^2 - X_C^2)} \qquad \text{(Eqn. 5.2)}$$

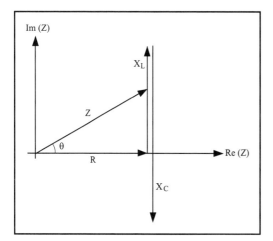

Figure 5–2. *Impedance phasor diagram.*

When electrical impedance is represented as a phase angle, the following formula is used:

$$\varphi = \tan^{-1}\left(\frac{X_L \times X_C}{R}\right) \qquad \text{(Eqn. 5.3)}$$

When electrical impedance is represented as a vector quantity, it is represented as $Z = R + jX$ Ω or $Z = R - jX$ Ω. Where $Z_t = R + jX$, the system is inductance-loaded (analogous to a mass-loaded system in a mechanical system) and where $Z_t = R - jX$, the system is capacitance-loaded (analog to a stiffness-loaded system in a mechanical system). Even though an imaginary number is represented by the letter i in mathematics we use the letter j for imaginary numbers in electronics as i is used to represent current. This provides further explanation for the question asked in Chapter 2, that is, why do we use $+j$ and $-j$ rather than i to represent the imaginary line?

When impedance is described as a phase quantity, then $Z = Z < \emptyset$ or $Z = Z > \emptyset$. The symbol preceding $\emptyset$, whether $<$ or $>$ is dependent on the quadrant in which the phase quantity is plotted. As seen in Figure 5–2, the upper quadrant, as indicated by the upward-pointing arrow, is inductance-dominated and will carry the greater than sign $(>)$. The lower quadrant, as indicted by the downward-pointing arrow, is capacitance-dominated and will carry the less than sign $(<)$.

We hope that you understand the concept of phase angle. Remember that $X_L - X_C$ is net X. Phase angle can be positive or negative depending on whether net X is X_L or Xc. X_L is positive and X_c is negative.

Based on the above discussion, we can describe electrical impedance in two ways: (1) using both imaginary and real numbers as described above (rectangular notation), and (2) polar notation. In polar notation, both impedance Z (vector impedance) and associated phase angle are used. Phase angle is derived using the above mentioned formula.

Admittance Y, on the other hand, is the opposite of impedance. We came across the term admittance in Chapter 2. Admittance is the measure of how readily the circuit allows current to flow through it and is given by the ratio of current to voltage in a circuit. This is the analog of mechanical admittance, which is equal to V/F. The unit of admittance is siemens or mho. Admittance, like impedance, is a complex quantity with the real component (conductance G, the inverse of resistance) and the imaginary component (susceptance B, the inverse of reactance as shown in Eqn. 5.4):

$$Y = 1/Z = \sqrt{G^2 + jB^2} \text{ siemens or mhos}$$
(Eqn. 5.4)

Impedance (or admittance) is a frequency-dependent quantity. In a DC circuit impedance is the same as resistance as reactance is zero. However, as a change in frequency of alternating current signal can change the impedance of a circuit, and therefore its characteristics, many frequency-dependent applications are designed around circuits with different combinations of R, L, and C. Signal filtering is a major area where frequency dependent circuits is signal filtering.

FILTERS

Unlike resistors, inductors and capacitors are frequency-dependent components, that is, they have a particular response characteristic to every frequency component of an AC signal. Each of these two components will give specific reactance to the

signal depending on the frequency of the AC signal used. In practical applications such as communications, signal processing, and acoustics the signals used contain a mixture of many components with different frequencies. It is often necessary to separate out or filter signals by maintaining some frequency components while significantly attenuating others. Because of their frequency selective properties, inductors and capacitors are ubiquitous, found in TV sets, radios, cell phones, hearing aids, amplifiers, assistive listening devices, audiometers, and all electrophysiologic measuring devices. Different combinations of resistors, inductors, and capacitors are used to implement passive filtering circuits that can select or reject specific frequency bands in a given signal.

Depending on the application, a filter passes certain frequencies and attenuates others. The frequencies to be selected or passed lie in the pass-band of the filter. The frequencies to be rejected are outside of the pass-band within the stop-band. The frequencies outside the pass-band are attenuated to a level much lower than the pass-band. The frequency at which the pass-band transitions into the stop-band is called the cutoff frequency f_c. In an ideal filter the pass-band frequencies stay completely unaffected while the frequencies outside the band are infinitely attenuated. The transition from pass-band to the stop-band happens at the cutoff frequency. The frequency response of a filter is plotted on a logarithmic scale graph (Figure 5–3).

In practical terms, however, it is not possible to implement a filter with an instantaneous cutoff. The stop-band attenuation is chosen to be a certain number of decibels (dB) below the pass-band gain. There is a transition band between the pass-band and the stop-band. The midpoint of the transition band is generally taken as the cutoff frequency. The width of

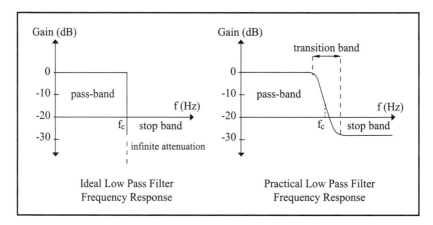

Figure 5–3. *Ideal and practical low-pass filters.*

the transition band depends on the complexity of the filter. The number of elements and the complexity of the filter increase as we try to decrease the width of the transition band. The frequencies in the pass-band may also undergo minor attenuation due to the losses in the filter. Active filters with amplifiers can be used to make up for this attenuation of the signal.

Depending on the range of frequencies to be passed through to the output and the frequencies to be suppressed, the filters are classified as low-pass filters, high-pass filters, band-pass filters, band-stop filters, and so forth.

Low-Pass Filter

In certain applications it is necessary to truncate the high-frequency components from a signal source and pass only the low-frequency signals ahead for further processing. A low-pass filter as the name suggests allows low-frequency components to pass ahead to the next stage while rejecting the higher frequency components. It is also called a high-cut filter or a treble-cut filter in audio applications.

Ideally, it will attenuate all the frequencies above the cutoff frequency while leaving the lower frequencies totally unaffected. In a practical low pass filter however the transition from pass-band to stop-band is not immediate.

A resistor and a capacitor connected in a particular order can be used to implement a low-pass filter (Figure 5–4). The alternating current flows through the resistor and the output voltage is taken across the capacitor. Thus, the load or the next processing stage is supplied with the filtered voltage across the capacitor.

The alternating current from the mixed frequency voltage source v passes through the resistor R into the capacitor C. The capacitor impedes the flow of current through it selectively. As the reactive impedance given by a capacitor to the flow of current decreases with the increase in frequency, the higher frequency components will pass through the capacitor without generating much voltage drop across it. The lower frequency components of the current will be met with high impedance by the capacitor and will generate a higher voltage drop across the capacitor. This voltage consisting of

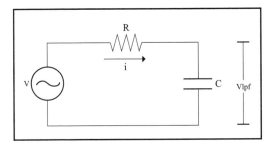

Figure 5–4. *Circuit for low-pass filter.*

lower frequencies will be taken as the output of the low-pass filter v_{lpf} and supplied ahead for further applications. The cutoff frequency of this filter is given as f_c:

$$f_c = \frac{1}{2\pi RC} \ \text{Hz} \qquad \text{(Eqn. 5.5)}$$

Here the product of R (resistor) and C (capacitor) is called the time constant τ ($\tau = RC$ seconds) of the circuit. A time constant is defined as the time required for a charged capacitor to reach 63% of its ultimate peak value in voltage, or 37% of its decay value from the peak. The time constant in seconds is also defined as the product of the capacitor in farads times the resistor in ohms, or the product of the inductor in henrys times the resistor in ohms. The time constant varies depending on the values of R, C, and L. In Equation 5.5, f_c is therefore equal to the reciprocal of 2p (cycle).

Figure 5–5 shows the output of a low-pass filter as seen on the monitor of a real-time analyzer. A real-time analyzer is a device that displays the component frequencies and relative amplitudes of a complex signal. The screen in this case shows the frequency spectrum of the output of a low-pass filter fed with a mixed frequency noise signal or white noise at the input. We can see how the lower fre-

quencies in the signal are passed at higher amplitude whereas the higher frequencies in the signal are suppressed beyond a certain frequency, which is the cutoff frequency of the connected low pass circuit.

We can also use a combination of a resistor R and an inductor L (Figure 5–6) to implement a low-pass filter. However, the manner in which they are connected will change. The alternating current from the mixed frequency voltage source v first flows through the inductor L into the resistor R to produce a voltage drop v_{lpf} across R. When the mixed frequency current flows into the inductance, the higher frequency components of the current are met with high reactive impedance by the inductor and are attenuated. Thus, they generate a low-voltage drop across R. However, the lower frequency components of the signal are met with much lower impedance and pass through to the resistor without much attenuation, thereby generating most of the voltage drop across R. This total voltage drop v_{lpf} generated across R is the output of the filter and contains the frequencies below the cutoff frequency f_c Hz. In this case the f_c is calculated differently:

$$f_c = \frac{R}{2\pi L} \ \text{Hz} \qquad \text{(Eqn. 5.6)}$$

The time constant of the circuit is $\tau = R/L$ seconds. All the frequencies above f_c Hz comprise the pass-band and appear in the output whereas all the frequencies above f_c Hz will lie in the stop-band and will be attenuated.

Apart from the RC and RL combinations, active low-pass filters are also implemented using amplifiers to boost the signal strength along with filtering and provide a better quality filtered signal by improving its signal to noise ratio.

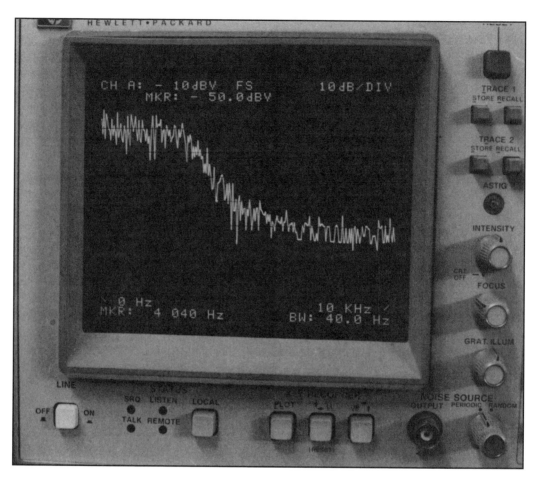

Figure 5–5. *Low-pass filter as shown on a real-time analyzer.*

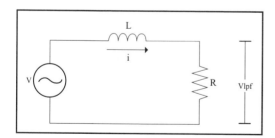

Figure 5–6. *RL low-pass filter.*

Applications of low-pass filters include communication circuits to reject high-frequency noise to protect the low-frequency communication signal from corruption (distortion). Radio transmitters use high power amplifiers to boost the signal strength for transmission. These amplifiers are nonlinear devices that generate high-frequency harmonics along with the useful low-frequency signal to be transmitted. Low-pass filters are used to block high-frequency harmonics being generated in these high power amplifiers to prevent them from being transmitted. A subwoofer in our music systems uses a low-pass filter to suppress the high frequencies in the audio signal and deliver low-frequency sounds or bass more effectively. Low-pass filtering is used extensively to sculpt sounds for electronic music and electronic sound synthesis. It is used in image processing to reduce the sharpness of a picture and induce blur effects.

It is important to use a low-pass filter in Audiology to ensure that we obtain the best response for cortical and subcortical auditory evoked potentials. The optimum response for cortical and subcortical auditory evoked potentials exists between 1 to 30 Hz such as late- and middle-latency response. Ironically, this is the same range of frequencies, as you will see later, that is filtered out to obtain other evoked potentials that are measured in microvolts such as brainstem auditory evoked potentials that can be contaminated by the presence of low-frequency noise. Luckily, cortical and middle-latency responses, ideally located at low frequencies, have high amplitude as opposed to the waveform of ABR and cochleography. A low-pass filter is also used in assessing speech perception in low-frequency noise such as cafeteria noise and speech babble.

High-Pass Filter

A high-pass filter also called a low-cut filter is the exact opposite of a low-pass filter. When an ideal high-pass filter is connected to a mixed frequency voltage signal source, it will completely suppress all the low-frequency components below a certain frequency called the cutoff frequency, while leaving all the frequency components above that point unchanged. The band of frequencies that is below the cutoff frequency therefore forms the stop-band in this case and the band of frequencies about the cutoff frequency forms the pass-band. The transition from stop-band to pass-band ideally should be immediate; however, like the low-pass filter in practical terms, it is not possible. The sharpness of the cutoff increases and the width of the transition band decreases with the increasing complexity or order of the filter. It is also called a bass-cut filter or a rumble filter in audio technology.

A simple first-order high-pass filter can be implemented using a resistor R and a capacitor C (Figure 5–7) like the low-pass filter. However, in this case the capacitor is connected in series before the resistor and the filtered output voltage is taken across the resistor. This output signal consists of high-frequency components from the input signal with the low-frequency signals attenuated to a much lower level.

The alternating current i from the mixed frequency voltage source v flows into the capacitor where the low frequency components of the current are met with high capacitive inductance and are attenuated. The attenuated low frequency current components generate a very small voltage drop across R. The high frequency components of the current experience a much lower impedance and therefore generate a maximum voltage drop across the resistor R. The resultant output voltage v_{hpf} taken across the resistor R contains mainly the frequencies above the cutoff frequency f_c Hz as shown in Eqn. 5.7:

$$f_c = \frac{1}{2\pi RC} \text{ Hz} \qquad \text{(Eqn. 5.7)}$$

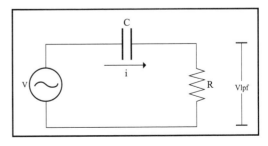

Figure 5–7. *RC high-pass filter.*

The frequencies above f_c Hz lie in the pass-band and are almost unaffected whereas the frequencies below f_c Hz form the stop-band, which is greatly attenuated. Thus, this filter passes high frequencies and suppresses low frequencies. Multiple RC circuits can be connected in cascade to increase the order of the filter thereby increasing the sharpness of the cutoff.

Figure 5–8 shows the output of a high-pass filter on the monitor of a real-time analyzer screen connected to a white noise signal at the input consisting of all the frequencies. The band of frequency components below the cutoff frequency point is attenuated greatly or stopped. The frequency band above the cutoff frequency is not affected by the filter and is passed through. Thus, the filter is "high-pass."

Just like the low-pass filter, we can also implement a high-pass filter with a resistor and an inductor combination but with reversed order of the components (Figure 5–9). The alternating current i consists of a mixed frequency voltage source v that passes through the resistor R first and then into the inductor L. The filtered output voltage v_{hpf} is taken across the inductor.

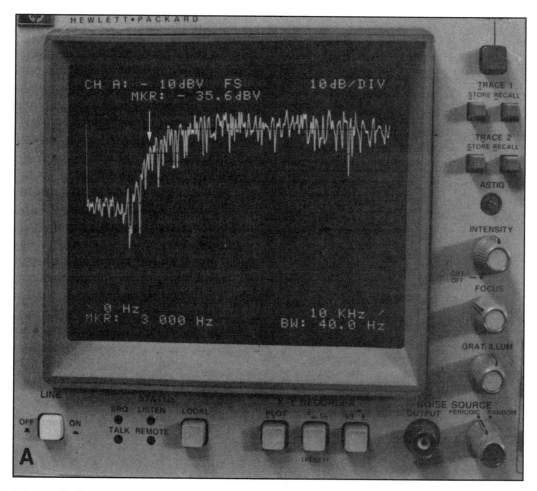

Figure 5–8. High-pass filter as seen on an RTA.

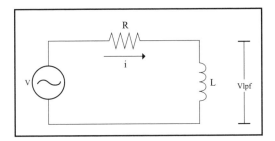

Figure 5–9. *RL high-pass filter.*

The current flowing through the resistor R and into L is met with inductive reactance frequency selectively. The low-frequency components experience low impedance to their flow and thus do not generate much voltage drop across the inductor L. The high-frequency components are met with high impedance to their flow and thus generate most of the voltage drop across the inductor L. This voltage is the output v_{hpf} of the high-pass filter and contains mainly the high-frequency components of the input signal that lie above the cutoff frequency f_c Hz as shown in Eqn. 5.8:

$$f_c = \frac{R}{2\pi L} \text{ Hz} \qquad \text{(Eqn. 5.8)}$$

All the frequencies below f_c Hz are suppressed whereas all the frequencies above f_c Hz are passed through to the output. The time constant τ is R/L seconds. Cascading multiple RL circuits will increase the complexity of the filter but will also improve the cutoff characteristics of the filter.

Active high-pass filters can also be implemented similar to low-pass filters using amplifiers that boost the filtered output and improve the signal to noise characteristics.

High-pass filters are used in music systems to pass only the high frequen-cies to the tweeter while blocking low frequencies that can damage the tweeter circuitry. They are used in some devices to block the frequencies near the lower end of the audible range of frequencies to avoid overloading of the equalization circuits. They are also used to connect amplifier circuits to each other. This is called AC coupling. High-pass filters also find application in image processing, communications, audiology, and speech pathology, in particular in systems where it is desirable to eliminate low frequencies (e.g., hearing-aids, assistive-listening devises, and some electrophysiologic systems).

Band-Pass Filter

In many communication applications it becomes extremely important to separate a particular band of frequencies for observation and further processing. The frequencies below and above this band are either useless or harmful to the further processing of our selected band of frequencies. Thus, for filtering out a particular band of frequencies and suppressing all the other frequencies we use what is called a band-pass filter. A band-pass filter is a combination of a low-pass filter and a high-pass filter in such a manner that the cutoff frequency f_{cl} of the low-pass filter is above the cutoff frequency f_{ch} of the high-pass filter. Thus, the low-pass filter attenuates the frequencies above f_{cl} Hz whereas the high-pass filter blocks frequencies below f_{ch} Hz. The band of frequencies between f_{cl} Hz and f_{ch} Hz form the pass-band and are passed out as the output of the band-pass filter. All the frequencies outside the pass-band fall in the stop-band.

We can implement a band-pass filter by any combination of low-pass filter and high-pass filter mentioned above as long as $f_{cl} > f_{ch}$. However, an RLC combination is used practically to implement a band-pass filter. It consists of a series combination of a resistor R, an inductor L, and a capacitor C connected to an input source. The filtered output is taken across the resistor R (Figure 5–10).

When the alternating current i consists of a mixed frequency voltage source v and is connected to the input of the filter, the inductor impedes the flow of high-frequency components while easily passing the low-frequency components of the signal ahead to the capacitor. The capacitor will block the lower frequency components of the signal while passing on whatever high-frequency components are present in the signal coming out of the inductor. In between the high and low frequencies lies a small band of frequencies that is passed by both the inductor and the capacitor for a well-designed circuit. At this point the inductive reactance equals the capacitive reactance and effectively cancels it out (we discussed this point in Chapter 2). This makes the circuit purely resistive. This is called series resonance and the frequency is called the resonant frequency f_r Hz (Eqn. 5.9):

$$f_r = \frac{1}{2\pi\sqrt{LC}} \text{ Hz} \qquad \text{(Eqn. 5.9)}$$

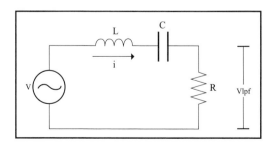

Figure 5–10. *RLC band-pass filter.*

Figure 5–11 shows the output of a band-pass filter on a CRO (cathode ray oscilloscope) screen. A white noise signal is given at the input of the filter and the output of the filter is given out to the input of the CRO. The screen shows a band of frequencies that is unaffected and lies at a higher amplitude than all the other frequencies. These frequencies form the pass-band. The frequencies on either side of the pass-band fall in the stop-band and are greatly attenuated.

Similarly, we can implement a band pass filter using a parallel combination of L and C in series with resistor R. The filtered output is taken across the parallel LC combination at the resonant frequency f_r Hz given by the same formula as a series combination.

A band-pass filter is found in almost every device that processes mixed frequency signals. It is used in communications to isolate channels and to recover information from a mixture of channels. Band-pass filters are used in music synthesizers to synthesize electric music. Apart from audio and communications, band-pass filters are used in signal processing, image processing, and atmospheric sciences, and most important to us in Audiology, in generating narrow-band noise (NBN) used in masking and in selected portions of auditory evoked potentials. For example, the waveform of ABR can be surrounded by low- and high-frequency noise that can negatively impact the waves. An appropriate band-pass filter needs to be used to eliminate both low and high frequency noise. It was determined that the best band-pass filter for ABR is between 1500 and 3000 Hz. Frequencies below 1500 Hz and above 3000 Hz may have an adverse effect on ABR, especially when the amplitude of the waveforms is measured in microvolts.

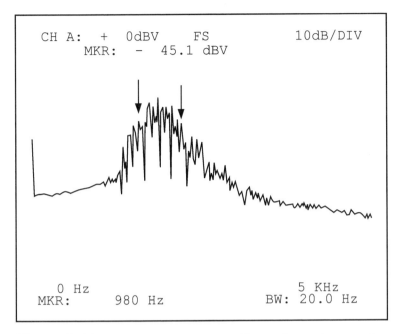

```
CH A:   +   0dBV        FS          10dB/DIV
      MKR:   -   45.1 dBV



        0 Hz                        5 KHz
      MKR:       980 Hz            BW: 20.0 Hz
```

Figure 5–11. *Illustration of band-pass filter, redrawn from monitor of real-time analyzer.*

As we will see in Chapter 9, the band-pass filter plays an important role in oscillators used in audiometers.

Band-Reject Filter

In certain applications it is necessary to suppress just a particular band of frequencies from the spectrum of the mixed frequency signal. A band-reject filter blocks or stops a band of frequency components from appearing at the output. It is also called a band-reject filter. A band-stop filter can be implemented similar to a band-pass filter using a high-pass filter and a low-pass filter except for the fact that the cutoff of the low-pass filter f_{lpf} is lower than the cutoff of the high-pass filter f_{hpf}. The frequencies between these two cutoffs now lie in our stop-band filter. The center of this pass band is the resonant frequency

f_r Hz where the circuit is purely resistive (Eqn. 5.10):

$$f_r = \frac{1}{2\pi\sqrt{LC}} \text{ Hz} \qquad \text{(Eqn. 5.10)}$$

The same RLC series circuit can be implemented as a band-stop filter except for the fact that the output v_{bsf} is taken across the capacitor and inductor pair instead of the resistor. At the resonant frequency the resultant reactance of the LC pair is zero and the voltage drop across them is negligible whereas the frequencies in the pass-band will generate a voltage drop across the LC pair and will give an output voltage. The resultant output voltage v_{bsf} will contain all frequencies except those in the stop-band.

A special type of band-reject filter called a notch filter is designed to have a very narrow stop-band. It generally is used to reject one particular frequency or a narrow strip of frequencies. The stopband looks like a notch in the spectrum (Figure 5–12). The filter is generally a very high order filter with extremely sharp cutoffs to give the desired filter outputs.

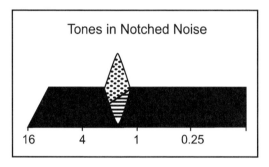

Figure 5–12. *Tones in notched noise. Adapted from Stapells, Picton, Perez-Abalo, Read, and Smith (1985) with permission.*

We hope that the information that you have gained from this chapter will assist you in understanding forthcoming concepts, for example, the principal operation of an immittance device, generation of various stimuli used in clinical audiology such as a pure tones, narrow-band noise, the operation of an oscillator, and so forth.

Acknowledgment. William Resnick photographed Figures 5–5, 5–8, and 5–11 in this chapter.

REFERENCE

Stapells, D. R., Picton, T. W., Perez-Abalo, M., Read, D., & Smith, A. (1985). Frequency specificity in evoked potential audiometry. In J. T. Jacobson (Ed.), *The auditory brainstem response* (pp. 147–177). Austin, TX: Pro-Ed.

6

Building Communication Systems

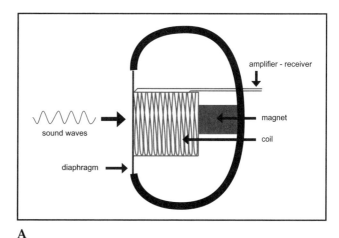

A

Figure 6–1. **A.** *Cross-section of dynamic microphone.*
continues

We now incorporate many of the concepts described in this text in building a communication system. The microphone is the first component in a communication system.

MICROPHONES

A microphone is an electronic device that converts sound pressure into an electrical signal. This signal can be amplified, modified then converted into an acoustic signal through a device called a receiver. There are many types of microphones but all have one thing in common: a diaphragm. The most commonly used microphone is the *dynamic* microphone. See Figures 6–1A and 6–1B for a cross-section of a dynamic microphone and hand-held microphone, respectively.

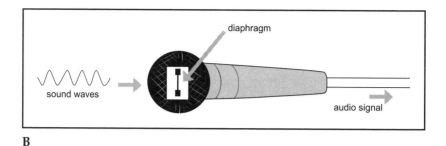

B

Figure 6–1. continued **B.** *Cross-section of dynamic hand-held microphone.*

Note that the dynamic microphone has the following components: diaphragm, magnet, coil, and wires that carry the electrical signal into an electrical system. The diaphragm is attached to the coil. The coil moves in synchrony to the sound wave when the diaphragm vibrates in response to an incoming acoustic signal. Dynamic microphones are known for noise reduction and bass roll-off. These microphones are used for public address systems, recording, and have a cone shape to concentrate energy. They are usually low in cost. Dynamic microphones, also called moving-coil microphones, can record both digital and analog signals. Figure 6–1B shows the location of the microphone diaphragm. The dynamic microphone is often used in clinical audiology especially for the test-microphone monitor on the audiometer. Neodymium, rather than conventional, magnets are sometimes used for the dynamic microphone as they are more powerful. Neodymium microphones are smaller, with a uniform frequency response and higher volume output.

Ribbon microphones are part of the family of dynamic microphones that use a thin piece of aluminum or microfilm for the diaphragm. Figures 6–2A and 6–2B show cross-section and hand-held versions, respectively, of a ribbon micro-

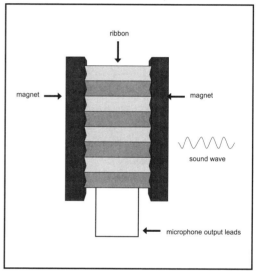

A

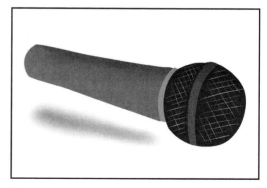

B

Figure 6–2. **A.** *Cross-section of ribbon microphone.* **B.** *Hand-held ribbon microphone.*

phone. This ribbon is placed in front of a magnetic plate. Acoustic stimuli will cause the ribbon to vibrate, thereby producing an electrical wave mimicking the sound wave. A ribbon microphone responds to a wide frequency range and produces a natural sound.

Condenser microphones can also be referred to as capacitor microphones. Figures 6–3A and 6–3B show cross-section and hand-held condenser microphones, respectively.

Recall from Chapter 4 (Alternating Current) on electronics, a capacitor has two plates. One plate serves as a diaphragm that is sensitive to sound pressure. This diaphragm is connected to one pole of the battery. The other plate, a back plate, is connected to the other pole of the battery. Sound pressure impinges on the

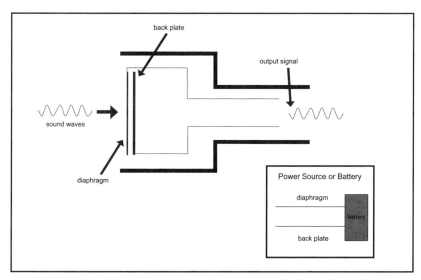

A

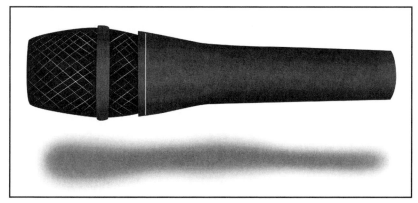

B

Figure 6–3. **A.** *Cross-section of condenser microphone.* **B.** *Hand-held condenser microphone.*

diaphragm; the two plates of the capacitor come closer together causing capacitance of the plates to increase, that is, to become charged (compression). When the plates separate, the capacitance will decrease, that is, discharge (rarefaction). The charged and discharged conditions follow the pattern of the sound wave. Many audiometers use a condenser microphone for the talk-back mic for the patient. Condenser microphones draw their power from an external source like an electrical outlet or from a battery. The audio signal is stronger and more sensitive than that of a dynamic microphone allowing it to pick up subtleties in sound. However, their sensitivity makes them prone to distortion and therefore less appropriate for high-volume tasks.

The electret microphone (Figure 6–4) part of the family of condensor microphones, is the smallest and the most commonly used microphone in Audiology and Hearing Science for delicate equipment. For example, the electret microphone is used in immittance devices, sound level meters, and otoacoustic emission systems, and so forth. This mic is self-biased (having its own charge) and can last for more than 100 years. Unfortunately, this means that an electret microphone has the potential to live longer than a human. It has a wide dynamic range in terms of frequency and a flat frequency response, that is, equal energy across the wide dynamic range. Foil electret microphones consist of a thin film of insulating material that is electrically charged to produce an external field. The diaphragm is made of Teflon material about 0.5 to 1-mm thick on one side. Some present day electret microphones, for example, Etymotic Research ER-10B+ and the ER-10C[1] have a frequency response up to approximately 20 kHz.

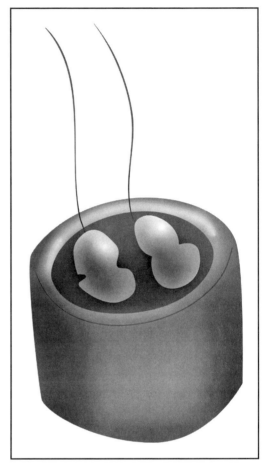

Figure 6–4. *Electret microphone.*

Pickup microphones include unidirectional, bidirectional, and omnidirectional microphones. Unidirectional mikes, also called cardiod mics because they are similar in configuration to the human heart, pick up sound from one direction (the front), and separate speech and other desired signals from background noise. Figures 6–5A and 6–5B show cardiod sound contours and illustration, respectively. The unidirectional microphone is good for live-voice speech audiometry, lectures, and so forth. However, on occasion, the unidirectional microphone exhibits an undesirable *proximity effect* that boosts low

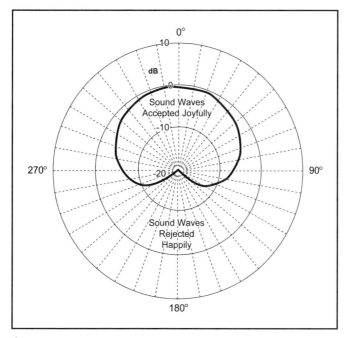

A

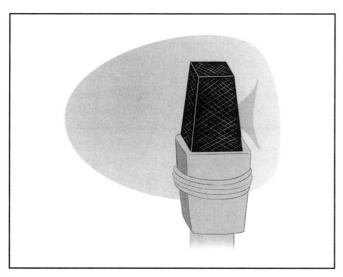

B

Figure 6–5. *A. Cardiod contours. B. Illustration of cardiod microphone.*

frequencies, especially when the speaker's mouth is near the microphone. This is why we often see TV interviewers moving the mic back and forth to avoid a prox-

imity effect. An experienced microphone user will be able to control this effect.

Bidirectional microphones pick up sounds from front and back while rejecting sound from both sides. Figures 6–6A and 6–6B show bidirectional sound contours and illustration, respectively. These microphones are excellent for interviewing and face-to-face therapy.

Omnidirectional microphones (Figure 6–7 for omnisound contour) pick up sound waves from all directions. These are excellent for group discussions, vocal groups, and so forth.

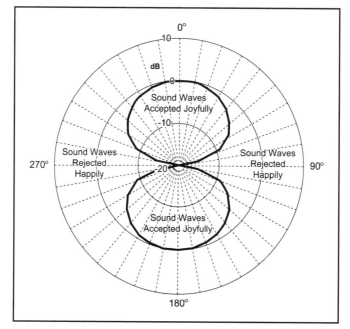

A

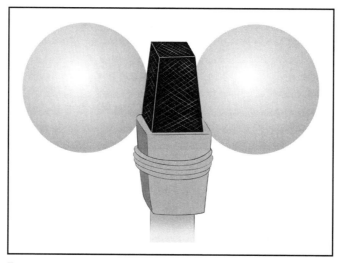

B

Figure 6–6. *A. Bidirectional sound contours. B. Illustration of bidirectional microphone.*

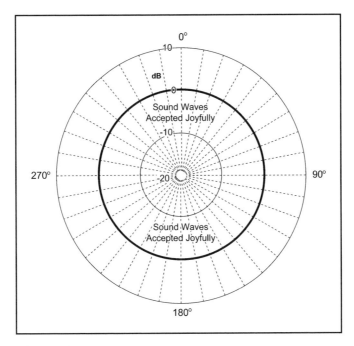

Figure 6–7. Omnidirectional microphone contour.

The moving-coil microphone is possibly the most often used microphone. It is simple in design, strong, fairly inexpensive to produce, and effective across most of the frequency response.

LOUDSPEAKER/EARPHONE/ INSERT RECEIVER

These devices all convert electrical energy into sound energy. The way in which they work is the opposite of the microphone. Remember that a microphone converts acoustic energy into electrical energy. We use the term "loudspeaker" to refer to earphones, insert receivers, and loudspeakers because all are based on the same principle. First, let's talk about a dynamic loudspeaker. It consists of a diaphragm (thin sheet of foil) that vibrates in response to the alternating electrical signal coming from the amplifier. In the dynamic loudspeaker, the reverse of the dynamic microphone, the diaphragm consists of a thin and flexible sheet. The diaphragm is cone shaped and attached to a coil of wire. The coil of wire is exposed to a magnetic field produced by a permanent magnet (Figure 6–8).

When a signal presented by an alternating current (this can be a sound picked up by a microphone) passes through the coil, it creates an electromagnetic field that interacts with the magnetic field generated by the permanent magnet. This interaction causes the diaphragm attached to the coil to vibrate. In other words, when the positive part of the current appears in the coil, the negative part of the magnet will pull (attract) the coil and the diaphragm. When the negative part of the current appears in the coil, the positive part of the coil is attracted to the permanent magnet. The positive part of the magnet

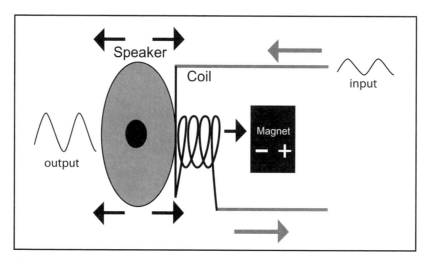

Figure 6–8. Schematic drawing of loudspeaker.

will repel the positive part of the wave in the coil. When this occurs, the diaphragm will vibrate and create a sound.

Although all dynamic loudspeakers operate on the same principle they differ in their frequency response depending on their purpose. The frequency response of the loudspeaker is determined by the size and shape of the diaphragm, the size of the coil, and the thickness of the materials.

A capacitor loudspeaker functions in a manner opposite to that of the condenser/capacitor microphone. As mentioned above, there as a front plate and a back plate to the condenser mic. When these plates come together rarefaction is produced, and when they part compression is produced. These states of rarefaction and compression will produce an alternating wave that goes through the electrical system. The wave will encounter two plates in the loudspeaker, one similar to that of the diaphragm in the mic and the other similar to the back plate of the mic. The motion of the plates will mimic the electrical signal and produce an acoustic signal. Generally, the mic and the speaker are part of the same family.

AMPLIFIERS

Earlier in this chapter we described electrical characteristics and function of microphones and receivers. We also reviewed various types of microphones and receivers. In this section, we look at the topic of amplifiers, devices that are placed between microphones and receivers. Don't forget the filtering process that takes place between the mic and the amplifier to shape the signal by passing some frequencies and attenuating others, reduce noise, and so forth. Filtering also takes place before the output.

In the majority of electrical appliances, for example, home appliances, audiometers, OAEs, and so forth, the power weakens or is reduced due to the losses in various electrical components of the systems, for example, in audio systems the amplitude of the processed audio signal before it is sent to the speakers is decreased due to losses in the processing circuitry the signal has passed through. In other cases like radio receivers and earphones, sometimes the received signal is weak and produces a very low amplitude current signal. In order to process or extract information or to work further with these low amplitude current signals, we need to increase their amplitude without changing other characteristics like shape, phase, and so forth. This process of boosting the amplitude of a current signal or a voltage signal is called amplification and is performed by a device called an amplifier.

An amplifier is an electrical instrument that changes the amplitude (usually increases) of the signal fed at its input, while keeping all other characteristics of the signal like phase and shape intact. Thus, it only boosts the energy of the signal without changing its information content. In the case of electronics and audio applications, for example, audiometer or hearing aid, the input signal is a voltage or a current signal. The term *signal* therefore will be used interchangeably with a voltage or current signal. An amplifier is required at different stages of a circuit to boost the signal for processing in the next stage, to improve the signal-to-noise ratio of the signal, or to boost the signal amplitude at the output device like a speaker for maximum power. The measure of amplification of a signal is called the amplifier gain or just gain and is denoted by the letter *A*. The gain *A* of an amplifier is simply defined as the ratio of the amplitude of the output signal to the amplitude of the input signal. Gain is a dimensionless quantity. The amplifier is symbolized as a triangle with an input and an output terminal. The gain *A* is shown on the triangle in Figure 6–9.

Recall from Chapter 4 that electrical components such as resistors, capacitors, and inductors are passive and therefore do not require power for their operation and are incapable of providing gain or manipulating the current flowing through them. Therefore, these devices cannot be

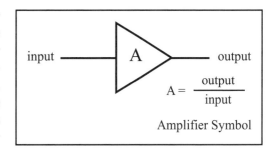

Figure 6–9. *Amplifier symbol.*

used for amplifying signals. Active components on the other hand are capable of changing their operational characteristics depending on the manner in which they are connected in a circuit. They need power to function and are capable of performing different types of operations including some interesting mathematical operations on the current passing through them, for example, $Z = V/I$. Active components also have the ability to control the flow of current passing through them using some other voltage or current signal. Thus, these active components can be used to construct amplifiers that can provide voltage gain or current gain in a circuit. Examples of active components are vacuum tubes, transistors, silicon-controlled rectifiers (SCR), and so forth.

Before the invention of transistors, vacuum tubes were used for amplification of a signal. Some of you may have seen an early hearing aid. Amplification for the early hearing aids (in the 1930s) was based solely on vacuum tube amplifiers. Likewise, the original audiometers contained vacuum tubes for amplification of a signal. Early hearing aids were quite large to accommodate the large vacuum tubes. A vacuum tube is composed of a cylindrical glass tube consisting of a cathode *filament*, a control *grid,* and an anode *plate* placed in a vacuum (Figure 6–10). The filament is

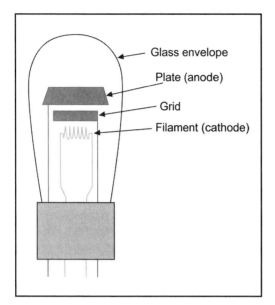

Figure 6–10. *Vacuum tube (triode).*

heated using an external source causing it to emit electrons into the vacuum forming an electron cloud. The plate (anode) has a very high positive potential to attract the electrons emitted by the filament.

The controlling action (like a volume control) is performed by the control grid. The grid is a thin metallic mesh placed very close to the plate so that it can influence the electrons collected by the plate. The low voltage input signal to be amplified is connected to the grid. This changes the electric field around the grid as per the input signal and modulates the flow of electrons from the filament to the plate. As the input signal is used to modulate the flow of electrons in the tube, the output signal taken from the plate is an amplified version of the input signal. Vacuum tubes are robust, inexpensive, and provide better amplification for high power applications like radar, television transmission, and so forth. However they are bulky and need extra power to heat up the filament. This makes it impractical for use

in low power applications where there are power supply and space constraints. Bipolar junction transistors are used for this purpose.

Bipolar junction transistor (BJT) commonly known as a transistor is a 3-terminal semiconductor device capable of controlling the flow of current that flows through it. BJTs are small and consume less power because they do not require an external heating supply for operation as do vacuum tubes. They are made of semiconductor crystals and are sturdy components with a size comparable to resistors and capacitors. This makes it possible to implement it in a circuit. Millions of transistors can also be fabricated onto small microchips that can be used as switching devices. Thus, almost every modern day electronic device uses many transistors for multiple applications. To understand the working of the transistor we need to understand its construction and internal operations.

SEMICONDUCTORS

Electrical conductivity of a material is used to classify it as a conductor or an insulator. All the wires that connect the electrical components mentioned in Chapter 3 and Chapter 4, that is, resistors, conductors, inductors, are defined as conductors because they conduct electricity from one component to another. Examples of good conductors are iron, copper, and so forth. Insulators are unable to conduct electricity. Examples of good insulators include glass, wood, and so forth. However, there are some materials that have conductivity between that of a conductor and an insulator. These materials are called semiconductors. A transistor is a semiconductor device, that is, it is made up of a semiconductor material. There are several known semiconductor materials that possess characteristics between that of a conductor and an insulator, for example, silicon and germanium.

A process called doping (impurity) can change the above mentioned semiconductors to conductors. The process of doping can either increase the number of electrons in the material so that the electrons move within the material and conduct electricity or steal from the number of electrons thereby creating holes in their place so the holes can attract electrons. In the first example, the material is n-type semiconductor material because of an excess of electrons. In the second example, called p-type semiconductor material, the holes attract electrons. Phosphors have excess electrons and can create impurity thereby increasing conductivity of the semiconductor. Likewise, by adding gallium, the number of holes will increase, also increasing conductivity of the semiconductor.

The p-type and n-type materials are not of much use by themselves but when they are brought together they exhibit some interesting and useful characteristics.

PN JUNCTION

When the surface of a p-type material is brought in close contact with the surface of an n-type material a PN junction is formed (Figure 6–11). The PN junction forms the operational basis for all the semiconductor devices like diodes, BJTs, thyristors (a semiconductor device used as an electronic switch), and so forth. When a pure semiconductor crystal (e.g., silicon crystal) is doped with a p-type impurity from one side and with an n-type impurity from the other, a PN

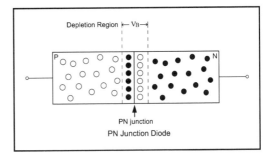

Figure 6–11. PN junction diode.

junction is formed where the two regions meet. This assembly forms the simplest semiconductor device called the diode.

When a junction is formed the electrons from the n-type region diffuse through the junction into the p-type region. At the same time the holes defuse from the p-type region into the n-type region. An electric field is set up due to diffusion of charges, which opposes any more diffusion. This process of diffusion continues until the strength of the electric field equals the force of diffusion and a point of potential equilibrium is reached. Charges from either side of the junction can no longer pass through the PN junction beyond this point. There is a thin region on either side of the junction, which is devoid of any free charges. This region is called the depletion region formed during the diffusion. The electric field around the PN junction is due to a potential difference V_B across the depletion region set up by the defused charges. This potential difference is called a potential barrier and it opposes any further diffusion. The potential barrier is a function of the semiconductor material used. It is close to 0.7 volts for silicon and around 0.3 volts for germanium. The majority charge carriers can cross this barrier only if they have enough energy supplied to them by an external source. The upper portion of Figure 6–12 shows the electrical symbol for a diode and the lower portion shows the semiconductor diode.

A diode is a one-way component. The PN junction in the diode allows the flow of current only in one direction. However for the current to flow through the diode it needs to be supplied with external power by connecting to a voltage source. This is called biasing of the diode. Depending on the way in which the battery is connected across the diode it is said to be forward biased or reverse biased.

The lead of the diode coming out of the p-type region is called the anode (A) of the diode whereas the one coming out from the n-type region is the cathode (K). A diode is said to be forward biased when the positive terminal of the battery is connected to the positive lead of the diode and the negative terminal is connected to the negative lead of the diode (Figure 6–13).

A minimum voltage of V_B volts needs to be supplied by the battery to overcome the potential barrier. The width of the depletion layer keeps on reducing when the voltage V_f of the forward bias is slowly increased from zero until V_B where the depletion region disappears and the potential barrier is overcome. The electrons now can freely flow from the negative terminal of the battery to the positive terminal of the battery and the holes can

flow freely in the opposite direction without any obstruction like current flowing through a good conductor. The forward bias conventional current I_f flows into the anode of the diode and out through the cathode before flowing back into the battery.

When the cathode (K) of the diode is connected to the positive terminal of the battery and the anode (A) is connected to the negative terminal of a battery the diode is said to be reverse biased (Figure 6–14).

In this case the potential difference V_r applied across the diode adds up to the potential barrier field and the width of the depletion region increases. The diffusion of electrons and holes becomes further difficult under the influence of this growing electric field. Forward current due

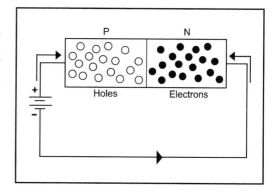

Figure 6–13. *Forward-biased diode.*

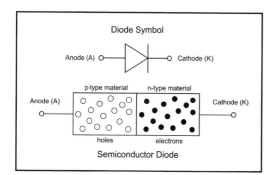

Figure 6–12. *Semiconductor diode.*

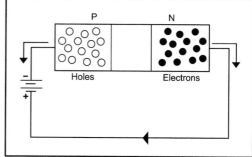

Figure 6–14. *Reverse-biased diode.*

to majority charge carriers cannot flow through the circuit loop under this reverse bias condition. However there is a small leakage current I_r flowing through the diode under the influence of the potential barrier electric field due to the drifting of minority charge carriers. This amplitude of this leakage current is very low and therefore negligible. Thus, practically no current flows through a reverse biased diode. When the reverse bias increases the width of the potential barrier to a point called breakdown voltage, the potential barrier collapses and a very large current flows through the diode (from cathode to anode). The diode gets physically damaged and cannot be used further. Certain diodes called Zener diodes are made to work in breakdown mode and are not damaged by the breakdown voltage.

This one-way property of the diode (PN junction) is the working principle of many devices that need to allow the flow of current only in one direction. For example, in a rectifier, a diode is used to convert an AC signal, which changes polarity (and therefore direction of flow) periodically into a DC signal flowing only in one direction.

Figure 6–15 shows a simple half-wave rectifier. The input to the circuit is an AC signal of i amperes. The diode D connected before the resistor R performs the rectifying action on the AC signal. During the positive half of the current cycle the diode

is forward biased. Thus, it allows the current to pass through it as I and into the resistor to provide a voltage drop across it.

When the polarity of the input signal i changes and becomes negative the diode D becomes reverse biased and blocks the complete negative current. There is no current across R to create a voltage drop across it. The current I flows only in one direction and is thus a DC signal.

This circuit rectifies only the positive half of the input AC signal and converts it to a DC signal while rejecting the remaining negative half negative signal. Thus, it is called a half-wave rectifier. A more complicated circuit called the full-wave rectifier (Figure 6–16) can convert both the positive and the negative halves of the AC signal into DC output. The output DC signal can be smoothed by passing it through low-pass filters to reject the high-frequency components and obtain a near-constant DC signal.

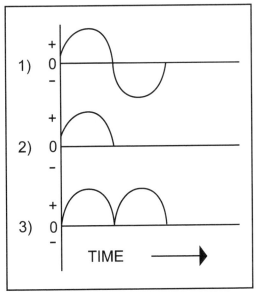

Figure 6–16. Rectified waves. Number 1 shows a full sinusoidal wave, number 2 shows the results of half-wave rectification, and number 3 shows the results of full-wave rectification (see text).

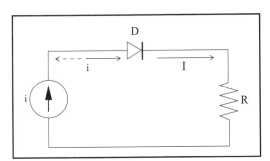

Figure 6–15. Half-wave rectifier.

TRANSISTORS

A bipolar junction transistor (BJT) is a 3-terminal device consisting of two PN junctions sandwiched between three layers of doped semiconductor material. A thin layer of a one type of semiconductor material (p-type or n-type) is placed between layers of the other type of semiconductor material. So, we can have a layer of p-type material sandwiched between layers of n-type material to form a NPN bipolar junction transistor or a layer of n-type material sandwiched between layers of p-type material to form a PNP bipolar junction transistor. The layers on either side are called the emitter *E* and the collector *C* and the middle layer sandwiched between the emitter and the collector is called the base *B*. Figure 6–17 shows us

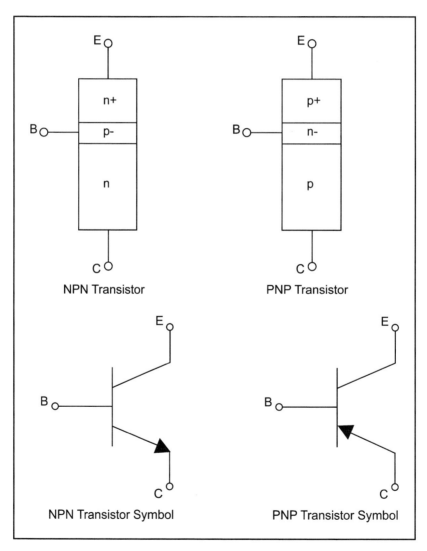

Figure 6–17. *The upper portion of this figure is a schematic drawing of NPN and PNP transistors. The lower portion of this figure shows electronic symbols for NPN and PNP transistors. The arrows represent the direction of the current.*

schematic and electronic representations of NPN and PNP transistors. The arrows indicate the direction of the current.

The emitter and the collector on either side of the base are doped with the same type of impurity but to different concentrations depending on their purpose. The purpose of the emitter is to inject approximately 90% of the electrons (in the NPN transistor) or holes (in the PNP transistor) from the emitter into the collector through the base, which is very thin compared with the collector and emitter and is lightly doped to allow most of the majority charge carriers from the emitter that scatter into the base across the emitter-base junction to be swept into the collector and to reduce the recombination of electrons and holes, keeping the base current low. The collector is moderately doped but is longer than the emitter to effectively collect the electrons or holes that are swept across the base-collector junction (Figure 6–18). This figure shows an NPN transistor. As you can see, the collector is longer

than the emitter and more lightly doped than the emitter. The transistor is not operational in this figure because both batteries are off. The operation of this transistor involves the flow of electrons as well as holes at the same time. Thus, it is called the bipolar junction transistor.

Although the second stage of amplification requires both batteries to be on so that the transistor will be operational, we chose to turn on only the base-emitter circuit (Figure 6–19), which is usually around .7 volts. Note that the positive side of the battery is connected to the holes, which are also positively doped, and the negative part of the battery is connected to the emitter, also positively doped. This is a forward-biasing circuit. At this stage, the hole in the base attempts to grab electrons but the electrons cannot go further but continue to rotate in the base-emitter because the small base cannot contain all the holes.

When the battery on the right-hand side (Figure 6–20) is also turned on, a new

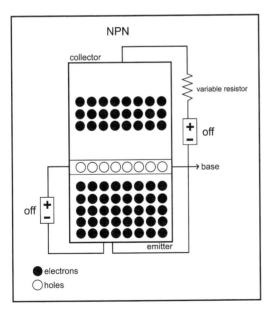

Figure 6–18. *Doped circuit with unconnected batteries.*

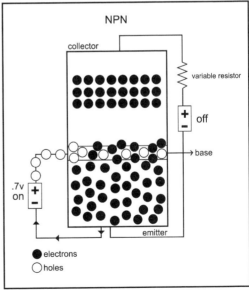

Figure 6–19. *Base-emitter on.*

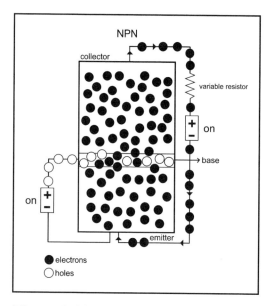

Figure 6–20. *Both batteries on.*

picture emerges. The base-collector is reverse-biased. The base cannot absorb all the electrons coming from the emitter. The electrons jump across the depletion region into the collector and are attracted by the positive pole of the battery on the right-hand side. As previously noted, approximately 90% of the electrons from the emitter end up in the collector. The current that reaches the battery (remember that $I = V \times R$) depends on the variable resistor, which can increase or decrease the current, that is, the current will determine the level of amplification.

In Figure 6–21, we see Ms. Smith singing in a natural voice. The signal is transduced from an acoustic to an electric signal via the microphone. As

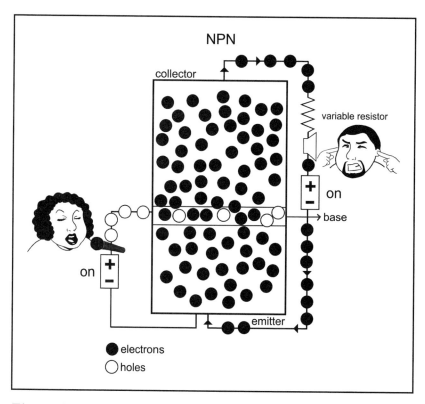

Figure 6–21. *Ms. Smith's singing has been added. Her boyfriend is listening (Ouch!).*

the signal creates an alternating current, the positive-going portion of the signal will create base-emitter forward bias and base-collector reverse bias. This will further increase the depletion region, which accommodates more electrons. The holes in the base will pull the electrons, but because the base is thin, it cannot handle all the electrons and they will jump into the collector. The battery on the right-hand side will further pull the electrons. The current at the speaker is now very large (about 90% greater than the initial current). The signal reaches the listener, Mr. Jones, through the speaker, the transducer that converts electric energy to acoustic energy.

We have learned that a forward-bias circuit will conduct electricity and a reverse-bias circuit will stop the flow of electricity. However, in the case of an amplifier, the base collector, which is reverse bias, behaves like a forward-bias circuit because it is collecting the electrons from the base to the speaker.

We can draw an analogy between the base of a transistor and the gas pedal of a car. When you minimally press the gas pedal, the car moves in a way that is not proportional to the small movement of the gas pedal, that is, it speeds up. Similarly, in the transistor, a small current at the input to the microphone is amplified 90 to 100% at the output of the receiver. In most cases, the impedance of a microphone is low whereas the impedance of the receiver is appreciably higher. Electrical current that travels through low resistance in a transducer such as a microphone will be significantly increased at the high impedance element like the receiver.

We will soon be transported to a digital world and then to a combination of both digital and analog.

7

Acoustic Immittance and Power Reflectance

You might wonder why we didn't introduce this chapter earlier in the text. We believe that to fully understand acoustic impedance and admittance (immittance refers to both impedance and admittance), it is important to have a foundation in general physics, mechanical impedance and admittance, electronics, filtering, microphones, receivers, amplifiers, and so forth. When we discussed mechanical impedance driven by an alternating force, we pointed out that each mechanical system naturally contains the following components: stiffness, mass, and friction. Whether a system is dominated by mass or stiffness depends on which element is the larger of the two. When the system is in resonance, neither mass nor stiffness dominates, as they will cancel each other; only friction remains.

The three major components mentioned in our discussion of mechanical and electrical immittance will be revisited when we describe acoustic immittance. Before we describe the major methods and techniques for measurement of acoustic admittance and impedance, we must describe acoustic immittance.

ACOUSTIC IMMITTANCE

Let's begin with acoustic impedance. Acoustic impedance is the analog to the electrical and mechanical impedance described earlier. The air volume in a tube closed at one end, for example, air in the human ear canal and middle ear (in this case we are considering the outer and middle ear as one tube where air molecules are compressed in both parts of the ear), is the acoustic analog to a mechanical spring in mechanical impedance and a capacitor in an electrical circuit. As the air in a tube open at one end is compressed, it will behave like a spring. The air volume in a tube open at both ends, for example, the air molecules in the mastoid cells, is the acoustic analog to a mechanical mass and to an inductor in an electrical circuit. The air volume in a tube open at both ends exhibits inertia and thus will behave like an acoustic mass. The collision of air molecules that represents acoustic friction is an analog to friction in a mechanical system and to a resistor in an electrical system.

Van Camp, Margolis, Wilson, Creten, and Shanks (1986) added mechanical variables to the acoustic impedance of the middle and outer ear and labeled the impedance of the outer and middle ear as "acoustico-mechanical impedance." The investigators considered the elastic tympanic membrane as a mechanical spring, the ossicular chain as a mechanical mass, and the friction among the various components of the middle and outer ear as mechanical friction. Figure 7–1 illustrates the mechanoacoustic model of the middle ear. The mechanoacoustic impedance of the middle ear is referred to in the literature as the acoustic impedance (Z_a) of the middle ear. The total acoustic impedance (Z_a) consists of acoustic mass reactance ($+X_a$), which is the acousticomechanical mass, acoustic stiffness reactance ($-X_a$), which is the acousticomechanical stiffness reactance, and acoustic resistance (R_a), which is the acousticomechanical resistance.

In Chapter 2 (Mechanical Impedance) we derived the impedance from F/V, that is, $Z = F/V$. Recall that in an electrical system, voltage is applied and the electrical impedance is measured, $Z_e = V/I$. In an acoustic system sound pressure expressed in dynes/cm² is applied to the system and the resultant volume velocity (expressed in cm³) is measured. Volume velocity is defined as the volume (cm³) of the sound-conducting medium, which flows in a given area in a given amount of time (in sec). The total acoustic impedance, therefore, can be expressed as:

$$Z_a = P/U \qquad \text{(Eqn. 7.1)}$$

where P is sound pressure (in dynes/cm²), U is volume velocity (in cm³), and Z_a is acoustic impedance (in acoustic ohms).

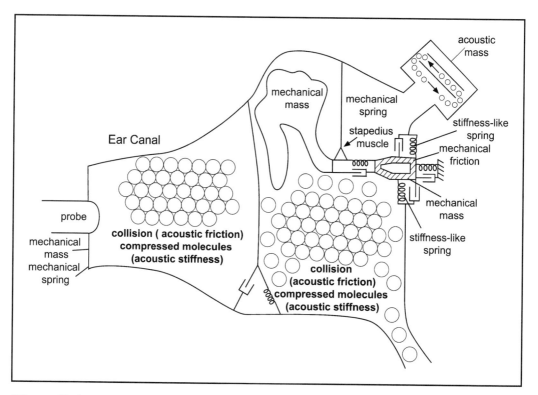

Figure 7–1. Proposed model of mechanoacoustic impedance.

The formula for acoustic impedance having a net acoustic reactance that is acoustic stiffness reactance is:

$$Z_a^2 = (-X_a)^2 + R_a^2 \qquad \text{(Eqn. 7.2)}$$

where Z_a is total acoustic impedance, $-X_a$ is acoustic stiffness reactance, and R_a is acoustic resistance, or

$$Z_a^2 = [S/(2\pi f)]^2 + R_a^2 \qquad \text{(Eqn. 7.3)}$$

where S is stiffness and f is frequency.

The formula for acoustic impedance having a net acoustic reactance that is acoustic mass reactance is:

$$Z_a^2 = (+X_a)^2 + R_a^2 \qquad \text{(Eqn. 7.4)}$$

where $+X_a$ is acoustic mass reactance, or

$$Z_a^2 = (2\pi f M)^2 + R_a^2 \qquad \text{(Eqn. 7.5)}$$

METHODS FOR MEASUREMENT OF STATIC-ACOUSTIC MIDDLE-EAR IMMITTANCE

Recall that the calculation of impedance for direct and alternating current is different for impedance in series compared to impedance in parallel circuits (refer to Chapters 3 and 4). The middle ear and outer ear in humans are considered analogous to two parallel electrical systems as described in these chapters. Therefore, if one wishes to calculate the impedance of the outer or middle ear, the same principle of an electrical parallel system applies. The input impedance of a parallel system of the outer and middle ear is shown in Figure 7–2 and can be calculated using the formula:

$$1/Z_a = 1/Z_1 + 1/Z_2 \qquad \text{(Eqn. 7.6)}$$

A similar formula was described in Chapters 3 and 4 when we discussed electrical impedance systems with direct and alternating current.

Recall from Chapters 3 and 4 that if the total impedance of the system and the impedance of one of the two parallel components are known, the impedance of the other parallel component can be derived using $1/Z_a = 1/Z_1 + 1/Z_2$ where Z_a is total impedance of the outer and middle ear, Z_1 is a known impedance and Z_2 is the unknown impedance. $1/Z_a = 1/Z_1 + 1/Z_2$ can be rewritten as:

$$Z_2 = (Z_1 \times Z_a) / (Z_1 - Z_a) \qquad \text{(Eqn. 7.7)}$$

where Z_2 is the impedance of the unknown component, Z_1 is the impedance of the known component, and Z_a is the total impedance.

According to Margolis (1981) the relationship between the total ear impedance (combined middle and outer ear impedance) and the impedance of the middle ear is nonlinear. On the other hand, the relationship is linear for acoustic admittance (Margolis, 1981). Using admittance rather than impedance is advantageous for two reasons that are described in Chapter 9.

Acoustic admittance is defined as the ease with which acoustic energy passes through a system (we defined electrical admittance and mechanical admittance in previous chapters). Acoustic admittance is mathematically expressed as the ratio of volume velocity to sound pressure ($Y_a = U/P$). The unit of acoustic admittance is mho; 1 mho = 1000 mmho. Middle-ear admittance is measured in mmhos.

As acoustic admittance is the reciprocal of acoustic impedance, it can be written as:

$$Y_a = 1/Z_a \qquad \text{(Eqn. 7.8)}$$

where Y_a is total admittance and Z_a is total impedance.

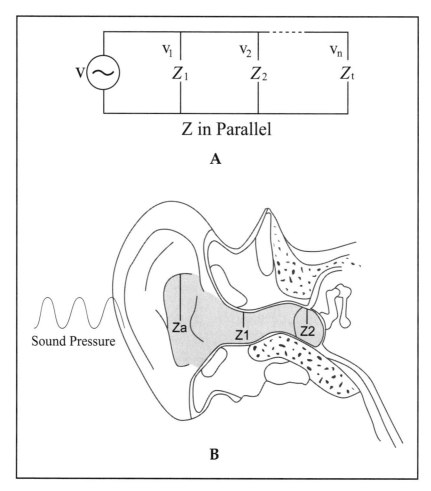

Figure 7–2. This figure shows parallel electrical impedance in **A**, and parallel acoustic impedance in **B**. V represents the voltage source for electrical impedance. Z_1 and Z_2 represent impedance in parallel in the outer and middle ear. Z_a represents total impedance of the parallel system. In this case, Z represents the combined value of stiffness reactance, mass reactance, and resistance.

As the impedance of the total middle and outer ear is expressed in the formula $1/Z_a = 1/Z_1 + 1/Z_2$ as mentioned above, and as $Y_a = 1/Z_a$ we can write the admittance formula as $Y_a = Y_1 + Y_2$. Therefore, if we assume Y_2 is the middle ear, then $Y_2 = Y_a - Y_1$. The admittance components include acoustic stiffness susceptance $(+B_a)$, which is the reciprocal to acoustic stiffness reactance, acoustic mass susceptance $(-B_a)$, which is the reciprocal to acoustic mass reactance, and acoustic conductance (G_a) which is the reciprocal to acoustic resistance. The total acoustic admittance can be calculated from the formula:

$$Y_a^2 = B_a^2 + G_a^2 \qquad \text{(Eqn. 7.9)}$$

Thus far, we have described how to obtain total admittance or admittance of the outer or middle ear. In calculating each individual component, that is, G_a, or $-B_a$, we follow the same format as for Y_a. If you want to calculate total Y_a from B_a and G_a, the Pythagorean formula should be used.

Acoustic admittance or impedance, like electrical impedance described in Chapter 5, is expressed using rectangular or polar notation. In rectangular notation, one value is given to the acoustic conductance or resistance component and one value is given to the net acoustic susceptance or reactance component. For example, acoustic impedance can be written as $Z_a = 1500 - j\,3000$ using rectangular notation, where j is the square root of -1. As j represents an imaginary number, it cannot be added to real numbers, for example, 1500 in the given example (Figure 7–3).

In polar notation, one number is given to the magnitude of the acoustic impedance and one number represents the phase angle of the acoustic impedance. For example, $Z_a = Z\,2121 <$ or $-45°$. We use either the less than symbol or the minus sign because both represent the lower quadrant.

We can also express admittance in either rectangular or polar notation. In polar notation, for example, $Y_a = 0.6 >$ or $+30°$ (Figure 7–4). We can use either the greater than symbol or the plus sign, because both represent the upper quadrant in admittance (the reciprocal of impedance). In rectangular notation, $Y_a = .500 + j >$ or $+ .300$. We derived the values using cosine of a 30° angle.

CALCULATION OF ACOUSTIC ADMITTANCE OF THE MIDDLE EAR

Figure 7–5 illustrates the static-acoustic admittance (Y_a) of the total ear (outer ear and middle ear) obtained using an absolute immittance device.

The tympanogram (immittance pressure function) in this figure indicates that the total admittance, Y_a, includes both middle and outer ear admittance. The arrow (labeled A) from the baseline to the abscissa indicates ear canal volume (ear canal admittance) and B is the middle-ear admittance value.

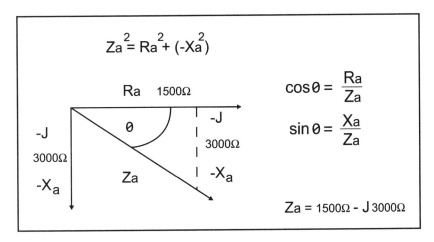

$$Za^2 = Ra^2 + (-Xa^2)$$

Ra   1500Ω

$$\cos\theta = \frac{Ra}{Za}$$

$$\sin\theta = \frac{Xa}{Za}$$

-J 3000Ω

-J 3000Ω

θ Za   -Xa

-Xa

$$Za = 1500\Omega - J\,3000\Omega$$

Figure 7–3. Example describing Z_a using rectangular notation.

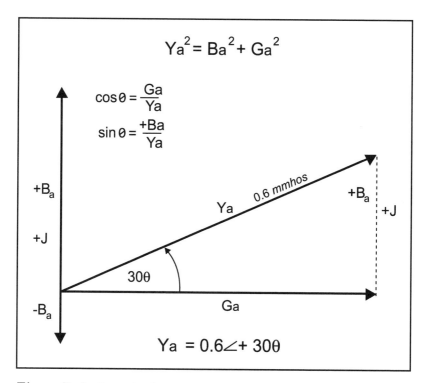

Figure 7–4. *Example of* Y_a *described in polar notation.*

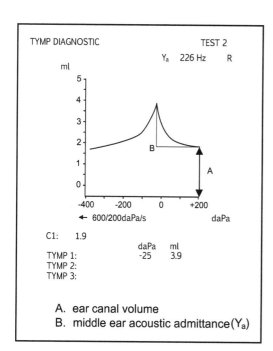

Figure 7–5. *Tympanogram describing ear-canal volume and middle-ear compensated static for an 8-year-old child.*

Caveat: Over the years, we have read in the literature and heard anecdotal accounts of professionals who label ear-canal admittance as equivalent ear-canal volume. It is correct to label admittance of the outer ear in cm^3 equivalent ear-canal volume when using a 226-Hz probe tone because the admittance of a 1-cc cavity is equivalent to 1 mmhos. However, because admittance is directly proportional to frequency, the admittance of the 1-cc cavity, will be 3 mmhos using a 660-Hz probe tone and approximately 5 mmhos when using a 1000-Hz probe tone.

Modern electroacoustic admittance devices (to be described in detail in Chapter 9) include, in addition to Y_a, the capability of measuring the three components of Y_a, that is, $G_a + B_a$ or $- B_a$. Generally, the net susceptance (B_a) is recorded.

The acoustic impedance vector (Z_a) and its components, acoustic net reactance (X_a) and acoustic resistance (R_a) can be calculated by obtaining the reciprocals of B_a, G_a, and Y_a as follows:

$$X_a = B_a/(B_a^2 + G_a^2) \quad \text{(Eqn. 7.10)}$$

$$R_a = G_a/(G_a^2 + B_a^2) \quad \text{(Eqn. 7.11)}$$

$$Z_a = \sqrt{(X_a^2 + R_a^2)} \quad \text{(Eqn. 7.12)}$$

The tympanogram in Figure 7–5 was recorded for an 8-year-old child using a 226-Hz probe tone. However, a newborn infant demonstrates different patterns than older children and adults. As shown in Figure 7–6, the pattern at low-frequency probe tones in infants is significantly different from the pattern at high-frequency probe tones. The patterns are opposite those we expect to see in older children and adults. This reversal of tympanometric shape in newborn infants is consistent with those reported by Sprague, Wiley, and Goldstein in 1985. These investigators attributed the reversal to the mass-loaded

system of the middle ear of a newborn at low frequencies (Figure 7–7).

As you can see in Figure 7–7, the majority of newborns in the Sprague et al. (1985) study demonstrate tympanograms similar to these patterns. The B pattern in Sprague et al. (1985) appears more frequently than that in A.

The patterns in Figure 7–7 are likely to fit tympanometric patterns B and C proposed by Vanhuyse, Creten, and Van Camp (1975) as shown in Figure 7–8.

Before we relate aspects of Figure 7–8 to Figure 7–7 we describe the different tympanometric patterns in Figure 7–8. The pattern of 1B1G with a single susceptance maximum and a single conductance maximum is obtained when the middle ear is a stiffness-dominated system and when the resistance of the middle ear is less than the stiffness reactance at tympanometric peak pressure. This is illustrated in Figure 7–8A. The pattern of 3B1G (Figure 7–8B) is obtained when the resistance of the middle

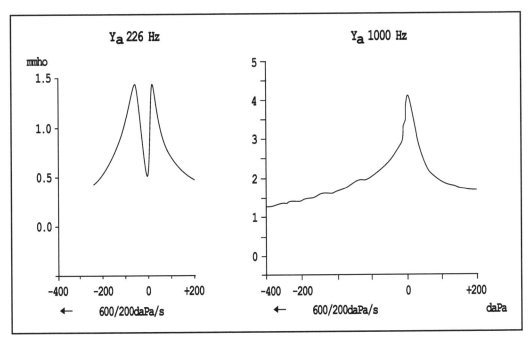

Figure 7–6. *Tympanometric shapes for infants at 226-Hz and 1000-Hz probe-tone signals.*

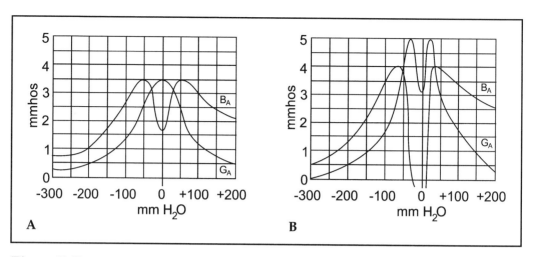

Figure 7–7. *Tympanometric patterns obtained by Sprague et al. (1985) in newborn infants using a 220-Hz probe tone. In that study, 58% of the infants showed the pattern in* **B***. 25% showed the pattern in* **A***.*

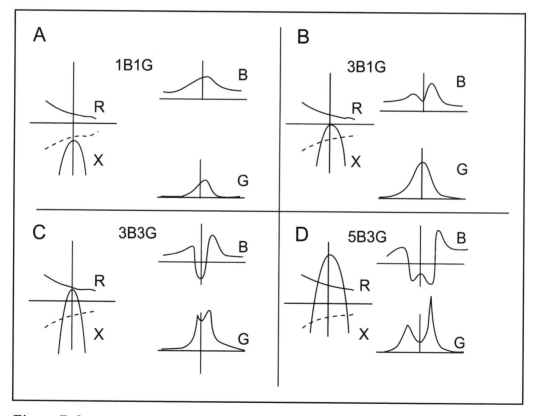

Figure 7–8. *Shown are four normal high-frequency tympanometric patterns expressed in acoustic impedance (resistance [R] and reactance [X]) and acoustic admittance (conductance [G] and susceptance [B]). After Vanhuyse, Creten, and Van Camp (1975) in Shanks (1984) and Silman and Silverman (1991, 1997).*

ear is higher than the value of the stiffness reactance at zero peak-pressure point and when the resistance of the middle ear is smaller than the value of the stiffness reactance at both extreme pressures. 3B3G (Figure 7–8C) is obtained when the middle-ear system is mass dominated at zero peak-pressure point and resistance is higher than reactance. 5B3G (Figure 7–8D) at zero peak-pressure point occurs when the system is mass dominated and mass reactance is larger than stiffness.

Figure 7–7B fits tympanometric pattern C in the Vanhuyse et al. (1975) classification in which the system is dominated by mass at zero peak-pressure point. Also note that the resistance is higher than mass reactance in this case. Furthermore, note that Figure 7–7A fits tympanometric pattern B in the Vanhuyse et al.'s (1975) classification system. At 0 daPa pressure point, the system is at resonance and resistance is the only component.

Weatherby and Bennett (1980) contend that the absence of the acoustic reflex at low probe frequencies in a newborn is due to the reduction of the impedance at the eardrum at birth (flaccid drum) and the higher impedance of the middle ear (this significantly increases the resistance). There is, therefore, a mismatch in impedance between the tympanic membrane (low impedance) and the middle ear (high impedance). The small impedance change caused by the reflex cannot be measured. In other words, high impedance cannot be measured through a low-impedance medium using a low probe tone (Figure 7–9 shows the acoustic reflex in the neonate). These authors also reported that by 800 Hz, the reflexes of a newborn are present in the same proportion as those of an adult. Silverman (2010) proposed using an ipsilateral BBN activator with a pass/fail based on Mazlan, Kei, and Hickson's

(2009) 95th percentile for healthy babies and Rhodes, Margolis, Hirsh, and Napp's (1999) findings for NICU babies. As the 95th percentile is 80 dB HL, the intensity for ipsilateral acoustic reflex testing can be 50 to 80 dB HL, incorporating 5-dB steps. Silverman (2010) using high-probe admittance norms (Margolis, Bass-Ringdahl, Holte, and Zapala, 2003) in combination with the ipsilateral reflex and OAEs, proposed an interesting approach for the diagnosis of middle ear effusion in infants.

Figure 7–10 shows the acoustic reflex for older children and adults. The acoustic reflex presents different patterns and different frequency effects for these two populations.

POWER REFLECTANCE

Think back to what you've learned in anatomy and physiology regarding the impedance mismatch of the middle ear. Recall that when energy flows into the outer and middle ear, it travels via air conduction. When it reaches the inner ear, the energy faces opposition from the fluid in this space. The opposition is caused by a change in the medium from air to fluid (an impedance mismatch). Without the middle ear's impedance-matching mechanism only 0.1% of airborne energy would be transmitted to the cochlea, whereas about 99.9% would be reflected back (this corresponds to a 40 dB drop in energy transmission from an air-filled medium to a fluid-filled medium). The middle ear transfer from the tympanic membrane to the cochlear fluids (dB gain from eardrum to cochlea) varies greatly across the frequencies with the greatest gain at the mid-frequencies (also refer to Chapters 2, 3, and 4). Light, heat, and other forms of energy also face opposition when changing mediums.

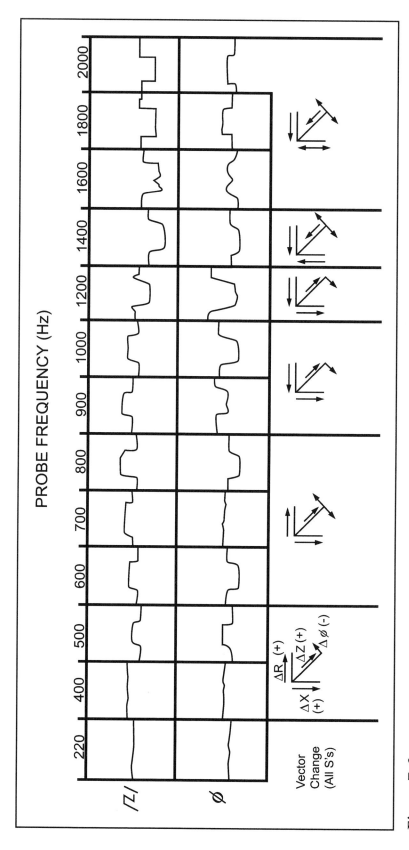

Figure 7–9. The impedance Z and phase angle Φ with the corresponding vectorial change of the acoustic reflex in neonates. Note that there is no response for the reflex at low frequencies. The figure reveals a reversal of the direction of the acoustic reflex occurring between 1000 Hz and 1200 Hz. The arrows indicate either an increase or decrease of the impedance components as well as the direction of the vector impedance. The horizontal direction toward the right indicates an increase in resistance. The direction of the horizontal arrow to the left indicates a decrease in resistance. The downward-pointing vertical arrow indicates an increase in the reactance component. The arrow pointing 45° to both the upper and lower corners represents an increase in both resistance and reactance.

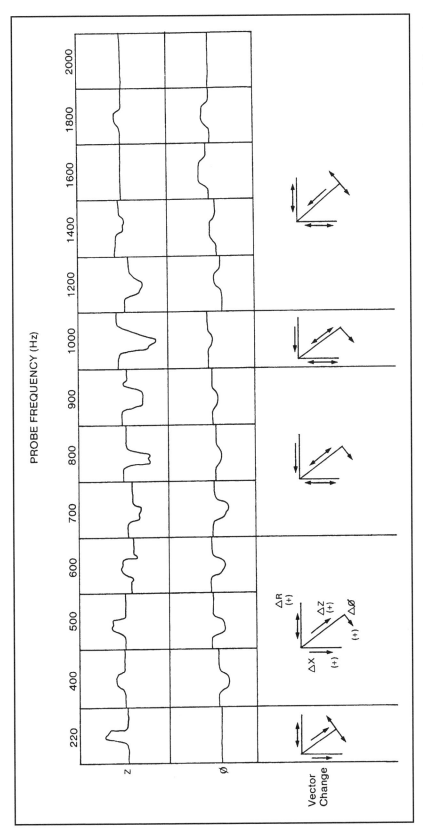

Figure 7–10. *The impedance Z and phase angle Φ with the corresponding vectorial change of the acoustic reflex in older children and adults. Note that the reversal of the direction of the acoustic reflex occurs earlier than in neonates (700 Hz).*

To avoid confusion, let us first clarify the difference between impedance as described in the literature (and in the current text) throughout the years, and reflected energy. Impedance, as traditionally taught, and reflectance of energy are not precisely the same, as we will see. Recall that the formula for impedance is $Z_A = P/U$. Therefore, when energy moves from one medium to another, there will be rejection (impedance) by the second medium. Impedance is proportional to sound pressure. This means that Z can be derived from the sound pressure level. The higher the Z, the higher the sound pressure level and the higher the sound pressure level, the higher the impedance. The increase in sound pressure level indicates that air molecules are pressed together, thereby preventing the flow of energy. This is an analog to reflected energy in that only part of the energy will pass through the system, and part will be reflected. So, for example, when sound is introduced into the ear canal, the sound's energy is partially reflected at the level of the tympanic membrane, a result of the acousticomechanical properties of the auditory system, namely, the middle ear and cochlea.

The efficiency of the system's ability to pass the energy can be measured by a method called power reflectance. Power reflectance is sometimes referred to as energy reflectance, or wideband reflectance. (*Explanatory note*: Although the ratios of reflected to incident power and reflected to incident energy are the same in the steady-state transmission, the terms energy and power should not be used interchangeably, as power in the physical sense refers to time rate at which energy is transferred [power is measured in watts and $W = J/s$] and energy refers to the capacity of a physical system to perform

work [energy is measured in joules and $J = N.m.$]. Please refer to Chapter 1.)

The power reflectance method is based on the concept of the transmission line theory. Power refers to the rate of energy transfer. Power reflectance and power transmission are used in monitoring and maintaining power transmitters as well as the measurement of power efficiency in engineering, industrial, and medical fields (Chapter 3). A power reflection meter generally measures power transmission and reflectance in these fields. The power is directed through a load and measured before and after the load. A load refers to the system that is being evaluated for reflectance, that is, resistor, capacitor, or inductor. The initial power or initial energy is the incident power or incident energy, respectively. The reflectance is then the ratio of the reflected quantity over the incident quantity. Thus, the reflectance is "unitless" and may be expressed as a percentile.

Recently, some investigators (Khanna & Stinson, 1985; Lawton & Stinson, 1986; Stinson, Shaw, & Lawton, 1982) questioned the accuracy of traditional impedance measurement *in high frequencies*. As we know, in order to derive middle ear impedance, we first have to obtain the impedance of the space between the probe and the tympanic membrane. However, it is difficult to assess the impedance of the space between the probe and the tympanic membrane because the curves of the ear-canal curve make it difficult to calculate the distance between the probe and the tympanic membrane. The traditional impedance measurement is based on the concept of the lumped element model that assumes that the acoustic pressure at the ear canal measurement point (at some unknown distance from the tympanic membrane) is the same as the acoustic pressure at the tympanic membrane. This equality is maintained only in the frequencies below approximately 2000 Hz (Khanna & Stinson, 1985).

At higher frequencies, the ear canal may be modeled as a transmission line with varying acoustic pressure along its length and the tympanic membrane as its terminating load. (There are no contraindications to applying this model in the low and mid frequencies as well.) The transmission line theory allows for the prediction of the energy reflectance at the tympanic membrane from the ear canal sound pressure measurement.

Thanks to sophisticated calibration procedures (Allen, 1985; Keefe, Ling, & Bulen, 1992) the acoustical reflectance can be computed even though the precise distance between the measurement point and the tympanic membrane is unknown. Energy reflectance is assumed to be uniform along the length of the ear canal. The acoustical energy reflectance is a ratio of the reflected energy to the incident energy and is equal to the square of the ratio of reflected sound pressure to the incident sound pressure (Figure 7–11).

Recently, power reflectance has been cleverly introduced by researchers in the field of middle ear diagnosis (Allen, 1985; Feeney & Keefe, 1999; Keefe, 1997; Keefe, Bulen, Arehart, & Burns, 1993; Keefe et al., 1992) using reflectance as a measure of the

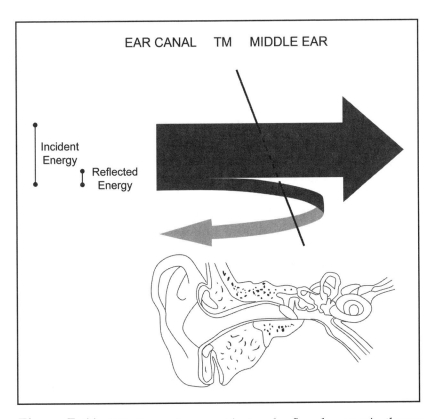

Figure 7–11. This figure shows incident and reflected energy in the ear canal. The figure was adapted, with permission, from Salus, H. R. (doctoral dissertation).

inefficiency of the middle ear and cochlea. These investigators have highlighted the advantages of using reflectance rather than admittance or impedance to detect middle ear pathology. Reasons include: (a) in measuring power reflectance the middle ear is not pressurized. Pressurizing the TM has a disadvantage in measuring middle ear static. For example, at +200 daPa, the eardrum of a newborn infant may be pushed inward creating artificial middle ear pathology and exaggerating ear canal volume. Similarly, at –400 daPa, we may artificially expand the middle ear compensated static. In this case, one might miss middle ear pathology; (b) whereas traditional tympanometry uses a single probe-tone frequency, for example, 226 Hz, 678 Hz, or 1000 Hz, wideband power reflectance employs a chirp stimulus that consists of a broad range of frequencies from low (approximately 100 Hz) to high (approximately 8000 Hz). This has the advantage of providing the reflectance of all frequencies along the continuum between the low and high ends of the range thereby enhancing the diagnostic appeal of power reflectance; (c) the above mentioned investigators have taken advantage of the fact that the ear canal is essentially uniform up to the eardrum so energy will not be lost along the path; and (d) impedance measurement is influenced by the location of the probe. Probe location does not influence power reflectance measurement.

A normal ear, one free of middle ear pathology, will have optimum transmission and therefore minimum reflectance of sound energy between 1000 and 5000 Hz as the imaginary impedance component barely exists (mass reactance and stiffness reactance). Only the resistive component remains. Resistance is not significantly affected by frequency. It is interesting to see how various middle ear pathologies affect transmission and reflectance of energy in the range of frequencies described. Preliminary data appear to hold promise regarding the use of reflectance in the detection of various middle ear disorders. Furthermore, data for noise-tone difference (NTD) of the acoustic reflex using power reflection for prediction of hearing loss in the elderly indicate promise. The NTD of the acoustic reflex using power reflection appears to be much wider than that using the traditional acoustic reflex (Salus & Silverman, in preparation). We are awaiting additional data and details from labs around the world before reflectance joins our clinical armamentarium in the diagnosis of various middle ear pathologies. We suggest that clinics for which the device is affordable purchase the reflectance instrument and compare their clinical data for middle ear pathologies identified using admittance testing with results from reflectance.

The following formulas explain power reflectance as a physical quantity: Reflectance (sometimes called pressure reflection coefficient) = $K(\omega)$ = $pR(\omega)/pI(\omega)$. (ω) refers to angular velocity (or angular frequency) ($\omega = 2\pi f$); pR refers to sound pressure reflected, and pI refers to sound pressure incident. Therefore, Energy Reflectance = R = $/K(\omega)/^2$ = $/pR(\omega)/pI(\omega)/^2$. Figure 7–12 shows normative data from three different studies. The shaded area represents the 5 to 95% normal range and the three curves indicate normative data for the three studies.

Figure 7–13 shows an example of a wideband power reflectance recording for a young healthy normal-hearing female child with a normal middle ear.

The efficiency of the middle ear and cochlea are not only measured via power reflectance but through power absorption. Figure 7–14A shows mean norms for reflectance (dotted line) and reflectance results for an individual with otitis media with effusion. Figure 7–14B shows mean absorption (dotted line) and results absorption results for the same individual with otitis media with effusion.

The calibration procedure (Figure 7–15 gives calibration cavities) is performed in order to determine the sound delivery system's characteristics, so-called equivalent Thevenin parameters (equivalent source pressure and equivalent source impedance). Measurements of sound

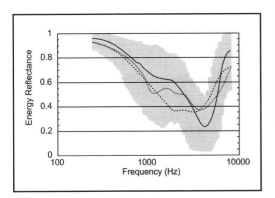

Figure 7–12. *Normative data for ear reflectance from Feeney, Grant, and Marryott (2003) by permission. The abscissa shows frequency (note that at approximately 6000 to 8000 Hz, reflectance is minimal. The ordinate shows energy reflectance where 1 is maximum reflectance and 0 is minimum reflectance.*

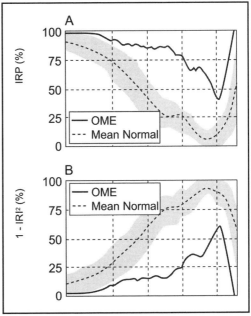

Figure 7–14. *Reflectance and absorption tracings for an individual with OME (with permission of Allen, Jeng, & Levitt, 2005).*

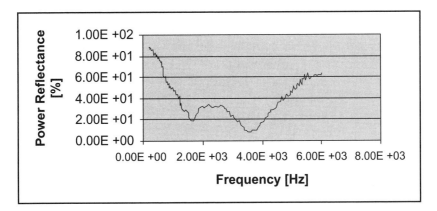

Figure 7–13. *Wideband power reflectance for a young female with normal hearing.*

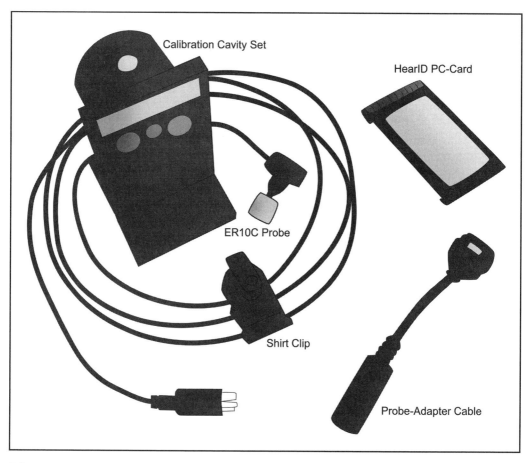

Figure 7–15. *Calibration cavities for calibration of power reflectance instrumentation.*

pressure and impedance in four calibration cavities, four closed tubes, (four pairs of measurements) are used to compute the two Thevenin parameters. Essentially, the calibration computation consists of matching the response data to a closed tube model. All the measurements are frequency dependent. Thus, the chirp stimulus yields a multitude of the tubal sound pressure measurements, tubal impedances and Thevenin parameters. The Thevenin parameters are later used together with the ear canal sound pressure measurements to compute the ear canal impedance and ear canal reflectance.

The reflectance, although representing the ratio of the reflected energy to the incident energy, is not obtained directly from those two values but indirectly, using the values of ear canal sound pressure, impedance, and Thevenin parameters.

REFERENCES

Allen, J. B. (1985). Measurement of eardrum acoustic impedance. In J. B. Allen, J. L. Hall, A. Hubbard, S. T. Neely, & A. Tubis (Eds.), *Peripheral auditory mechanisms* (pp. 44–51). New York, NY: Springer-Verlag.

Allen, J. B., Jeng, P. S., & Levitt, H. (2005). Evaluation of human middle ear function via an acoustic power assessment. *Journal of Rehabilitation Research and Development, 42*(4), 63–78.

Feeney, M. P., Grant, I. L., & Marryott, L. P. (2003). Wideband energy reflectance measurements in adults with middle-ear disorders. *Journal of Speech Language Hearing Research, 46*(4), 901–911.

Feeney, M. P., & Keefe, D. H. (1999). Acoustic reflex detection using wide-band acoustic reflectance, admittance and power measurements. *Journal of Speech, Language, and Hearing Research, 42,* 1029–1041.

Keefe, D. H. (1997). Otoreflectance of the cochlea and middle ear. *Journal of the Acoustical Society of America, 102,* 2849–2859.

Keefe, D. H., Bulen, J. C., Arehart, K., & Burns, M. E. (1993). Ear canal impedance and reflection coefficient in human infants and adults. *Journal of the Acoustical Society of America, 94,* 2617–2638.

Keefe, D. H., Ling, R., & Bulen, J. C. (1992). Method to measure acoustic impedance and reflection coefficient. *Journal of the Acoustical Society of America, 91,* 470–485.

Khanna, S. M., & Stinson, M. R. (1985). Specification of the acoustical input to the ear at high frequencies. *Journal of the Acoustical Society of America, 77,* 577–589.

Lawton, B. W., & Stinson, M. R. (1986). Standing wave patterns in the human ear canal used for estimation of acoustic energy reflectance at the ear drum. *Journal of the Acoustical Society of America, 79,* 1003–1009.

Margolis, R. H. (1981). Fundamentals of acoustic immittance. Appendix A. In G. R. Popelka (Ed.), *Hearing assessment with the acoustic reflex* (pp. 117–143). New York, NY: Grune & Stratton.

Margolis, R. H., Bass-Ringdahl, S., Holte, L., & Zapala, D. A. (2003). Tympanometry in newborn infants — 1000 Hz norms. *Journal of the American Academy of Audiology, 14,* 383–392.

Mazlan, R., Kei, J., & Hickson, L. (2009). Test-retest reliability of the acoustic stapedial reflex test in healthy neonates. *Ear and Hearing, 30,* 295–301.

Rhodes, M., Margolis, R., Hirsch, J., & Napp, A. (1999). Hearing screening in the newborn intensive care nursery: Comparison of methods. *Otolaryngology-Head and Neck Surgery, 120,* 799–808.

Shanks, J. E. (1984). Tympanometry. *Ear and Hearing, 5,* 268–280.

Silverman, C. A. (2010). Multifrequency tympanometry and otoacoustic emissions in infants and children. *AudiologyOnline.* Invited article.

Sprague, B. H., Wiley, T. L., & Goldstein, R. (1985). Tympanometric and acoustic-reflex studies in neonates. *Journal of Speech and Hearing Research, 28,* 265–272.

Stinson, M. R., Shaw, E. A., & Lawton, B. W. (1982). Estimation of acoustic energy reflectance at the eardrum from measurement of pressure distribution in the human ear canal. *Journal of the Acoustical Society of America, 72,* 766–773.

Van Camp, K. J., Margolis, R. H., Wilson, R. H., Creten, W. L., and Shanks, J. E. (1986). *Principles of tympanometry.* ASHA Monograph No. 24. Rockville, Maryland: American Speech-Language-Hearing Association.

Vanhuyse, F. J., Creten, W. L., & Van Cam, K. J. (1975). On the W-notching of tympanograms. *Scandinavian Audiology, 4,* 45–50.

Voss, S. E., & Allen, J. B. (1994). Measurement of acoustic impedance and reflectance in the human ear canal. *Journal of the Acoustical Society of America, 95*(1), 372–384.

Weatherby, L. A., & Bennett, M. J. (1980). The neonatal acoustic reflex. *Scandinavian Audiology, 9,* 103–110.

Signal Processing and Digital Technology

Before the digital technology era, microphone and camera recordings of audio and video signals were accomplished using the analog format. The analog signal modulated the surface of a gramophone platter or the magnetic properties of a tape cassette. These media could then be read to generate a good replication of the original recorded signal. Disadvantages of these storage systems included bulkiness, susceptibility to noise, and signal degradation over time. All other non-audio or non-video types of information such as accounting or research data could not be stored using these analog recording systems. The technologic advances in modern times led to the need for more streamlined, accurate, and easier means of storage of information to facilitate recording and sharing of various types of files including, for example, audio, video, research data, business data, and accounts. These were the conditions under which digital technology emerged.

Information embedded in analog signals, for example, sine waves, comprises infinite data points along a continuum. Let us use an example based on temperature. Suppose the temperature on a hot day generally ranges between 85° and 90° Fahrenheit and we use an analog temperature sensor to measure the actual temperature at a given moment. The sensor generates an analog voltage signal that is read by the instrument and then displayed on a screen. The screen displays a value such as 85°, 87.89°, 88.9236°, or even 89.79462176° Fahrenheit, depending on the precision of the sensing equipment. Thus, the number of unique values between two ends of a range can be infinite, and attempts to continuously track temperature, even for a short time, can yield an infinite number of data points. The infinite analog information becomes impossible to store in any real-life electronic system. So, the amount of recorded data and the amount of storage space for the data need to be finite, and the data stored need to allow for later accurate generation of a replica of the original signal. This goal can be accomplished by obtaining samples or select, discrete values of the original analog information signal at regular time intervals or at critical time points in the signal. Returning to our temperature measurement example, if we obtain discrete val-

ues from the analog voltage signal of the temperature sensor at 5-second intervals, and then display these sampled values (in 0.5° steps), then a finite amount of data (e.g., 85.0°, 87.5°, or 88° Fahrenheit) will have been extracted that represent the information embedded in the original signal and which can be stored as finite numbers or digits. Electronic systems that represent information signals using discrete numerical values are called digital systems, and the data stored in this format are called digital data.

Analog signals such as audio signal output from a microphone can be inputted into analog amplifiers and filters to yield a louder and noise-free audio signal. In this process, the audio signal is not automatically stored in analog format. On the other hand, a video camera recording produces analog signals containing all the audio and video information seen through the camera, and analog processing can be employed to change the signal parameters such as brightness, film-grain (noise), and color tones. But this analog information cannot readily be stored in analog format without using bulky and noisy analog media tapes that are subject to degradation over time. Instead, these analog signals can be sampled at discrete points in time, converted to numbers or digitized, and then stored on magnetic media (e.g., hard disk drives or optical media such as DVD disks). The stored digital data or numbers represent the values of the original signal and can be used to regenerate the original audio or video at a desired later time. As data in digital format are converted into specific, unique digits, they are more impervious to noise and are easier to store than analog data. Even textual and graphical data such as databases, research documents, accounting documents, pictures, and charts can be digitally formatted, stored, duplicated, and distributed using digital media (e.g., floppy disks, CD disks, and DVD disks).

In the electrical domain, electronic circuits can be constructed based on electronic components (e.g., resistors, capacitors, diodes, and transistors) that perform analog processes such as filtering and amplification on analog data. But such circuits generally are bulky and high quality analog components are expensive. Although some audio professionals employ these bulky analog tube amplifiers because of their high power output and clarity, digital circuits can provide similar quality with less bulkiness, greater portability, and lower cost. Moreover, in contrast with analog circuits, digital circuits are readily programmable for achievement of various audio effects. As digitized video signal from a camera requires considerable storage capacity, compression techniques based on digital processing circuits can be employed to reduce storage needs. Digital technology has enabled the use of high quality special effects, postprocessing effects, video editing, and audio mixing. Many individuals perform these effects using their personal computers. Digital technology has pervaded nearly every aspect of our lives; our cell phones, high definition televisions, MP3 players, personal computers, and Internet—just to name a few examples—rely on digital technology. This technology has brought within the reach of everyday convenient and inexpensive use, many impractical devices and services and has made many previously impossible and impractical devices and services inexpensively and conveniently available to all of us. Consequently, digital technology has led to the replacement or phasing out of analog devices.

Digital data can be stored and processed using computers, which are called digital computers. Computers use digital code to store, process, transmit, and receive data.

DIGITAL AND BINARY CODES AND BINARY NUMBERS

A digital code is a series of numbers representing some information or data. With a digital code, a unique number is mapped to a unique aspect of the data. Consider an elevator. An elevator has a panel of buttons, each of which designates a specific, unique floor. So, pressing "9" means the elevator goes only to the ninth floor and pressing "2" means that the elevator goes only to the second floor. The elevator does not stop in between floors. It is as if an elevator uses a digital code to deliver individuals to a specific floor. In this example, the digital code is a decimal code as each digit assumes any one of the 10 (decimal) values from 0 through 9. The decimal system represents a regular part of our everyday lives as we count and calculate using the decimal code. Our 10 fingers on our two hands facilitate the use and understanding of the decimal system.

The language of computers uses another form of the digital code, which is called the binary code. A binary digit assumes one of two possible states or values. Consider the following examples of two possible states or values:

➤ ON versus OFF
➤ Positive versus negative
➤ 1 versus 0
➤ hot versus cold
➤ high versus low

For further explanation of the binary code, see Appendix B for digital circuitry. These examples show two possible states or values for the binary digit in contrast with the decimal digit that has 10 possible values. To represent *ON* versus *OFF* states, a binary digit uses only two values that is, *0* to represent the *OFF* state and *1* to represent the *ON* state of the digital system; these two states generally are accomplished by using two fixed voltages in the computer chips and memory. Any numerical value can be represented using a series of binary digits that form a binary number. Using simple mathematical operations, each decimal number can be converted into the corresponding binary number and vice versa. Table 8–1 illustrates decimal numbers and their equivalent binary numbers. Binary numbers can be derived from the decimal numbers as follows: Carry out a series of divisions by 2 (binary numbers are base 2 in contrast with decimal numbers which are base 10), and the remainder of each division, 0 or 1, represents successive digits going from right to left. For example, consider the number 67. Divide 67 by 2 yields 33 with a remainder of 1, so *1* is the rightmost digit. Now, divide 33 by 2, which yields 16 with a remainder of 1, so *1* is the next digit (going from right to left). Now, divide 16 by 2, which yields 8 with a remainder of 0, so *0* is the next digit (going from right to left). Now, divide 8 by 2, which yields 4 with a remainder of 0, so *0* is the next digit (going from right to left). Now, divide 4 by 2, which yields 2 with a remainder of 0, so *0* is the next digit (going from right to left). Now, divide 2 by 2, which yields 1 with a remainder of 0, so *0* is the next digit (going from right to left). Now, divide 1 by 2, which yields 0 with a remainder of 1, so *1* is the last digit (going from right to left). So, the binary number equivalent of 67 is 1000011.

Let us now convert from a binary number into the decimal equivalent. The process involves looking at each digit of the binary number (starting with the rightmost digit and moving leftward). Each digit is multiplied by the number 2 raised to successively higher exponents, beginning with 0. The resultant numbers for each multiplication step then are summed to yield the decimal equivalent. For example, let us consider the binary number 1010. This binary number has 4 digits, and the rightmost digit is 0. The rightmost digit of 0 is multiplied by 2^0 (any number raised to the power of 0 equals 1) which yields 0 (the resultant number for the first multiplication step). The next digit (moving from right to left) is 1, so 1 is multiplied by 2^1, which equals 2 (the resultant number for the second multiplication step). The next digit (moving from right to left) is 0, so 0 is multiplied by 2^2, which equals 0 (the resultant number for the third multiplication step). The last digit (moving from right to left) is 1, so 1 is multiplied by 2^3, which equals *8* (the resultant number for the fourth and

Table 8–1. Decimal Numbers and Their Binary Equivalents

Decimal	Binary
0	0
1	1
3	11
10	1010
15	1111
67	1000011
100	1100100
111	1101111
235	11101011
345	101011001
999	1111100111

last multiplication step). The sum of these resultant numbers is the sum of $0 + 2 + 0 + 8 = 10$.

Let us take another binary number, 1100100, and convert this binary number into its decimal equivalent. There are 7 digits, and we begin with the rightmost digit which is 0, and 0 multiplied by 2^0 equals 0 (the resultant number for the first multiplication step). The next digit (moving from right to left) also is 0, and 0 multiplied by 2^1 equals 0 (the resultant number for the second multiplication step). The next digit (moving from right to left) is 1, and 1 multiplied by 2^2 equals 4 (the resultant number for the third multiplication step). The next digit (moving from right to left) is 0, and 0 multiplied by 2^3 is 0 (the resultant number for the fourth multiplication step). The next digit (moving from right to left) is 0, and 0 multiplied by 2^4 is 0 (the resultant number for the fifth multiplication step). The next digit (moving from right to left) is 1, and 1 multiplied by 2^5 is 32 (the resultant number for the sixth multiplication step). The last digit (moving from right to left) is 1, and 1 multiplied by 2^6 is 64 (the resultant number for the seventh and last multiplication step). The sum of these resultant numbers is the sum of $0 + 0 + 4 + 0 + 32 + 64 = 100$.

Our digital computers are fabricated from processor microchips, memory chips, and digital devices that store and process data in binary format. Inside computers, binary representation is accomplished with digital switches (generally, transistors on microchips) whose output is either *OFF* (usually 0 volts) or *ON*. Each digit of a binary number is called a *bit*, and the number of bits specifies the number of switches. Thus, an *n*-bit binary number can be represented by *n* switches. The decimal number 345 is a three-digit number and its binary number equivalent,

101011001, is a nine-bit number that can be represented by nine switches, each of which represents one of the bits with an *ON* (1) or a *OFF* (0) state.

Each time a computer receives some data, it converts the data into its own binary code and all computer processes occur in binary code. The resultant binary output then is converted into a format that we can recognize and understand. Thus, binary code is the internal language of all digital systems.

As previously mentioned, each digit of a binary number represents one bit. A binary number is a string of bits such as 0, 1, 100, 1010, 00001, 00010, 0100, and so forth. In the aforementioned example, the binary number 101011001 is a 9-bit number. A series of four bits is termed a nibble (e.g., 1000, 1010, 0101) and 8 bits form one byte (e.g., 10100101, 00110011). Thus, one byte represents 8 bits of information. A byte is a commonly used unit of measure for binary code. We often specify computer memory in terms of mega-bytes and we often describe the computer hard disk drive in terms of giga-bytes of storage space. These terms represent measurement units in binary code. Table 8–2 shows the terms for series of bits and

Table 8–2. Terms for Series of Bits and Bytes

Number of Bits or Bytes	Equivalent Measure
4 bits	1 nibble
8 bits	1 byte or 2 nibbles
1 kilo-byte	1024 bytes
1 mega-byte	1024 kilo-bytes
1 giga-byte	1024 mega-bytes
1 tera-byte	1024 giga-bytes

bytes. Computers store data on hard disk drives or DVD disks, etc., converting the data into binary code (series of 1s and 0s) and into bits that we can read at some later point in time.

REPRESENTING LETTERS WITH A BINARY CODE

Binary codes can be used to represent the letters of the alphabet, numerals, common symbols, and commands such as space or enter. This is done using bytes, each with a unique sequence of eight bits to represent different characters. A series of 8 bits enables the generation of 256 different combinations, each of which can be mapped to a different meaning. Each byte can represent an individual letter, numeral, symbol, or command in a text document, in which case every character in the document uses a byte.

An ordinary computer keyboard has 47 keys, and each key can be used with or without the Shift key, resulting in 94 basic symbols that can be encoded for numbers, small letters, capitals, and common punctuation. (The Space bar and the Return key increase the number of symbols from the basic 94 to 96.) The ASCII code (American Standard Code for Information Interchange) for computers uses a 7-bit code to represent 128 symbols, which are sufficient to encode all ordinary keyboard symbols. For example, the lowercase alphabet character *a* is encoded by the byte 1100001, whereas uppercase alphabet character *A* is encoded by the byte 1000001. A grouping of eight bits (furnishing 256 possible combinations) yields many "extra" codes for special symbols found in an extended ASCII system. These symbols usually are encoded using the Control or the Alternate key in conjunction with one of the 47 basic keys, yielding an additional 94 symbols. Codes also exist for the 12 keyboard Function keys and for the other special keys (e.g., arrow keys) located to the right of the basic keys on the keyboard. Encoding of the keystrokes in binary format enables the computer to recognize differences among numbers and symbols so that appropriate operations can be performed.

DIGITAL COMMUNICATIONS

Binary codes are found not only in computing, they are found wherever digital technology is found, including the field of communications. When the telephone, invented by Alexander Graham Bell, was initially used, it was costly because it required telephone operators to connect the sender and receiver of the telephone communications. Telephone communications involved transmission of analog signals (spoken speech signals converted into electric voltage signals by the telephone microphone at the caller end) over copper wires. So this represented the age of analog communications. Problems plaguing the early telephone transmissions included susceptibility of the analog signal to noise; and decrease in signal voltage with distance resulting from degradation of the signal from the resistance of the copper wires; and high cost associated with the expense of copper. But digital technology has led to the use of multiple cordless phones and cell phones, many of which allow Internet browsing.

With digital communication, information (voice, data, video, etc.) transfer occurs as a digital bit stream through a transmission medium (metal wires, optical fibers, air, etc.) from one point to another point (e.g., one person calling another person on the cell phone) or one point to multiple points (e.g., a global positioning system [GPS] satellite transmitting information to GPS units in people's cars). The analog data such as spoken speech into a cell phone is digitized and transmitted as a binary stream from the caller to the receiver's cell phone for decoding and conversion back to analog speech that enters the recipient's ear. The transmitted data are digital, represented in the form of 1s and 0s, and, as such, are more impervious than analog signals to noise. Any drop in signal strength over distance can overcome with amplification and retransmission by devices called repeaters. Various digital signal-processing techniques can be employed to improve any noise susceptibility of the data transmissions, and error coding techniques to detect and even correct errors also can be employed. To ensure privacy and secure communications, the signal can be encrypted. These techniques and capabilities are not possible with analog communication. Modern telecommunication standards for our cell phones include GSM (Global System for Mobile Communications), CDMA (Code Division Multiple Access), and most recently 4G (fourth generation of cell phone network technology). There are standards for wireless routers to enable wireless connections to the Internet in our homes. Ethernet standards that govern how computers and devices in a local area network communicate with each other include the less efficient CSMA/CD (Carrier-Sense Multiple Access/Collision Detection) protocol, and, more recently, the full-duplex protocol. In June, 2009, analog television (TV) broadcasting was replaced by digital broadcasting, and individuals who did not own digital televisions had to install digital converter boxes to receive the digital television transmission. High-definition television allows the receipt of the increased bandwidth and resolution of the digital television signal. Digital signal processing techniques also are employed in radios, for example, to reduce signal noise.

DIGITAL SIGNAL PROCESSING (DSP) PRINCIPLES

Digital signal processing or DSP involves representation of real world signals using numbers or digital code and signal processing techniques such as filtering, amplification, transformation, and modulation. As previously mentioned, DSP is useful and has many applications such as audio processing, video processing, image processing, and digital communications. As real-world signals are analog in origin, they need to be digitized to enable their being digitally processed. Digitization is accomplished through sampling and quantization.

Analog signals can have a unique value at any given point of time and they represent the signals in their complete, raw form. As previously mentioned, representing a signal at each moment of time would place high demands on storage and computing power to process such large amounts of data. As mentioned earlier, an approach is to select values at regular time intervals. Such an approach reduces the amount of data that need storage and processing, and judicious selection of time intervals for sampling the data values can enable reasonably good representations of the original signal for practical applications. The original signal is discretized by being reproduced as an array of discrete values. The sampling or discretizing process is shown in Figure 8–1. To obtain the discretized representation of the original analog signal, samples of the analog signal are obtained at regular time intervals and stored in discrete format.

The time period between two consecutive samples represents the the the sampling period (T_S) for which the unit commonly is seconds. The sampling frequency (f_S) in Hz represents the inverse of T_S (see Eqn. 8.1):

$$F_s(Hz) = 1/T_s \qquad \text{(Eqn. 8.1)}$$

It represents the number of samples taken from a continuous time signal during each time interval to yield the discretized representation of the original signal. Dis-

cretization does lead to signal loss as it involves taking only selected values while discarding all other values. So, the signal reconstructed from these sampled values may not always faithfully represent the original, continuous time signal. Better representation of the original continuous signal using sampling can be achieved by increasing the number of samples per second, but the tradeoff is the need for increased storage space and computing power. The Nyquist-Shannon sampling theorem can be employed to achieve a good balance between number of samples and required storage space and processing power. According to this theorem, any continuous time signal can be well reproduced from its discretized version if the sampling frequency exceeds a value that is twice the maximum frequency within the signal. If the highest frequency component in a given continuous time signal is f_{MAX} Hz, then sampling frequency should be at least $2f_{MAX}$ Hz (Eqn. 8.2) to yield a discretized signal that is a faithful reconstruction of the original continuous signal:

$$F_s(Hz) \geq 2f_{MAX} \qquad \text{(Eqn. 8.2)}$$

where f_{MAX} is the highest frequency component in the continuous time signal.

The Nyquist-Shannon sampling theorem can be applied to telephone transmissions. Although persons with normal-hearing sensitivity can hear sound in the frequency range of approximately 20 Hz to 20,000 Hz, telephones generally cut off frequencies above 4000 Hz. So, if 4000 Hz is the highest frequency component passed by a telephone, then the sampling frequency should be 2 × 4000 Hz or 8000 Hz to yield a satisfactory and accurate reproduction of the original voice at the recipient's ear.

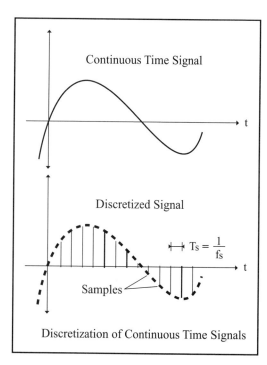

Figure 8–1. *The continuous, time analog signal is shown in the top graph and the process of sampling of the values in the continuous time signal leads to the discretized signal in the bottom graph.*

A signal sampled according to the sampling theorem can be reconstructed back into the original continuous time signal by passing through a digital to analog converter. This is possible if the discretization had occurred with a sampling frequency greater than f_s Hz. This sampling frequency is referred to as oversampling. A sampling frequency less than f_s Hz is referred to as undersampling, and the original signal cannot be reconstructed faithfully with undersampling, which causes aliasing or folding. Aliasing is the distortion in the discretized, reconstructed signal from undersampling of the original signal. Figure 8–2 illustrates aliasing.

Because f_s Hz is less than $2 \times f_{MAX}$ Hz, sampling is not in accordance with the Nyquist-Shannon sampling theorem, and the reconstructed, discretized signal is distorted. The reconstructed signal clearly is not a faithful replica of the original signal. An anti-aliasing filter, which essentially is a band-limiting pass filter, is sometimes used to minimize the adverse effects of alias-

ing. Such a filter assists in band-limiting the input analog signal according to the Nyquist-Shannon sampling theorem.

After the signal is discretized, then the discrete values need to be quantized. As the discretized values of the original signal represent the instantaneous values of the original signal at the moment of sampling and have real-life fractional values, they may not directly and accurately be converted into binary code, which is the language of computers. Quantization is the process of converting these discrete values into the closest digital or binary equivalents that can be read, processed, and stored by a computer. Specifically, this means that the A/D converter breaks the signal into discrete voltage steps based on the number of bits. For example, if the range of the A/D converter is 10 volts, then a 16-bit converter breaks this 10-volt range into 2^{16} discrete steps of about 1.5 µV each. With quantization, the continuous time signal is represented as a sequence of steps that attempt to

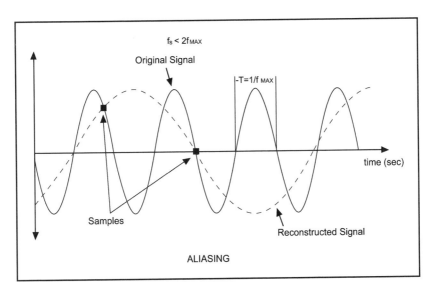

Figure 8–2. The original, continuous signal, and the discretized, reconstructed signal. The filled squares represent the times at which samples were obtained.

mirror the shape of the original signal. Each step is a predefined voltage level representing a specific binary sequence, and its duration is T_S seconds or the sampling period. Figure 8–3 illustrates the quantization process that is applied to the continuous time signal. Note that the steplike quantized signal is superimposed on the original, continuous time signal. Sampling is done at the frequency f_S Hz, and then the sampled values are rounded off to the closest quantization level at the onset of the sampling event. The quantization level remains constant for the duration of the sampling period, after which the quantization level changes or remains unchanged, depending on the value of the next sample. Each quantization level represents a binary sequence. In this manner, the analog signal is mapped to a series of binary strings. As the quantization process involves rounding off the values, some loss of precision is incurred that can be minimized by increasing the number of steps or quantization levels. This will increase signal fidelity, but the tradeoff is an increase in required storage and computing power and, hence, digital

circuit complexity. So, quantization step size is calculated based on the specific application.

The original signal is now completely digitized after the two-step process of sampling and quantization. These processes are carried out in a device referred to as an analog-to-digital (A/D) converter. The digitized signal, which is in binary form, can undergo further digital signal processing by the computer.

DIGITAL RECORDING

Digital recording is a method used in digi-tal technology for storing audio and visual signals. These signals can be stored on media such as CD-ROM (compact disk read-only memory) or DVD-ROM (digital video disk read-only memory).

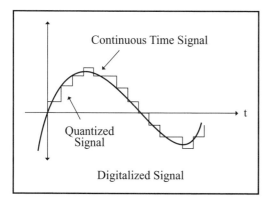

Figure 8–3. The original continuous time signal is the smooth curve. The steplike signal is the quantized, digitalized signal.

Before the age of digital technology, audio was recorded on storage media in analog format. Thomas Edison invented the phonograph, the first audio recording device, in 1877. The diaphragm of the phonograph vibrated when someone spoke into it. The back of the diaphragm had a needle that etched the diaphragm vibrations onto a tinfoil cylinder that the user rotated manually while recording. The playback system read the recorded etchings off the tinfoil cylinder and converted them back into the spoken voice. In 1887 Emil Berliner modified the audio recording design to use flat disks instead of a tinfoil cylinder; his modification was called the gramophone.

The year 1925 marked the introduction of gramophones that used a microphone to convert mechanical vibrations into electrical vibrations that controlled needle etchings onto the surface of a vinyl disk. During playback, a pinpoint head traces the etched grooves off the spinning vinyl disk, thereby generating electrical vibrations (analog signal) that then are transduced into the acoustic waveform in the loudspeaker. Later, the invention of magnetic tapes ultimately made it possible to store audio and video data on cassette tapes. The analog video signal from the camera and the analog audio signal from the microphone modified the magnetic properties of the cassette tape. During playback, the tape-head would read these magnetic variations on the cassette

tape and convert them back into the original audio and video signals.

The problems affecting the analog audio and video-recording systems were essentially the problems previously described that affected analog systems in general. The recording equipment was bulky and not very portable. The recording and playback equipment contained many mechanical components, which became degraded and would breakdown as they aged, and they required regular maintenance. Vinyl disks and cassette tapes were susceptible to dust damage and also degraded over time with use. Copying of analog data from one storage medium to another is accompanied by a 3-dB loss of signal-to-noise ratio in the copy, reflecting adverse effects of copying on the quality of analog recordings. Digital recordings do not have these disadvantages.

The process of digital recording involves multiple steps to acquire an analog signal, digitize the signal, process the digital signal, and then store it as a stream of binary numbers. The multiple step process of digital recordings is illustrated in Figure 8–4. The first step involves the use of a microphone to convert the spoken audio signal into the analog electronic form. The second involved addition of analog dither to the signal. Analog dither basically is random noise. Although we generally desire noise-free systems and use noise-reduction techniques towards this goal, in this case, we introduce a small amount of noise to reduce distortion in the recorded signal. The noise has a slightly adverse effect on the signal-to-noise ratio, but the resultant signal sounds less distorted and is more pleasant sounding to the listener. The analog signal with dither added then is sent through a low-pass filter to filter out frequencies above

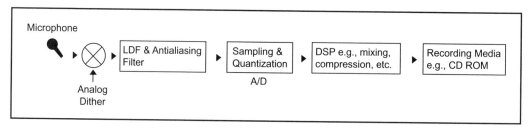

Figure 8–4. *Steps in digital recording. LPF is an abbreviation for low-pass filter.*

22,000 Hz (such frequencies are unnecessary) and through anti-aliasing filters to minimize any aliasing effects. The filtered analog audio signal subsequently passes through an A/D converter (also called ADC) to be sampled and quantized as part of the digitization process. As the highest frequency component is 22 kHz, sampling is performed at the Nyquist rate of at least 44.1 kHz to minimize aliasing distortion and to maximize the audio information in the discretized signal. Some audio professionals prefer to sample the signal at higher sampling rates such as 96 or 192 kHz for higher fidelity. These higher sampling rates frequently are employed in recording studios to make a master copy that can be mixed with other audio streams at those high sampling rates to maintain good fidelity. These discretized audio streams then need to be quantized. The number of quantization steps used by the quantizer substantially influences the quality of the recorded audio. As mentioned previously, more quantization steps mean longer binary sequences of words to define a binary sample also mean that more storage space will be required to record the data. A word length of 24 bits is considered optimum and practical nowadays for achieving a level of quality comparable to that associated with expensive analog equipment; this word length is commonly used in most new recording standards. Most modern recording systems have a signal processing stage for the application of various techniques to enhance the digitized audio stream. Data compression to reduce storage space needed without sacrificing recording quality can be accomplished using DSP techniques such as FFT (fast Fourier transform) or wavelet transform. The digitized, processed signal then is recorded to physical media such as CD-ROM or DVD-ROM.

A standard audio CD-ROM is recorded at a sampling rate of 44.1 kHz using 16-bit audio words. Using these parameters, the ADC obtains 44,100 samples of the analog audio signal being recorded per second and uses 65,536 (2 raised to the power of 16) levels or steps of quantization to represent each audio sample using a 2-byte (16 bits = 2 bytes) word. These 2-byte words are recorded onto the CD-ROM as a digital bit-stream. With audio playback from a CD-ROM, a digital-to-analog (D/A) converter (also called DAC) converts this recorded digital bit-stream into an analog output that faithfully reproduces the original analog audio waveform that was recorded. Hence, the sound quality of audio playback from a CD-ROM has high fidelity.

In summary, digital recording is highly advantageous as compared with the older analog recordings. Digital recording equipment has become extremely portable, easy to use, and much editing, filtering, and real-time enhancement of audio and video signals can be accomplished using just computer software.

Audio video recorders are almost omnipresent: they are present in our highly portable cell phones and media players. Digital recording equipment provides high quality recordings and has become relatively inexpensive as compared with good analog recording equipment. Making copies of digital media involves essentially just the copying of a digital bitstream of 1s and 0s which, if done properly, does not entail any loss of signal-to-noise ratio or quality. Recording quality remains high even when making numerous copies. Digital media do not degrade with use or age, and they maintain high fidelity unless they incur damage from physical impact. With digital technology, compression techniques can be employed to reduce storage needs without loss of quality. Examples of audio compression formats include MP3 (1 MPEG-1 Audio Layer 3) and, more recently, AAC (Advanced Audio Coding). Examples of video compression formats include MPEG (Moving Picture Experts Group), motion

JPEG (Joint Photographic Experts Group), and, most recently, H.264 (also known as MPEG-4 Part 10/AVC for Advanced Video Coding).

DIGITAL FILTERING

Various filtering operations (e.g., low-pass filtering, high-pass filtering, and band-pass filtering) can be performed in the digital as well as analog domains. Digital filtering applies DSP algorithms to the digital data such that the effects on the reconstructed signal are similar to the effects of the analog filter on the original analog signal. Unlike analog filters that require dedicated filtering circuitry, digital filtering can be performed using DSP algorithms on a computer. These DSP algorithms represent a series of mathematical operations (addition, multiplication, trigonometry, etc.) that are implemented to achieve the desired filtering effect. Digital filtering can be done without bulky circuits having components such as capacitors, resistors, and transistors. The computer processing power represents the limiting factor on the extent of digital filtering. More complex DSP applications may require dedicated digital signal processors, which are single chips that can be programmed for specific operations. Many new audiologic and speech and hearing sciences instrumentation use digital filtering. For example, digital filtering is incorporated in a variety of audiologic equipment where increasing signal-to-noise ratio is critical, e.g., audiometers, auditory evoked potentials, and some new sound level meters. These devices are described in detail in Chapter 9. In addition to digital filtering there is also fast Fourier transformation (FFT) filtering to be discussed below.

DIGITAL HEARING AIDS

An acoustic signal (e.g., speech) strikes the microphone of a hearing aid, which then converts the acoustic signal into an electrical signal (see the section on microphones in Chapter 6). In a digital hearing aid, a low-pass filter with an upper limit of approximately 6000 Hz (sometimes as high as 8000 Hz) is employed; and, based on the Nyquist-Shannon theorem, the sampling rate generally is 16000 Hz with a 16-bit word size. The frequency maximum of the low-pass filter is set to not exceed 8000 Hz in order to reject the unwanted high frequencies that cause the formation of the aliasing error previously mentioned. This allows for the passing of a high quality speech signal.

After the ADC converts the signal into digital form, the digitized signal receives DSP by a digital integrated circuit (IC) chip that has the processing algorithms. These algorithms store a set of commands that manipulate the digitized signal to fit a particular patient's needs. The DSP circuit in digital hearing aids implements the arithmetic operations specified by a particular algorithm (e.g., noise reduction). Because of space and memory limitations and limited power supply from the battery in hearing aids, the speed of DSP is markedly slower in hearing aids than in personal computers. These programs (algorithms) to alter the digitized signal and specific hearing-aid parameter values are stored in the Erasable Programmable Read-Only Memory (EPROM) of the hearing aid. During a hearing-aid fitting session, the desired hearing-aid parameters determined using the fitting software of the computer used by the professional who is performing the hearing-aid evaluation are set into the sound-processing algorithms stored in the reprogrammable EPROM of the hearing aid. Although the parameters and algorithms are stored in the EPROM, the moment-to-moment signal inputs and resultant outputs of the DSP are temporarily stored in random access memory (RAM) rather than in the EPROM permanent memory storage. Some small programs that do not vary with differences in algorithms can be stored on read-only memory (ROM), which places fewer demands for power than RAM.

A hearing with DSP can be classified as a closed platform or an open platform system. The former refers to a hearing aid with a processor that is programmed for a specific algorithm. A change in the algorithm requires a replacement DSP circuit. The latter refers to a hearing aid with a processor into which various program algorithms can be placed. Although an open platform is much more flexible than a closed platform, the former places a much greater demand on power consumption than the latter (Figure 8–5).

Although inserting a low-pass filter at the input to the A/D converter assists in reducing the aliasing error, some error may remain in some instances, necessitating the need for other measures such as dither to further reduce the aliasing error. Imaging distortion also can occur at the output of the hearing aid, which can be avoided by using a low-pass imaging filter at output of the D/A stage.

FAST FOURIER TRANSFORMATION (FFT)

FFT is one of the most important and commonly used tools in digital signal processing. It is a type of computer algorithm for performing a discrete Fourier transform. FFT is what allows computers to per-

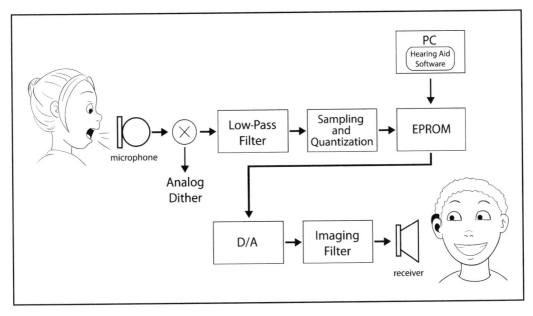

Figure 8–5. *Signal processing stages in a DSP hearing aid.*

form the mathematical computations that define the frequency representation of a signal in a fast and efficient manner. In practice, FFT is the computational tool most always used to perform discrete Fourier transforms. Therefore, the entire discrete Fourier transform process, from sampling an analog signal to graphing its power spectrum, is colloquially referred to as FFT and commercial software will frequently refer to a power spectrum as the FFT of an input signal.

We encounter the application of Fourier transform in almost every area. For example, in medicine, an MRI is often used to identify and analyze a brain tumor. Speech-language pathologists may also use instrumentation incorporating FFT to analyze the voice of patients with voice disorders in order to provide proper training and treatment. In digital photography, Fourier transform is applied with various filtering techniques to generate special visual effects. Audiologists

use FFT to analyze otoacoustic emissions, auditory evoked potentials, and auditory steady-state response (ASSR) where the amplitude of the response is measured in nV. The contribution of FFT to Audiology is explained in greater detail in Chapter 9 where we discuss instrumentation used in Audiology and Hearing Science.

We often describe a sound in terms of its pitch, that is, the highness or lowness of the sound, as we perceive it. We might describe an amplifier or headphones as having a good "bass" response. Perhaps we compare a baritone to a soprano and say, rightfully so, that the baritone's voice is in a lower range than that of the soprano. In each of these examples we are subjectively describing the frequency content of the signal that is generated by the device or the singer. Every complex signal can be synthesized by a number of different sinusoidal components, each one multiplied by a specific coefficient and each one having a different frequency. A coefficient in this context refers to the amplitude for each frequency. If we decompose the baritone and soprano's songs into their constituent frequencies, we will see that the lower frequency components of the baritone's song have larger coefficients and the higher frequency components of the soprano's song have smaller coefficients. This is what differentiates our perceptual decisions of low versus high pitch for baritone and soprano voices, respectively. Collectively, the frequencies and the coefficients of all these signals are referred to as the frequency content or the spectrum of the original signal.

To more comprehensively understand the concept of a spectrum, imagine a tone being played on a musical instrument. For example, if we decompose the signal for the A above middle C on a piano, we will see that there is a big coefficient for the frequency of 440 Hz and smaller coefficients for the other component frequencies. This large coefficient corresponds to the "pitch" of the tone, or the "fundamental frequency," whereas the other coefficients give the piano tones their distinct sound and are called "harmonics." Of course, more complicated signals will have a response distributed over a larger number of frequencies. In this chapter, we discover how to compute the frequency content of a complex signal using computers, with the help of the FFT mathematical algorithm. Specifically, we show, step by step, the conversion of a waveform (a signal represented in the time domain) to a power spectrum graph (the frequency domain representation).

Time Domain Representation

Before proceeding to the actual method used to acquire the frequency content of a signal, it is useful to review the way this signal is represented in its original form. This form, which is called the time domain representation, is nothing more than the waveform of the signal or, equivalently, the graph of the signal amplitude (y-axis) as a function of time (x-axis). In this form, the amplitude of the signal varies over time and this variation is mathematically described by a signal equation. The signal equations for analog signals are determined by functions of time:

$$y = f(t), \qquad \text{(Eqn. 8.3)}$$

where t is a continuous (analog) variable representing time, and y is the resultant amplitude at time t. The signal equation for a discrete signal written as a function of time would be:

$$y = f[n], \qquad \text{(Eqn. 8.4)}$$

where n is a positive integer representing time. Figure 8–6 illustrates analog (continuous) and discrete waveforms, on the left and right, respectively.

Frequency Domain Representation

As mentioned earlier, each signal has specific frequency content. This roughly means that each signal can be decomposed into "simpler" sinusoidal signals, each one with a corresponding amplitude and frequency. Recall that amplitudes are called the coefficients for each frequency and the total of these coefficient-frequency pairs can uniquely describe the original signal. So, instead of a time domain representation, we can have a graph that depicts these pairs. This graph is called the frequency domain represen-

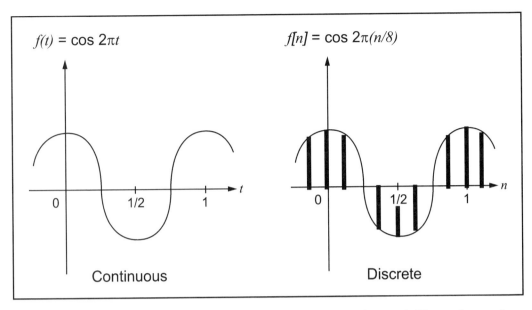

$f(t) = \cos 2\pi t$

$f[n] = \cos 2\pi(n/8)$

Continuous

Discrete

Figure 8–6. Graphs of a continuous and a discrete cosine signal (function). The continuous function is overlaid on the discrete, which is simply represented by vertical lines.

tation and all processing done on signals with this representation takes place in the frequency domain.

The mathematical tool we use to acquire the frequency domain representation of a signal is the Fourier transform. This applies to both stimulus and response signals, for example, OAE, auditory evoked potentials, and in particular, ASSR. The Fourier transform provides us with much more information about the signal than we need for the purpose of the applications we are discussing. Later, we will see how to extract the useful information from the output of the Fourier transform. The useful element is called the power spectrum and it is an approximation of the frequency content of the original signal. In Figure 8–7, we can see some examples of signals with their corresponding frequency content extracted with the help of the Fourier transform. In this figure, a simple sine signal (a) has a spectrum that is concentrated around a single frequency. In (b), where a small ripple has been introduced, we can see a second spike emerging. This spike represents the high frequency content and is smaller than the original dominant signal. In (c) there is a more complicated speech signal and its corresponding power spectrum. In the rest of this chapter, we generate and interpret these graphs using computer software.

TECHNICAL DETAILS OF THE FFT

As stated above, the FFT algorithm is a highly efficient computer algorithm for performing a discrete Fourier transform. Essentially, the FFT attempts to estimate the spectrum of the original analog signal by using the samples acquired from it.

Its efficiency relies on the fact that the FFT splits N samples into two sets and carries its calculations in these reduced

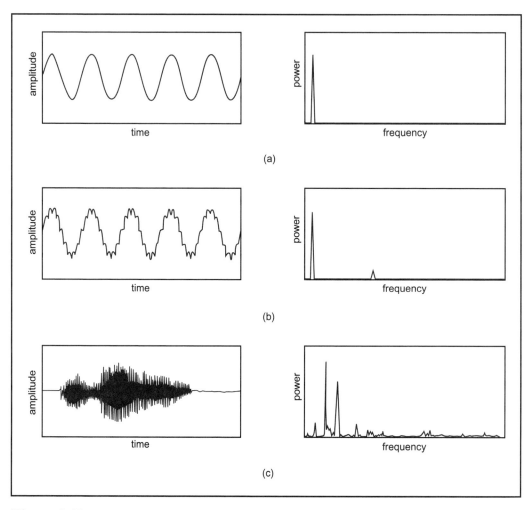

Figure 8–7. *Some examples of signals and their corresponding power spectra calculated with the help of a computer: (a) a sine signal, (b) the same sine signal with the addition of high frequency content, and (c) a speech signal.*

sets. Then it divides the sets again and again, each time performing calculations in a smaller set, until it reaches sets of size 2. This technique requires that the number of samples (N) taken for FFT analysis must be a power of 2, for example, 128, 256, 512, 1024, and so forth. In the event that we feed the FFT system with a number of samples that is not a power of 2, only the largest number, which is a power

of 2, will be selected, for example. 10,000 samples will result in $2^{13} = 8192$ samples being selected.

The output of the FFT is a sequence of N numbers (same as the number of samples) each one of which represents the contribution of a specific frequency of the original signal. The first number always represents the zero frequency and the last one the sampling frequency, which, according to the Sampling theorem, is the double of the maximum frequency contained in the original signal. This gives us a hint about which numbers of the FFT output actually contain useful data for us. Actually, only the first half of the sequence is useful. The rest is just a mirror image of the useful part (Figure 8–8).

Another peculiarity of the FFT is that it provides a sequence of complex numbers. Each complex number is actually a pair of numbers: the real part *a* and the imaginary part *b*. In order to be able to represent each frequency with a single coefficient, we have to calculate the magnitude of each complex number defined as the square root of the sum of the squares of the two parts, $\sqrt{a^2 + b^2}$.

The number of samples provided for analysis is also called a window. The tester selects the size of the window and the FFT, which can be expressed explicitly as an integer number of samples or it can be calculated by multiplying the amount of time during which the signal is being sampled by the sampling frequency. It should be understood that when digitiz-

ing a waveform and performing a discrete Fourier transform, the result is only an approximation of the mathematically defined continuous Fourier transform of the actual analog signal. This approximation improves with greater numbers of sampling points of the analog signal, that is, with finer digitalization. In order to measure how fine this representation is we need to define the notion of a *bin*. When we run the FFT on a signal, we will acquire *N* points that represent *N* different equally spaced frequencies from *0* to *fs*, where *fs* is the sampling frequency. Thus, the spectrum from the FFT will be a discrete spectrum. A bin is defined as the distance between two consecutive frequencies of this spectrum and can be easily calculated if we divide the sampling frequency by the window size. Hence, if we have a signal sampled at 44,100 Hz, and the window size is 512 samples, the bin size will be about 86.1 Hz, whereas a window of 8,192 samples will give a bin size of about 5.3 Hz, which yields a much more accurate power spectrum estimation. This effect is demonstrated in Figure 8–9.

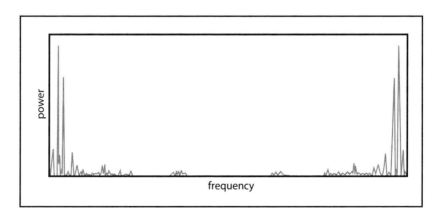

Figure 8–8. *An example of a signal and the magnitudes of the FFT coefficients. We can observe the symmetry of the FFT transform. The second half is redundant.*

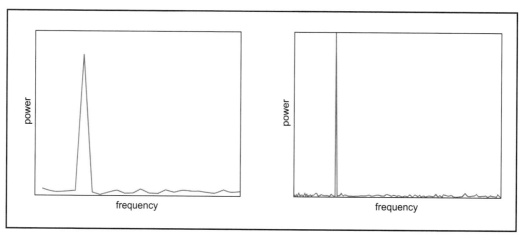

Figure 8–9. *Spectrum of a sine function with frequency = 500 Hz. In the left part, the bin size is 10 Hz and in the right part 1 Hz. The increased accuracy is obvious.*

FFT SYSTEMS SEQUENCE

Having discussed the basic ideas involved in FFT we now turn to outlining more carefully the process of obtaining the final output of commercial FFT software, i.e. the power spectrum of an input analog signal. Generally speaking, there are four steps in the process of using FFT to generate the power spectrum:

Step 1. An input analog signal is sampled, creating a raw sample sequence;

Step 2. The raw sample sequence is filtered (averaged);

Step 3. FFT algorithm is applied to the filtered (averaged) sample sequence;

Step 4. The power spectrum is plotted.

Step 1: Initially, an analog signal will be digitized by an A/D converter with sampling frequency *fs*. For example,

if the signal is sampled 96,000 times per second (96 KHz) for half a second we will get 48,000 raw samples. These data can be very rough and contain a lot of noise.

Step 2: To reduce the noise in the raw digitized sample sequence acquired in the A/D conversion process, filtering (averaging) is done. Filtering or averaging is a method of smoothing out the data by combining several raw sample values into one (see averaging in Chapter 9 in the section on auditory evoked potentials). This will reduce the noise because noise has the effect of bumping a signal up and down by small amounts. Averaging adds the up and down bumps together, thereby canceling them out.

As mentioned earlier, we can acquire a more accurate (less noisy) spectrum by widening the size of the window, that is, the number of samples taken from the original continuous signal.

Steps 3 and 4: After the samples have been filtered or averaged they can be fed into the FFT algorithm. The software usually selects the input samples automatically and extracts the power spectrum as described above.

Examples of the FFT Transform

In order to better understand the whole FFT sequence, we present a quantitative example. Let us suppose that the filtered sampling rate is 20 kHz, running for 0.5 sec. Then, 10,000 filtered samples are taken, from which only 8,192 real numbers are fed into the FFT algorithm. Thus, the output consists of 8,192 complex numbers. The first 4,096 of those complex numbers are converted into the sequence of their real number magnitudes, and this sequence of magnitudes is graphed to obtain the power spectrum. In order to read this graph, the x-axis must be interpreted by using the points along the x-axis of the power spectrum generated by FFT (FFT bins). The FFT bin width is 20,000/8,192 Hz $\approx$ 2.44 Hz. This means that every point along the x-axis of the spectrum is considered to be 2.44 Hz more than the last, starting from zero. In other words, the 4,096 magnitudes would be graphed along 4,096 discrete points along the x-axis, each separated by a distance of 2.44. The first point would be considered to represent the power at which the sampled analog input signal oscillates at 0 Hz while the last point would be considered the power at which the input signal oscillates as 20 kHz. Usually, these data points are plotted with connected lines, yielding an attempt to approximate the analog power spectrum.

Let us consider some interesting examples using FFT. We obtain an acoustic signal, which is the production of the word "audiology." For demonstration purpose, the sound file was obtained from the online Merriam-Webster dictionary. In real systems, such sound file are usually acquired by a microphone, and an A/D converter, for example, a computer audio card. Our sampling rate is 44,100 Hz, the duration of the signal is 0.204 sec, and our sample size is 9,000. We plot the sound wave in the time domain in Figure 8–10A. In this figure, we can see that the word "audiology" is composed of five syllables, each dominated by a certain pattern. Some syllables are short while somes are long. We conduct FFT on this sound signal and obtain the coeffients as shown in Figures 8–10B and 8–10C at half the sample size, that is, 4500. After we compute the power spectrum of the signal, shown in Figure 8–10D, we can observe a few characteristics of this spectrum. First, most engery is concentrated at the low to mid frequencies. Second, we see that the signal is dominated by a few frequencies (the spikes at lower frequencies). They correspond to the dominant frequencies in the five syllables (some syllables are dominated by more than one frequency). We also note that there is some noise at higher frequencies; this is possibly background noise. The noise can be removed by using a Finite Impulse Response Filter (see Figure 8–15) and transforming the signal back to the time domain. We may get a clearer production of the word "audiology." Note that both the real component in Figure 8–10B and the imaginary componenet Figure in 8–10C are integrated to form a clearer and more powerful spectrum in Figure 8–10D.

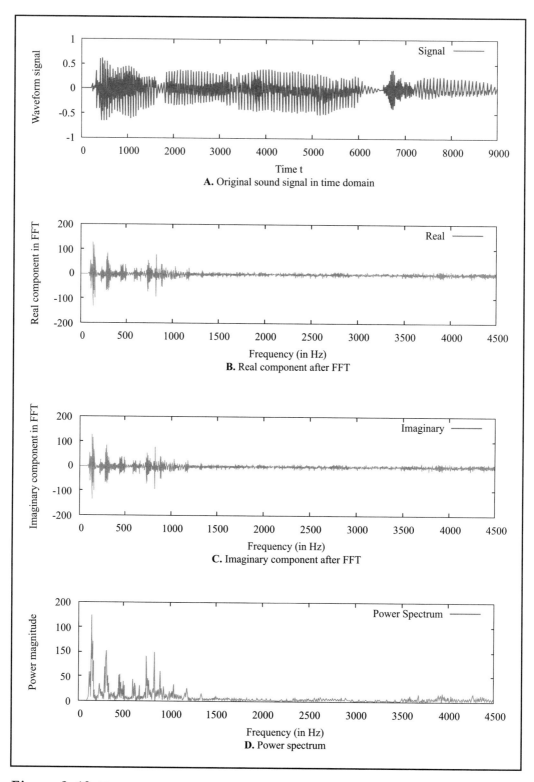

Figure 8–10. *Demonstration of computing FFT. Note that both real and imaginary FFT are important for the final power spectrum (D). The final power spectrum is clearer and stronger than each its components.*

Other examples of transformations from the time domain to the frequency domain using FFT are depicted in the next figures. In Figure 8–11, we have the recording of a male saying "hello" and in Figure 8–12 there is the corresponding power spectrum. The sampling frequency is 8000 Hz and the signal duration is 1 sec. Thus, the number of samples is 8000 and the bin size is 1 Hz. We can see two dominant frequencies in this signal that actually correspond to the different tones "he-" and "-low" of the speaker!

Analysis of ambient street noise provides another good example of FFT transformations. Figure 8–13 shows the recording of street noise and Figure 8–14 the corresponding power spectrum. In this case,

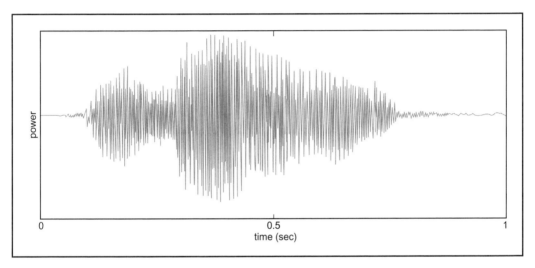

Figure 8–11. *Recording of a man saying "hello." fs = 8000 Hz.*

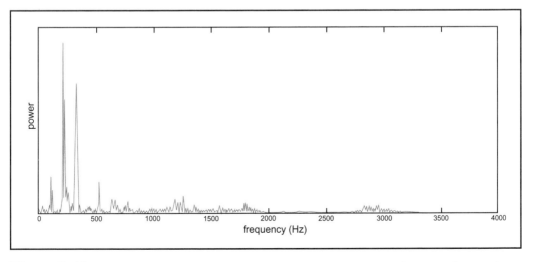

Figure 8–12. *Power spectrum of the "hello" recording. We can see two dominant frequencies.*

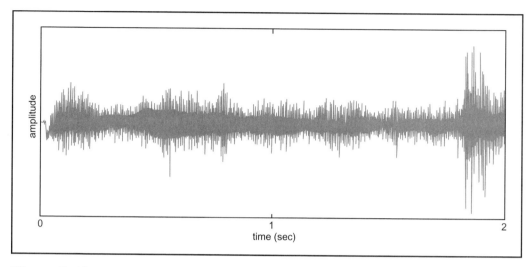

Figure 8–13. *A recording of ambient noise.*

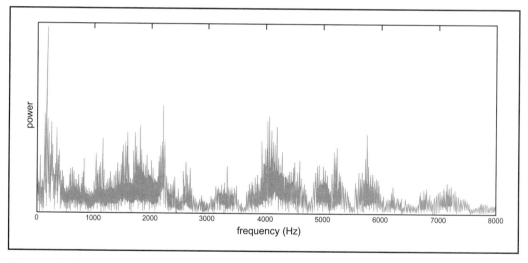

Figure 8–14. *Power spectrum of ambient noise.*

the signal contains a myriad number of different frequencies with random coefficients because there is no dominant frequency.

FURTHER PROCESSING

In many instances, the results of FFT analysis are filtered by an FFT filter (Figure 8–15) in order to obtain a specific com-

ponent of the FFT and to further shape the FFT result by filtering out unwanted noise. These filters are called FIR filters (Finite Impulse Response).

We hope we have presented a reasonably comprehensive explanation of FFT in general terms. We revisit the concept of FFT in Chapter 9 when we present some audiologic instrumentation that incorporates FFT algorithms.

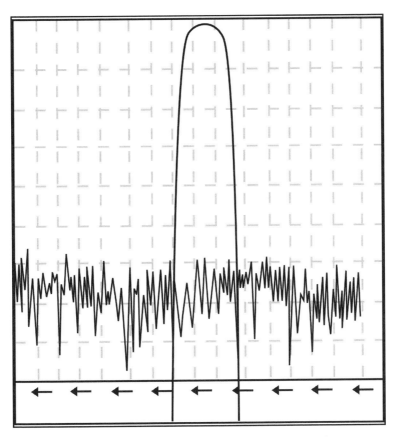

Figure 8–15. *Finite Impulse Response Filter.*

Test Equipment Used in Audiology and Hearing Science

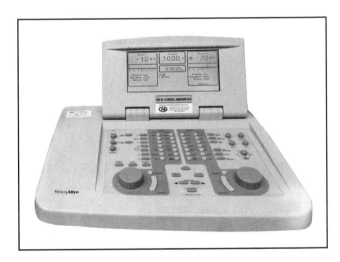

Figure 9–1. GSI-61 audiometer.

In this chapter we describe the principal equipment used in clinical audiology and hearing science: audiometers, immittance devices, otoacoustic emissions devices, and systems for the measurement of auditory brainstem response (ABR) and auditory steady-state response (ASSR). We also describe the operation of these instruments.

AUDIOMETER

An audiometer is an electronic instrument used to test human hearing. Figure 9–1 is a photo of the GSI-61 (Grason-Stadler, Inc.) audiometer, one of many audiometers on the market. All audiometers should adhere to American National Standards Specifications (ANSI) published by the American

Institute of Physics for the Acoustical Society of America (see Chapter 10). These standards describe specifications for all audiometers as well as audiometric transducers, that is, circumaural, supra-aural, insert receivers, bone oscillators, and loudspeakers. The basic components of a clinical audiometer include: (a) pure tone air-conduction in the range from 250 to 8000 Hz and bone conduction in the range from 250 to 4000 Hz. Some audiometers incorporate an extended high-frequency range between 8000 Hz and 20,000 Hz; (b) speech audiometry which includes live voice and/or recorded (analog or digital) speech signals; and (c) third-octave band narrow-band noise (NBN), broad-band noise (BBN), and speech noise.

Audiometers are classified as Types I, II, III, or IV. These classifications are based on: (a) type of test signal; (b) extent of the frequency range; (c) method of testing, that is, manual versus automatic, or computer controlled; (d) site/setting used by the tester, that is, clinical diagnostic, screening, industrial; and (e) number of channels. As the number of audiometric features decreases, the Type number increases. For example, Type I audiometers incorporate more features than Type II, Type II more than Type III, and so forth. Type I audiometers (whether analog, digital, or hybrid), are generally used in a clinical setting and differ from manufacturer to manufacturer. Table 9–1 presents frequencies and hearing levels recommended by ANSI 2010 for the four types of audiometers.

Audiometers in the field of Audiology and Hearing Science include analog, digital, and hybrid instruments. Although they differ in the way they are constructed, all audiometers have features in common. Certainly, they provide the same stimuli and adhere to ANSI standards.

We describe in brief the differences and similarities of analog, digital, and hybrid audiometers. We consider the hybrid audiometer first because it incorporates both analog and digital technology.

Hybrid audiometers are the most commonly used audiometers in our field. Let's look at the GS-61 hybrid audiometer as an example (this represents an example rather than a preference). We should mention that not every hybrid has precisely the same construction as the GS-61. Figure 9–2 shows our rendering of a simplified block diagram of one channel of a two-channel hybrid audiometer (in this case the GS-61). We chose this interpretation to avoid meandering through complex circuitry.

As you can see in Figure 9–2 the analog noise generator is on the left side of the diagram. Below that is a band-pass filter. The frequency control on the upper right allows us to select type of noise (speech noise, BBN, or NBN) based on the stimulus chosen. The selected type of noise will be routed to the equalizer that produces the proper intensity based upon audiometric zero; this differs for each type of noise. The attenuator dial, whose function is to change the power amplification of the signal, for example, 5 dB up, 5 dB down, controls the internal attenuator. The attenuator dial is usually located near the tester on the front section of the panel and is labeled on the block diagram as "tone control." The output of the power amplifier will be routed to the proper transducer, that is, earphone, bone oscillator, speaker, or insert receiver. If the system uses a digital noise generator, the process will be the same as that for the analog noise generator. The GS-61 audiometer used here as an example incorporates both analog and digital noise generators (see left-hand side of Figure 9–2).

Oscillators generate either sinusoidal tones or square waves. In the GS-61, the oscillator is only a square-wave generator. At the end of our discussion of the compo-

Table 9–1. Required Frequencies and Hearing Levels for Various Audiometers

	Hearing Levels (dB HL)[a]						
	Type[d]		*Type 2*[d]		*Type 3*[d]		*Type 4*[c]
Frequency	*Air*[b]	*Bone*	*Air*	*Bone*	*Air*	*Bone*	*Air*
125	70		60				
250	90	45	80	45	70	35	
500	120	60	110	60	100	50	70
750	120	60					
1000	120	70	110	70	100	60	70
1500	120	70	110	70			
2000	120	70	110	70	100	60	70
3000	120	70	110	70	100	60	70
4000	120	60	110	60	100	50	70
6000	110	50	100		90		70
8000	100		90		80		
Speech	100	60	90	55			

Source: Reprinted from ANSI/ASA S3.6-2010 with permission of the Acoustical Society of America.

[a]The maximum hearing level should be equal to the value listed in the table. The minimum hearing level should be −10 dB HL for Types 1 to 4.

[b]For Type 1 audiometers using circumaural or insert earphones the maximum hearing level is permitted to be 10 dB less than the table values.

[c]The maximum hearing level for Type 4 audiometers used for hearing conservation purposes is extended to 90 dB HL.

[d]Pure-tone, warble tone, or speech, sound field/loudspeaker output within the range of 250 to 6000 Hz should be within 20 dB of the values shown for air, for each instrument type.

Note: The maximum hearing level for audiometers that include test frequencies over 8000 Hz should be 90 dB HL from 8000 to 11200 Hz, and 50 dB HL for frequencies between 12000 to 16000 Hz. The minimum hearing level should be −20 dB HL at frequencies over 8000 Hz.

nents of the audiometer, we describe the two types of oscillators in greater detail: those that generate sinusoidal tones, and those that generate square waves.

The pure tones generated by the oscillator are routed through the appropriate filters for further shaping. The frequencies are checked internally by sending the signal to a counter-timer. Software compares the accuracy of the frequencies in terms of cycles/sec to the reference values. If these values do not match the reference values, the voltage is changed to bring the frequency to the proper value.

Sorry! But, because the audiometer does an internal check does not absolve you of the responsibility of using a frequency counter as part of your calibration process.

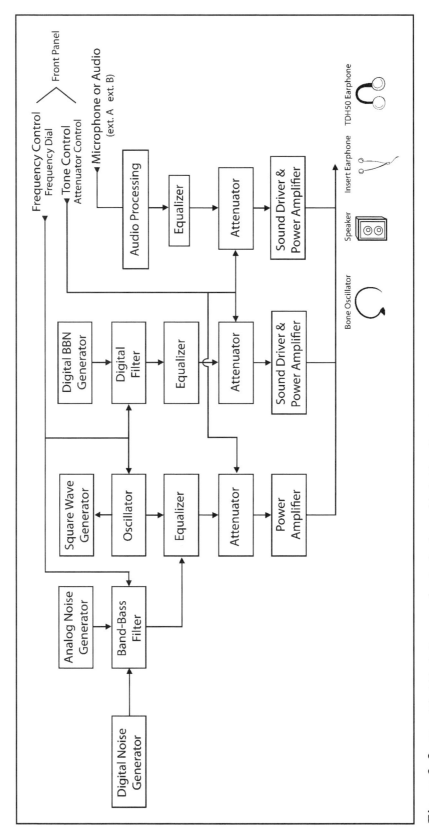

Figure 9–2. Simplified block diagram of a single-channel hybrid audiometer.

Again, the equalizer will serve a function similar to that described for noise. It equalizes each tone based on audiometric zero. The attenuator dial controlled by the tester will control the internal attenuator to increase or decrease the power amplifier.

At the upper right of the figure, below frequency and tone control, we see microphone and audio input. These inputs are routed to the back of the audiometer though circuitry for audio processing and subsequently into the soundproof booth. We use *microphone* with live voice and *talk-back,* and *audio* with an external input for speech stimuli. The electrical circuits (found in the rear of the audiometer and operated by buttons on the panel) for external A and B are similar, and their function is to direct the recorded signal from the external source, for example, analog or digital recorder, into the appropriate transducer. In order to achieve a 0 reading on the VU (Volume Units) meter, the input signal to the audiometer should be between 0.2 VRMS (voltage root mean square) and 1.0 VRMS.

The equalizer for the speech signal has the same function as the equalizers for tones and noise, that is, it adjusts the level for each speech stimulus (0 on the VU meter represents 19.5 dB SPL relative to audiometric zero). The attenuator will change the amplification of the signal.

The digital branch has a digital BBN generator, which generates digital noise with an energy spectrum evenly distributed over a range of 8000 Hz. The digital filter can filter out a narrow frequency band controlled by the frequency control knob. The equalizer and the attenuator serve the same functions as their analog counterparts but operate in the digital domain. The sound driver contains a digital-to-analog converter and other

processing stages that convert the digital stream coming from the attenuator to an analog narrow band of noise whose center frequency is that of the test tone. The power amplifier takes this narrow band and drives it into the output speaker or headphone.

The audiometer also provides for voice or recorded audio to be input through a microphone and driven to the output speakers in the test booth. Different knobs and buttons on the panel of the audiometer help control different parameters of the audio output from the audiometer.

The transducers drawn on the lower right of Figure 9–2 are routed into the test booth through the jacks at the back of the audiometer. Following is a description of various transducers: circumaural earphones (Figure 9–3A) HDA-200 are used for testing high frequencies above 8000 Hz. They have a cushion that fits around the pinna and usually come with a flat adapter to fit the IEC 60318-2 coupler for calibration. Insert receivers (Figure 9–3B) have a foam earpiece that fits comfortably in the ear canal.

Insert receivers afford several benefits: (1) they are useful if the patient has a collapsed ear canal; (2) in cases of masking dilemma with the TDH phones, the insert receiver will provide greater interaural attenuation than the traditional phones. According to Sklare and Denenberg (1987) insert receivers such as ER-3A have a range between 75 to 85 dB for interaural attenuation as opposed to 40 to 60 dB with traditional earphones, and (3) because they are more comfortable, insert receivers are frequently used for electrophysiologic measurements, particularly for infants and young children, especially while they are sleeping (Figure 9–4).

The bone conduction oscillator (Figure 9–3C) measures the integrity of the

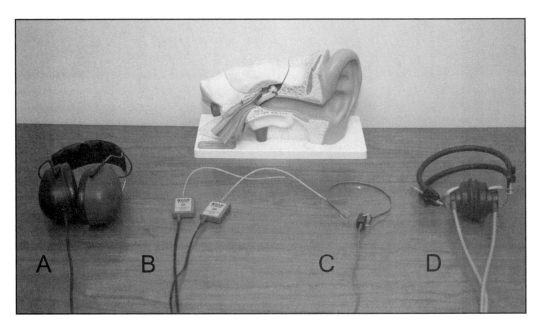

Figure 9–3. *Various transducers used in audiologic measurement.*

Figure 9–4. *Insert receivers for electrophysiologic test for sleeping baby.*

inner ear (for a complete description see Chapter 10). Supra-aural TDH 39, 49, and 50 headphones (Figure 9–3D) have a rubber cushion and sit directly on the pinnae. The speakers diagrammed in Figure 9–2 are located in the booth and, like all transducers, convert an electrical signal into an acoustic signal (see Chapters 6 and 10 for additional information).

OSCILLATORS

The following section describes the two major types of oscillators. One is commonly used in analog audiometers to generate sinusoidal tones and the other, which also generates sinusoidal tones, does so from a square wave.

Standard Oscillator

Before progressing with the description of these oscillators, we wish to remind you about the concept of resonance. An oscillator is an electronic circuit that generates a constant periodic signal (sinusoid). As you can see in Figure 9–5 thermal input noise (internal white noise commonly found in instrumentation) will be routed to the amplifier (you are already aware of the process of amplification), which is biased by a given voltage. The noise is amplified slightly and routed into a tuning circuit. A tuning circuit consists of inductors and capacitors that create sinusoidal signals when the value of the capacitors and inductors is equal (canceling each other) thus creating resonance and emphasizing a given tone while rejecting other tones. You can change the capacitors and inductors to change the tone you require. The resonance in this circuit allows us to generate pure tones. Such circuits can serve as oscillators in many audiometers. The signal returns to the amplifier for additional amplification and is then routed to the output as a sinusoidal signal.

The feedback loop controls the operation of the amplifier and thus the output of the circuit. Without the feedback loop continuously controlling the operation of the amplifier, the circuit will stop working.

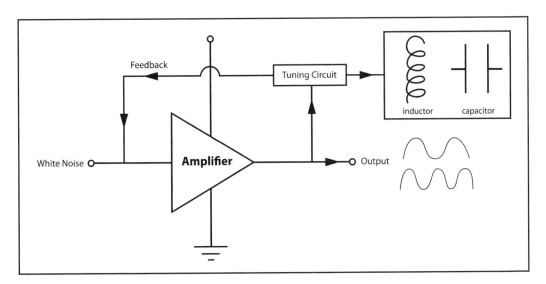

Figure 9–5. *Filtering circuit and pure-tone generator.*

As we do not have external input in an oscillator, the feedback loop takes some part of the output signal and gives it back to the amplifier as an input so that the circuit doesn't stop working.

Square Wave Oscillator

Figure 9–6 is a schematic drawing of a square-wave oscillator. Many recent audiometers use the square-wave principle to generate pure tones. Again, internal noise (thermal) is used as the basic signal for the square-wave generator. The amplifier labeled *A* in the figure amplifies the internal noise. The tuning circuit (R, R1, R2, and C) determines the fundamental frequency at which the amplifier changes the voltage (similar to the switching circuit described in Chapter 4). The square wave is analyzed and filtered as a pure-tone frequency. Therefore, the generation of a square wave is not significantly different from the switching circuit previously described.

The first PC-based audiometers entered the field over 15 years ago. How-ever, due to a number of drawbacks, they lacked popularity among clinical audiologists. Today, most of the drawbacks have been addressed and the digital audiometer has again appeared on the market again. The Madsen Astera (Figure 9–7) is an example of a PC-based audiometer. This audiometer represents an example and not necessarily a preference.

The Astera, as other PC-based audiometers such as the Maico MA 55 Audio-PC-System, is primarily a high-speed computer with a familiar audiometer interface. User tests are preset and the system has just about limitless data storage capacity, as well as a number of available calculations. In addition, digital audiometers allow integration with other diagnostic and fitting tools, for example, immittance tests.

Detailed Description of the Stimuli Generated by an Audiometer

Acoustic stimuli can be defined with reference to time and frequency. A waveform is displayed on a graph showing amplitude

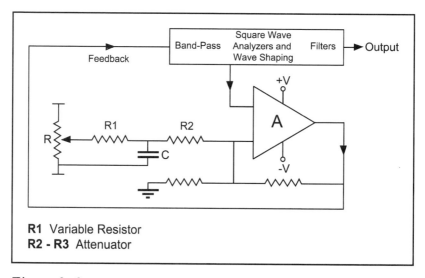

R1 Variable Resistor
R2 - R3 Attenuator

Figure 9–6. *Square-wave oscillator. Permission of Grason-Stadler.*

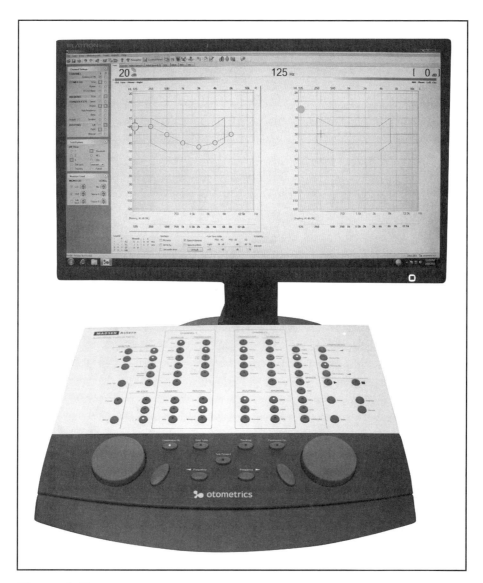

Figure 9–7. *Astera digital audiometer.*

as a function of time. A spectrum is displayed on a graph that shows amplitude as a function of frequency (see section on FFT in Chapter 8).

and spectrum, respectively, of a 2000-Hz pure tone. For detailed requirements see ANSI standards for rise, fall, and plateau of a pure tone (Chapter 10).

Pure Tones

A pure-tone signal has tonal quality and contains a single frequency component. See Figures 9–8 and 9–9 for the waveform

Warbled Tones

A warbled tone is a frequency modulated (FM) tone (a percentage change in frequency per second) of ± 5% of the test tone

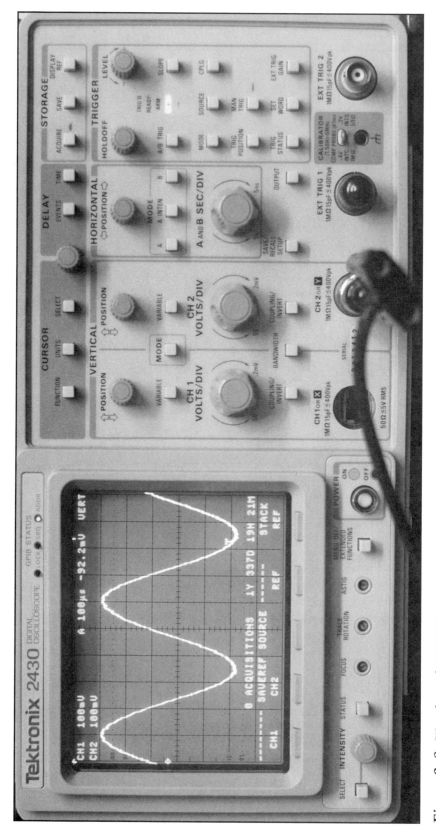

Figure 9–8. Waveform of a 2000-Hz signal as shown on an oscilloscope.

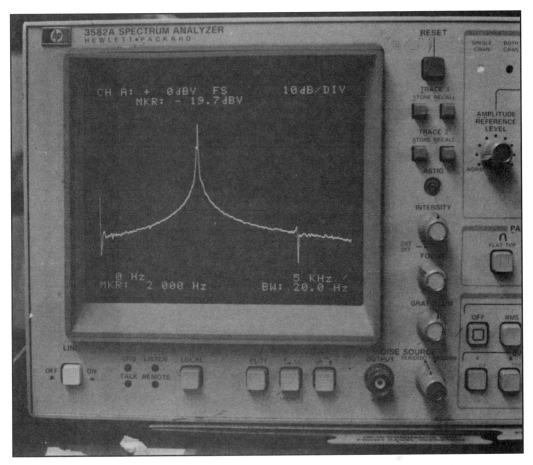

Figure 9–9. *Spectrum of a 2000-Hz signal as seen on a real-time analyzer.*

and is used to prevent standing waves. For example, a 1000-Hz warbled tone will fluctuate between 950 Hz and 1050 Hz (50 Hz warble), a 2000-Hz warbled tone will fluctuate between 1900 Hz and 2100 Hz (100 Hz warble).

Broad-Band Noise

BBN is derived from a white-noise signal. White noise consists of an infinite number of frequencies and essentially has equal power per cycle. When a white noise signal is routed through a transducer (e.g., earphone, bone oscillator, or speaker), its bandwidth is reduced because of the limitation imposed by the frequency response of the transducer. The transducer acts like a band-pass filter (Chapter 5). White noise shaped (filtered) by the transducer is called BBN. Figure 9–10 illustrates the waveform of a white-noise signal. Figure 9–11 illustrates the acoustic spectrum of BBN. Observe from this figure that the spectrum level is essentially uniform but falls off at the higher frequencies at approximately 6000 Hz because of the frequency response of the TDH 49 earphone.

The energy per cycle of a BBN signal can be determined mathematically by

Figure 9–10. *Waveform of white noise as seen on Adobe Audition.*

dividing the overall sound-pressure level (SPL) by the number of cycles of the BBN (Silman & Silverman, 1991). As dB SPL is a logarithmic quantity, whereas the number of cycles in a BBN signal is based on a linear scale, the number of cycles in a BBN signal first must be converted into decibels using the formula dB = 10 log ($N1/N2$) where $N1$ is the number of cycles in the BBN signal and $N2$ is the reference number of cycles (1 cycle). Using this formula, a BBN signal with 10,000 cycles will be equal in decibels to 10 log (10,000/1) or 40 dB.

To calculate the energy in 1 cycle of this BBN, the total SPL value of the BBN (e.g., 100 dB) is divided by 40 dB. Thus, the energy per cycle is 60 dB. (When dividing logarithmic quantities, the denominator quantity is subtracted from the numerator quantity). As a transducer such as an earphone shapes a white-noise signal, and since transducers differ in their frequency response characteristics, some transducers will pass more of the energy of white noise than other transducers. To determine the spectrum level or the energy level per cycle, the bandwidth characteristics of the transducer employed at a particular clinic should first be determined. Recall from Chapter 4 that the bandwidth of a signal is specified by the points at which the power is halved, or the intensity is 3 dB down from the maximum output of the stimulus. For example, the TDH earphones have a bandwidth of 6000 Hz. The number of cycles in decibels of a BBN signal with a bandwidth of 6000 Hz is 10 log (6000/1) or 37.8 dB. The spectrum level associated with 37.8 cycles is the overall

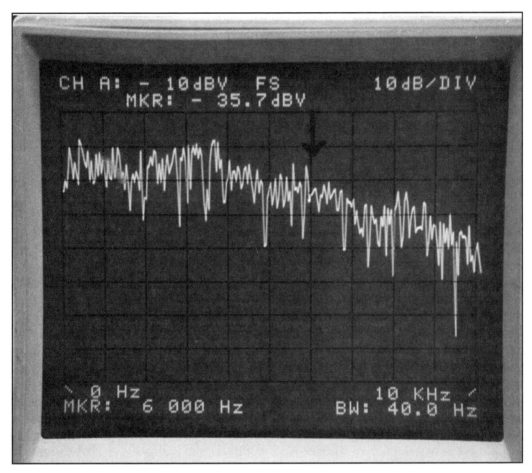

Figure 9–11. *Acoustic spectrum of BBN as seen on a real-time analyzer.*

dB SPL (100 dB) divided by 37.8 cycles, which is 62.2, that is, 100 – 37.8 dB SPL per cycle.

Narrow-Band Noise

NBN results from the passage of a wide-band stimulus through a band-pass filter (see description of filtering in Chapter 5). NBN (Figure 9–12) is used in clinical audiology to mask pure-tone signals or to obtain thresholds in sound field. To derive the NBN used in clinical audiology, the filter is set at 3 dB down from the maximum output (the half-power points) to produce a noise bandwidth containing a center frequency at the nominal frequency of the test tone to be masked. NBN contains bandwidths narrower than those of BBN. Many commercially available audiometers employ third-octave bandwidths for NBN signals.

Outside the third-octave band of the NBN, the rejection rate of the filter may vary between 10 and 60 dB per octave. Therefore, in cases of significantly rising or sloping audiograms, erroneous threshold responses may be obtained at frequencies outside the third-octave band rather than at the center frequency of the NBN,

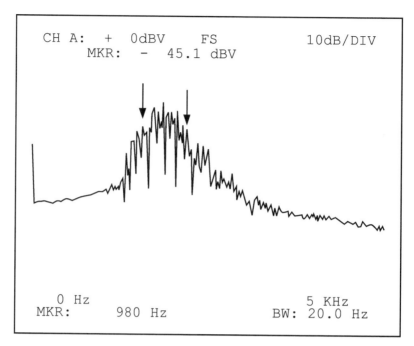

Figure 9–12. Spectrum of narrow-band noise.

when using filters with low rejection rates. Therefore, the audiologist should be cautious in interpreting the results of audiometric testing based on NBN signals.

CRITICAL BAND

Fletcher and Munson (1937) initially introduced the critical band concept. When a pure tone is masked by BBN, only a limited band of noise around the center frequency close to the pure-tone frequency is essential to mask the pure tone. This limited band of frequencies is called the critical band for masking. The critical bandwidths for the audiometric test frequencies are: (a) 50 Hz at 250 Hz, (b) 50 Hz at 500 Hz, (c) 56.2 Hz at 750 Hz, (d) 64 Hz at 1000 Hz, (e) 79.4 Hz at 1500 Hz, (f) 100 Hz at 2000 Hz, (g) 158 Hz at 3000 Hz, (h) 200 Hz at 4000 Hz, (i) 376 Hz at 6000 Hz, and (j) 501 Hz at 8000 Hz. The critical

band for masking a tone of 1000 Hz, for example, has a bandwidth of 64 Hz with a center frequency of 1000 Hz. Therefore, in a BBN signal with a 10,000 Hz bandwidth, only the energy in the critical band will contribute to the masking of the 1000-Hz pure tone. The rest of the BBN will contribute only to the loudness of the masking noise. Furthermore, when the pure tone is just audible in the presence of a masking noise, the energy of the critical band is equal to the energy of the pure tone. For example, a 1000-Hz pure tone of 40 dB SPL will be masked when the total energy of a critical band of 64 cycles is equal to 40 dB SPL. Figures 9–13 and 9–14 present the waveform and spectrum, respectively, of the critical band for 1000 Hz.

As illustrated by the critical band concept, critical band masking is preferable to BBN masking. The overall sound-pressure level of the critical band required to mask a pure tone is less than the overall

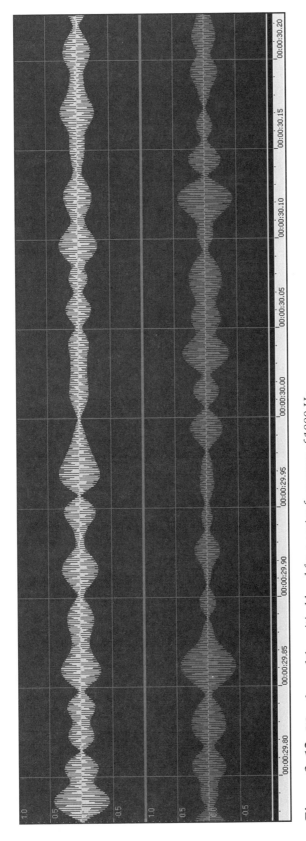

Figure 9–13. Waveform of the critical band for a center frequency of 1000 Hz.

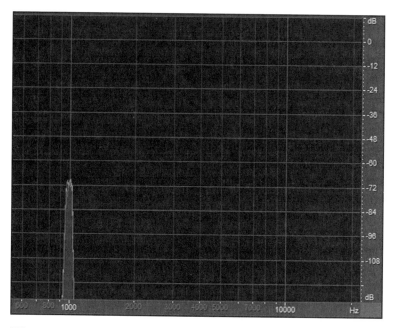

Figure 9–14. *Spectrum of a critical band with a center frequency of 1000 Hz using FFT.*

sound-pressure level of a BBN required to mask a pure tone. For example, as mentioned before, to mask a 1000-Hz tone of 40 dB SPL, a critical band with an overall sound-pressure level of 40 dB is required. As the critical band for masking a 1000-Hz tone has a 64-Hz bandwidth, the bandwidth in dB is equal to 10 log (64/1) or 2.5 dB. Therefore, the spectrum level per cycle of this critical band is equivalent to 40 dB SPL/2.5 dB or 37.5 dB per cycle. If the critical bandwidth is 64 Hz and a BBN masker with a bandwidth of 6000 Hz is used, the total sound-pressure level of the BBN required to mask the 1000-Hz tone with an intensity 40 dB SPL is equivalent to the number of cycles of the BBN masker in decibels: 10 log (6000/1 = 37.8 multiplied by the spectrum level per cycle (37.5 dB for a 64-Hz critical band), which is 75.3 dB SPL. This total sound-pressure level of 75.3 for the BBN that is needed to mask a 40 dB SPL tone at 1000 Hz is

approximately 35 dB more than the total sound-pressure level of 40 dB SPL needed for a critical band to mask this tone.

Although use of the critical band theoretically is ideal for masking, the major drawback is that the listener perceives the critical band as very close to the test tone; this can create confusion. Hear the audio of the critical bands for 500-Hz, 1000-Hz, and 2000-Hz. Listen to each critical band and determine whether the critical band is appropriate for masking a pure tone. Make a decision and then go to Chapter 10 for the answer and rationale.

SPEECH NOISE

Speech noise is BBN with a narrower frequency range extending from at least 250 to 4000 Hz. The slope of the speech noise spectrum is +3 dB per octave from 250 to 1000 Hz; the slope is –12 dB per octave from 1000 to 4000 Hz. The acoustic spectrum of speech noise follows the configuration of the acoustic spectrum of a speech signal. Masking of speech signals can be done using either BBN shaped by the earphone or speech noise. Many audiometers calibrate speech noise in effective masking, that is, 50 dB HL of speech noise will mask a 50 dB HL speech signal. BBN is generally not calibrated in effective masking; rather, it is calibrated in dB SPL. For NBN signals we recommend generating normative data on minimum effective masking (see MEMs in Chapter 10) using speech noise and BBN maskers; the MEM normative data for monosyllabic phonetically balanced (PB) words should be obtained separately from those for spondaic words. In order to obtain normative data on masking for spondaic and monosyllabic PB words, the speech signals should be introduced at a level of 50 dB HL and the speech noise or BBN noise increased in the same ear until the subjects can no longer repeat 6 out of 6 words.

INSTRUMENTATION FOR ACOUSTIC IMMITTANCE

Recall that acoustic impedance is the ratio of sound pressure to volume velocity, that is, $Z_a = P/U$. Also recall from Chapter 7 that acoustic admittance is the ratio of volume velocity to sound pressure, that is $Y_a = U/P$. In the impedance equation, if U is kept constant, then P is directly proportional to Z_a. This concept can be illustrated by considering water flow from a hose directly into a container. If the water flow is kept constant, the pressure of the water in the container is inversely proportional to the size of the container. The water flow is the analog to the volume velocity, the pressure

in the container is the analog to sound pressure, and the size of the cavity is the analog to the impedance of the ear. If the volume of the container decreases, the impedance increases; therefore water pressure (sound pressure) will be directly related to the impedance of the container (ear impedance) if the water flow (volume velocity) is kept constant. Modern commercially available acoustic-immittance devices are essentially constructed on the basis of the acoustic-impedance or acoustic-admittance formula. Devices constructed on the basis of the acoustic-impedance formula are called acoustic-impedance meters.

The acoustic-impedance meter, as shown in Figure 9–15, has a probe assembly that is inserted into the outer ear canal. The probe unit contains a loudspeaker that introduces a constant volume velocity (sound) in the ear canal by applying voltage from a source in the acoustic-impedance meter to the diaphragm of the loudspeaker. In Chapter 6 we described how an electric signal is converted to an acoustic signal. When the voltage is applied to the diaphragm, the air molecules in the ear canal are set in motion (the volume velocity). The probe assembly also houses a microphone that transduces the sound pressure resulting from the volume velocity into electrical voltage; the electrical voltage is read in acoustic-impedance units (acoustic ohms). Figure 9–15 illustrates the components of an acoustic-impedance meter.

One of the disadvantages of the acoustic-impedance meter shown in Figure 9–15 is that acoustic impedance at the probe tip is affected by the ear canal volume, as sound pressure and volume are inversely related.

Therefore, to avoid the effect of ear-canal volume on sound pressure and consequently on the acoustic impedance at

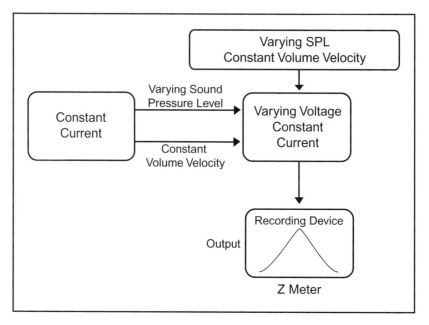

Figure 9–15. *Components of an acoustic-impedance meter.*

the probe, acoustic-immittance devices which measure acoustic impedance usually apply additional steps for keeping sound pressure constant at the probe. A balance meter in the acoustic-impedance device functions to maintain sound pressure at a predetermined level. That is, when the sound pressure level at the probe tip reaches a predetermined level such as 85 dB SPL, the balance meter will read 0 (arbitrary units). At the 0-unit balance-meter reading, the voltage and the microscope reaches a value equivalent to a reference voltage which produces 85 dB SPL in a cavity having specified volume. Adjustment of the balance meter cause the driver voltage to change, leading to changes in volume velocity so the pressure can be adjusted to 85 dB SPL in a given ear canal.

Another disadvantage (which cannot be offset) of the acoustic-impedance meter shown in Figure 9–15 is that the amplitude of tympanograms produced by such

a device cannot be expressed in physical units such as acoustic ohm because of nonlinearity in the impedance change during the ear canal pressure change. These acoustic-impedance meters express the amplitude of the tympanogram in arbitrary units, often erroneously referred to as compliance units. Because arbitrary units are employed, such devices are called relative acoustic-impedance meters.

In the acoustic-admittance meter (see Figure 9–16), acoustic admittance is derived from the volume velocity rather than from the sound pressure, as is the case for acoustic-impedance meters.

In acoustic-admittance meters, P is kept constant so Y_a is directly proportional to U. Therefore, the admittance Y_a is derived from U. This is carried out as follows: The voltage from the speaker is converted into sound pressure that is kept constant in the ear canal through an AGC (automatic gain control) circuit (see below for further information). This sound pressure will

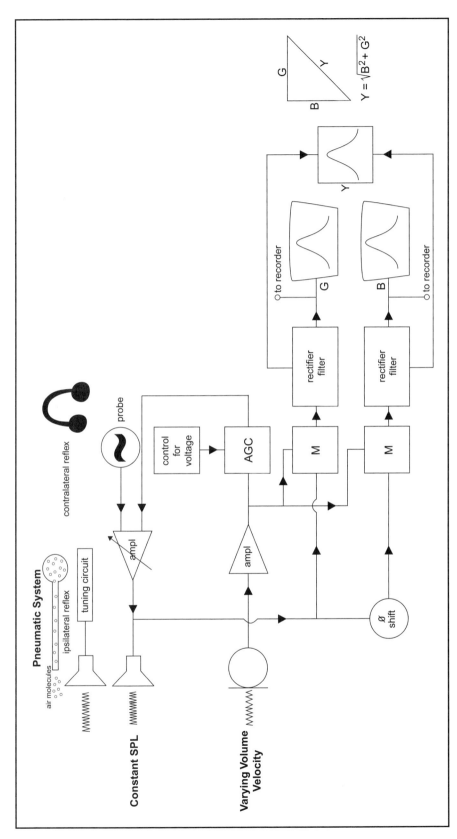

Figure 9–16. *General scheme for an acoustic-immittance meter. Reprinted with permission from Van Camp et al. (1986) and modified by Silman and Emmer to incorporate the Y component.*

cause the air molecules to flow into the ear (volume velocity). The volume velocity has two components, one in phase with the sound pressure and the second out-of-phase with the sound pressure. Both in-phase and out-of-phase volume velocities will be converted to current at the microphone. The in-phase and out-of-phase currents (previously in-phase and out-of-phase volume velocities) will be routed together to 2 multipliers (upper M and lower M in Figure 9–16). A multiplier is a phase-sensitive voltage amplifier that passes only in-phase signals and cancels the out-of-phase components. Therefore, the first multiplier (the upper M) will accept the in-phase current. The in-phase current will be smoothed by using a rectifier filter and then recorded as G (conductance). The second multiplier (the lower M) is connected to a phase-shifter, which will alter the phase of the incoming components from the speaker so that only the B component will be passed by the multiplier. The current is then smoothed by using a rectifier filter and recorded as B (susceptance). The B and G components, en route to the recorder, will first be routed to an analyzer that applies the Pythagorean theorem, and then routed to the recorder and displayed as Y. The device can record B and G separately or together.

This admittance concept can be illustrated with the water hose analogy. The driver voltage can be considered the source of the water flow. The admittance can be likened to the size of the container; the larger the container, the larger the admittance. Using the water hose analogy, to maintain constant water (sound) pressure, the flow of the water (volume velocity) has to be adjusted. The larger the container (admittance), the greater the water flow (volume velocity) needed to maintain the pressure.

The AGC circuit offsets the effect of ear-canal volume on sound-pressure level. That is, sound-pressure level is kept constant by a circuit, which continuously adjusts the driver voltage depending on the voltage at the microphone. As acoustic admittance is calculated from volume velocity rather than sound pressure, and does not have the disadvantage of nonlinearity found in the impedance meter, admittance change can be quantified in absolute admittance units, mmho. Admittance devices that measure the admittance change in absolute units are called absolute acoustic-admittance meters.

The early acoustic-immittance meters used only a single low-frequency probe tone. The use of a low-frequency probe tone was based on the results of early studies showing that the normal middle ear is stiffness dominated at all probe-tone frequencies. The results of later research, however, illustrate that the normal middle ear is stiffness dominated below 800 Hz; at probe-tone frequencies between 800 and 1200 Hz, the middle ear resonates (stiffness and mass reactance are canceled out) and at probe-tone frequencies above 1200 Hz, the middle ear is mass loaded (Margolis, Van Camp, Wilson, & Creten, 1985). Figure 9–17 illustrates the middle-ear impedance (reactance and resistance) as a function of probe-tone frequency.

At the present time, many commercially available acoustic-immittance devices incorporate a high-frequency probe tone such as 660 Hz or 1000 Hz in addition to a low-frequency probe tone. The incorporation of the high-frequency probe tones revolutionized the use of immittance technology by allowing differential diagnosis between the pathology of a mass-loaded system and a stiffening pathology. In the past few years a 1000-Hz probe tone has been used to identify the presence of mid-

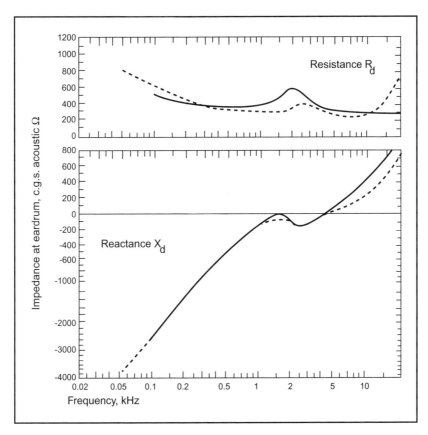

Figure 9–17. *Acoustic resistance and acoustic reactance modified and adapted from Margolis et al. (1985).*

dle-ear effusion in newborn infants. Low frequencies lack sensitivity and specificity in the identification of middle ear effusion and other middle ear pathologies.

Components of the Immittance Device

Probe Signal

In modern immittance devices, there are either two or three probe tones. Some introduce 226 Hz and 1000 Hz, whereas some incorporate 226 Hz, 678 Hz, and 1000 Hz. Each device has contralateral and ipsilateral acoustic reflex test capa-

bility. Current technology has improved the use of the ipsilateral reflex by introducing the multiplex circuit. This circuit is designed to prevent intermodulation distortion in the ear canal. In brief, intermodulation distortion can occur when two tones of different frequencies interact in a nonlinear cavity such as the outer ear. This interaction in the nonlinear cavity will produce other sounds that can be mistaken for an ipsilateral reflex. The artifacts generated because of intermodulation distortion obtain their energy from the primary tones (activator and probe tones). The "reflex" occurs as an increase rather than a decrease in admittance as is usual with the presence of a true reflex.

However, the increased admittance is not always an artifact. Some true reflexes have a pattern similar to the pattern of the artifact, that is, an increase rather than a decrease in admittance. This can occur with a decoupling of the stapes to the oval window, which results in an increase of the vector admittance. A multiplex system is designed to produce the stimulus and probe alternately.

Activating Signals

The immittance device also provides contralateral and ipsilateral activating signals for measurement of Acoustic Reflex Thresholds (ARTs). The maximum levels for contralateral and ipsilateral activating signals may differ from manufacturer to manufacturer, and the audiologist should review the manual that accompanies the device chosen. The upper limit of all activating signals for the GSI Tympstar Middle Ear Analyzer is shown in Table 9–2.

The transfer data from an IEC 711 to an ANSI HA-1 coupler were determined by GSI. Intensity levels are reduced as a function of volume at a rate of 1 dB SPL for each .1 ml. Intensity reduction begins at 1.2 mL.

Table 9–2. Upper Limit of HL Range in Reflex Threshold Mode

	Probe Tone	Pure-Tone Stimulus (Hz)					Noise Stimulus			Other Stimulus	
		250	500	1000	2000	4000	LBN	HBN	BBN	Click (SPL)	EXT (SPL)
Ipsi-Pulsed	226 HZ	95	110	110	105	100	95	95	95	110	110
	678 HZ	95	110	110	105	100	95	95	95	110	110
	1000 Hz	95	110	110	105	100	95	95	95	110	110
Contra-Pulsed	226 Hz	110	120	120	120	115	115	115	115	120	120
	678 Hz	110	120	120	120	115	115	115	115	120	120
	1000 Hz	110	120	120	120	115	115	115	115	120	120
Contra-Steady	226 Hz	n/a	120	120	120	115	115	115	115	120	120
	678 Hz	110	n/a	120	120	115	115	115	115	120	120
	1000 Hz	110	120	n/a	120	115	115	115	115	120	120

Note: These values are reported specifically for the GSI Tympstar Middle Ear Analyzer. Companies may differ in their values.

Figure 9–18 shows the mean ARTs, standard deviations, and the 90th percentiles as a function of hearing loss at 500, 1000, and 2000 Hz (Silman & Gelfand, 1981). The 90th percentile levels provide the upper limits for ARTs for cochlear hearing losses as a function of the magnitude of the loss at the aforementioned frequencies. Although the 90th percentile was established using TDH-50 earphones, when an instrument is calibrated using an HA-1 coupler, 5 dB should be added to the calibration values.

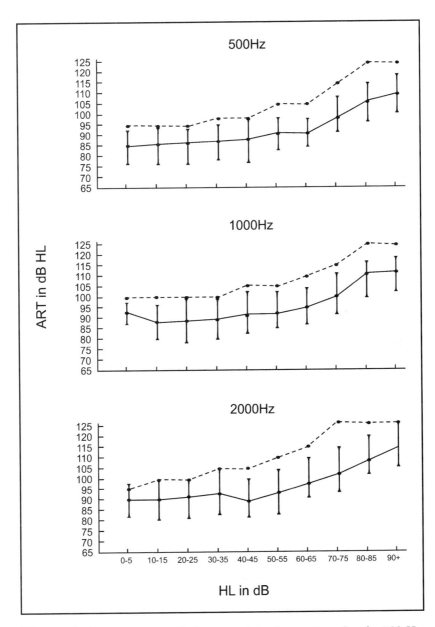

Figure 9–18. *90th percentile for contralateral acoustic reflex for 500 Hz, 1000 Hz, and 2000 Hz tonal activators (Silman & Gelfand, 1981).*

OTOACOUSTIC EMISSIONS— INSTRUMENTATION

"It is important to remember that otoacoustic emissions (OAEs) are only a byproduct of outer hair cell function and of the way that hair cells interact with basal membrane motion. A complete model of OAEs, therefore, must wait until there is a complete model of active cochlear mechanics" (Robinette & Glattke, 2007, p. 27). Therefore, the presence of OAEs is associated with healthy outer hair cells (OHCs). Damage to these cells will bring about a reduction in emissions.

Investigators assume the cochlear traveling wave that occurs in response to sound continues to build in amplitude from the oval window toward the apical end of the basal membrane hundreds of times in comparison to the amplitude seen at the oval window. At higher input levels the cochlea cannot sustain such amplitudes; thus, a very small portion of the traveling wave is reflected back to the oval window with a delay of a few milliseconds (ms) causing vibration of the tympanic membrane. These vibrations are labeled as OAEs.

The idea, however, that OAEs are reflected back along the basal membrane into the outer ear has recently been challenged by Ren (2004). This author has questioned the reverse traveling wave of all OAEs on the basis of his data measuring time of arrival of the distortion at the middle ear, and invasively measured time of arrival of the stimuli at the F2 place along the basal membrane. Ren's data did not show the expected delay in time based upon a reverse traveling wave. Thus, this investigator proposed that the distortion product might be reflected back to the middle ear and outer ear by a rapid pressure wave. The theory of a reverse traveling wave persists however.

The types of otoacoustic emissions known to be generated by OHCs include spontaneous emissions, which are like pure tones, and can be recorded from a sealed ear canal, and are present in approximately 30% of normal hearing individuals. The amplitude of spontaneous OAEs varies between 15 to 30 dB. Transient OAEs are elicited by a wide-spectrum signal of short duration such as a click. When TEOAEs are analyzed using a fast Fourier transform analysis (FFT, see Chapter 7 for discussion of FFT and OAEs), we see a wide frequency spectrum that in normal-hearing young individuals resembles the spectrum of the click stimulus. This type of emission is sometimes called a cochlear echo. The third type of otoacoustic emission is distortion product otoacoustic emissions (DPOAEs). This kind of distortion forms in the outer hair cells as a result of the interaction between two primary distinct frequency tones called f_1 and f_2. These tones are separated by a half-octave and the difference between f_1 and f_2 is the same spacing as between f_2 minus f_1 and f_1 (Gorga, Neely, Johnson, Dierking, & Garner, 2007). The newly generated signals are composed of nonharmonically spaced frequencies that are mathematically predictable. These new components (distortion products) reflect the sum and difference of the two primary tones (Figure 9–19). Recall that we encountered the concept of intermodulation distortion when we discussed the measurement of the ipsilateral reflex. As $2f_1 - f_2$ is generated close to the frequencies of the two primary tones, one of the primary tones is used for plotting the OAE audiogram as a function of the geometric mean of f_1 and f_2 (the square root of $f_1 \times f_2$). When the audiogram is plotted using a primary, we usually select f_2.

The intensity of the original input signals will be reduced in strength with

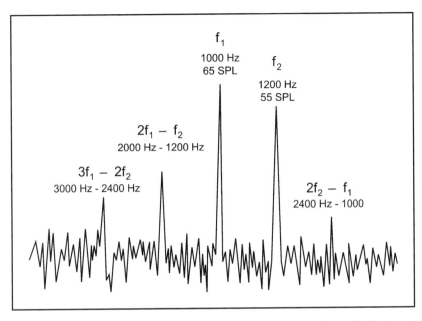

Figure 9–19. *Conceptualized example of a distortion product (DP). F$_1$ and f$_2$ are the primary tones whereas the others are distortion products. Note that 2f$_1$ – f$_2$ has the highest amplitude DP component.*

the production of the new sounds. Based on our explanation of the phenomenon of intermodulation distortion in the outer ear versus the inner ear, we can conclude that intermodulation distortion is an interfering factor when measuring the ipsilateral acoustic reflex, and is necessary when measuring the integrity of the outer hair cells when performing DPOAEs.

Both DPOAE and TEOAE instrumentation separate the response from background noise. The level of the noise is measured by averaging the noise level in several FFT bins on both sides of the DPOAE or TEOAE response, and then comparing the response level to the surrounding noise (refer to section on FFT in Chapter 8). Criteria for the signal-to-noise ratio is usually around 3 to 6 dB, that is, for a response to be detected it needs to be at least 3 dB greater than the surrounding noise.

Although it may appear that the instrumentation for TEOAEs and DPOAEs

differ from one another, components for both reside in a single computer system. Figure 9–20 shows that both TEOAEs and DPOAEs are incorporated in one computer: you can select one or the other.

In order to differentiate between the distortion product paradigm and the transient paradigm, both of which are accessible through the same computer, we have endeavored to illustrate the way in which both paradigms are incorporated within one computer. The active mode of each component is indicated by the black triangle at the top of the figure. In this case the DPOAE is active. This approach makes it easier for the reader to conceptualize how both TEOAEs and DPOAEs are incorporated in one computer (adapted from Lonsbury-Martin & Martin, 2007).

Lonsbury-Martin and Martin (2007) provide an excellent description of instrumentation for DPOAEs. All probe signals and response measurement systems are

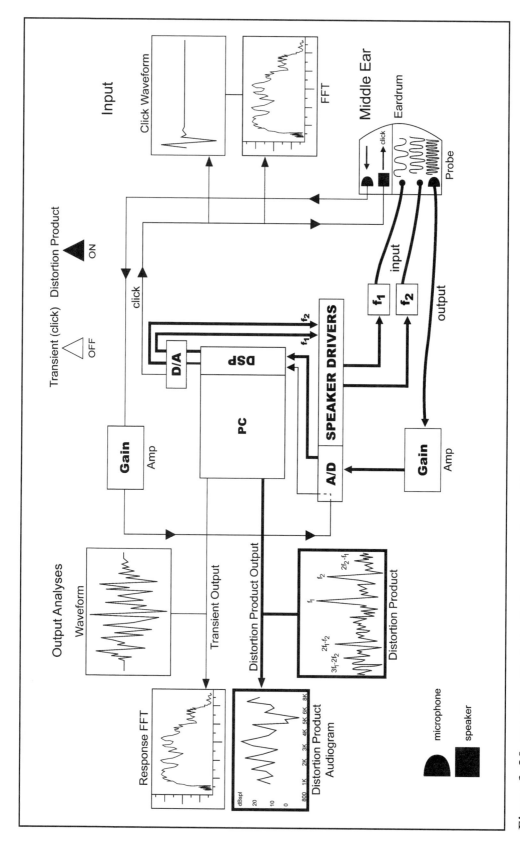

Figure 9–20. This figure illustrates the instrumentation used for measurement of both TEOAEs and DPOAEs.

incorporated in "plugboards" on a computer. The probe signals for both TEOAEs and DPOAEs are digitally stored in the computer using 24 bits. The 24-bit converter is needed due to the large dynamic range in intensity between the DPOAEs and the primaries as both stimuli and responses are present at the same time. During testing, the stimuli are converted from digital to analog (acoustic signals) via a digital-to-analog (D/A) converter. The microphone that measures the DPOAEs is encased in the acoustic probe inserted into the ear canal. In order to eliminate the artifact intermodulation distortion, both transducers are generally located away from the microphone, and the primary tones, f_1 and f_2, are separately introduced to the external ear canal through tubes passing through the probe. The input from the microphone is con-

verted from analog to digital (A/D) format for processing and analysis.

In order to reduce noise existing in the external auditory canal and to prevent leakage of the f_1 and f_2 signals and the low-intensity response, the probe must fit snugly into the external canal by using a removable soft immittance ear-tip. These conditions will provide a clear-cut DPOAE that can be measured in the presence of normal outer hair cells. The intermodulation distortion produced by the outer hair cells undergoes a reverse transduction from an electrochemical signal to an acoustic signal in the middle ear. Despite our precautions to eliminate the intermodulation distortion artifact, this artifact may occur as a result of a malfunction within the system itself, for example, a breakdown in the relay system.

Figure 9–21 shows the DPOAE response obtained using FFT on an ILO 88.

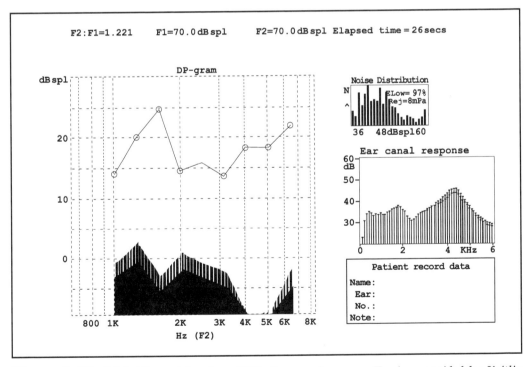

Figure 9–21. DPOAE resulting from FFT of a complex wave. Tracing provided by Kaitlin Calleja, AuD student.

The ratio of f_2/f_1 is 1.221. The stimulus intensity for f_1 and f_2 was 70 dB SPL. The figure shows the ear canal response on the lower right. The noise distribution in the ear canal is seen on the upper right.

Figure 9–22 shows a tracing of a DPOAE using a Bio-Logic OAE device. The first column of the table below the tracing shows the f2 stimuli. Column 2 indicates reproducibility (note that reproducibility is very high). Column 3 is the positive size of the response. Column 4 gives the values for the noise floor at each frequency. Column 5 (TE-NF) gives the net response above the noise floor.

For measurement of TEOAEs, both the speaker and microphone are housed in the same acoustic probe inserted in the ear canal. In this case, the input analog signal (transient) will be displayed as both a waveform and a FFT spectrum. The response will also be displayed as a waveform and FFT spectrum (Figure 9–23).

Figure 9–24 is a tracing for TEOAEs using the ILO-88 instrument. In the upper left hand corner of the figure, we see the stimulus click waveform with duration of 80 μsec and an intensity of approximately 89 dB SPL (roughly equivalent to 0.3 Pa). Patient information is indicated next to the

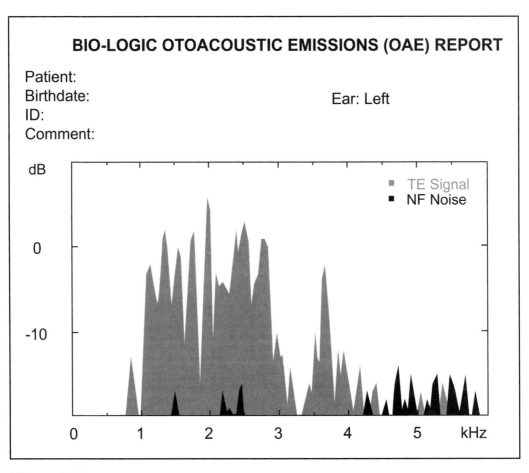

Figure 9–22. DPOAE tracing using Bio-Logic instrument. Tracing provided by Lauren Kaplan, AuD student.

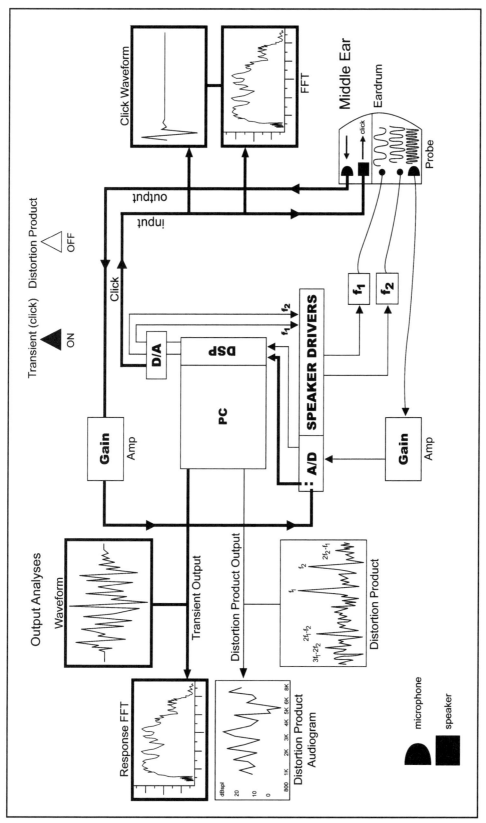

Figure 9–23. Schematic drawing of the instrumentation used for TEOAEs. This instrumentation is based on the concept of DPOAE instrumentation introduced by Lonsbury-Martin and Martin (2007).

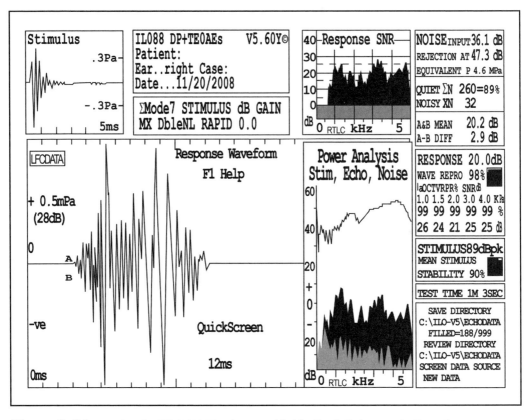

Figure 9–24. *Tracing for TEOAE. Tracing provided by Ruth Reisman, AuD student.*

stimulus. The frequency response of the transient emission as analyzed by FFT is indicated next to the patient information. This illustrates the FFTs that are based on the A and B tracings (waveform response). Noise input indicates the noise level in the ear canal. The rejection rate indicates the rejection threshold selected by the tester. There are some instances when the response is larger than the noise but the rejection rate is low thereby making it difficult to view the response. We can enhance the response by increasing the rejection rate. By increasing the rejection rate, we can see the response rising above the noise level. Quiet ΣN refers to the number of accepted responses. Noisy XN is the number of responses that were rejected. A and B mean refers to the SPL of

the average of the A and B response waveforms. In this case, the value is 28 dB SPL. The difference between A and B refers to the point-by-point difference between the A and B tracing as registered in the memories. A − B is the difference between A and B tracings. The larger the difference, the noisier the FFT response. Reproducibility in this tracing is 98%, an excellent percentage. Below wave reproducibility we see the test frequencies, percent reproducibility for each frequency, and the magnitude of response at each frequency in dB. Stability (in percent) indicates the change in stimulus intensity during the test. In this case, stability is 93%.

Let us see how FFT, first discussed in general terms in Chapter 8, can be applied more specifically to audiology. In an excellent example of FFT analysis (Figure 9–25) by Lonsbury-Martin et al. (1997), we see FFT displayed as two primary tones and the distortion product $2f_1$ minus f_2. The sampling rate was 44,100 Hz/sec. The samples for analysis (the window) contained 4096 points obtained during 93 ms as sampled at the output of the microphone; these points were averaged point-by-point 32 times in the time domain. Several windows of 4096 points were taken and averaged in a manner similar to averaging for ABR. The 4096 points FFT of the averaged waveform returned 2048 real points and 2048 imaginary points, used to compute the amplitude and phase of the complex signal. The bin width of the FFT was calculated by dividing half of the sampling rate, that is, 22,050 Hz/sec (Nyquist frequency). The FFT bin width was therefore approximately 11 Hz, obtained by dividing 22,050 by 2048 (half of the samples).

The small (12 dB SPL) peak at 2498 kHz is the $2f_1$ minus f_2 DPOAE. Figure 9–25 shows that a noise floor (NF) of 34 dB SPL was taken as the mean level of each spectral bin above and below the DPOAE frequency bin.

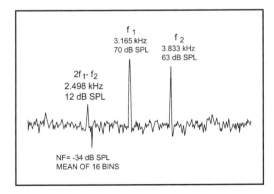

Figure 9–25. *The FFT of the DPOAE response including the two primary tones.*

ELECTROPHYSIOLOGIC INSTRUMENTATION

Auditory Evoked Potentials

Auditory evoked potentials, as the name implies, refers to electrical potentials that are evoked by introducing acoustic stimuli to the ear. Such potentials are so small that they are measured in μV (see Figure 9–25). These potentials begin at the cochlea and terminate at the level of the cortex. If we expand the time window from 0.13 ms to 600 ms, you will see a series of waves representing electrical activity from the cochlea to the cortex. Each pattern of waves depends on the latency of the response following the introduction of the stimulus. The groups of waves differ from each other in terms of latency and magnitude (Table 9–3 and Figure 9–26).

As shown in Table 9–3, the magnitude of the waves extends from .01 to .05 μV at the lower end (close to cochlea) to 10 to 30 μV at the upper end (close to the cortex). Under normal conditions these potentials cannot be seen because they are buried in both environmental and physiologic noise.

As mentioned above, we will concentrate on short (early)–latency potentials. The potentials are represented by a series of neurologic potentials recorded from electrodes placed on the scalp (far-field). Latencies for these potentials are up to 10 ms. Auditory brainstem response (ABR) has proven successful as a means of assessing the integrity of the auditory system from the cochlea to the lateral lemniscus. ABR has demonstrated a 95% success rate in the identification of pathology of the lower and upper brainstem. Although ABR was initially designed for prediction of hearing loss in infants and young children, recently some issues were raised

Table 9–3. Latencies, Amplitudes, Peak Components, and Origins of the Various Classes of Auditory-Evoked Potentials

Potential	Peak components	Origin	Latency	Amplitude (μV)
Very early				
Summating potential (SP)	DC wave	Cochlear haircells	~0.13	0.05–0.5
Cochlear Microphone (CM)	Waveform mirrors stimulus waveform	Cochlear haircells	~0.13	0.4–350
Compound action potential (AP)	$N_1 N_2$	Auditory nerve	1.5–4.5	0.1–20
Early/Short				
Brainstem auditory evoked potentials (Jewett waves)	I, II, III, IV, V, VI, VII	Brainstem, auditory nerve	1.3–8.1	0.05–1.0
Frequency following response (FFR)	Waveforms mirrors stimulus waveform	Brainstorm, auditory nerve, cochlea	7.0–10	0.2–1.0
Slow negative 10 (SN10)	V (P6)-N_1	Brainstem	6.0–17	0.05–1.0
Middle				
Middle latency response (MLR)	P_O, N_a, P_a, N_b, P_b, N_c, P_c, N_d	Auditory cortex	8.0–80	0.5–3.0
40-Hz Event-related potential (ERP)	N_a, P_a, N_b, P_b, N_c, P_c, N_d	Classic auditory pathway, reticular formation	12–50	0.1–3.0
Late/Long				
Slow vertex (SVR)	P_1, N_1, P_2, N_2	Primary and association areas of the cerebral cortex	50–250	3.0–15
Long (P300)	N_1, P_2, N_2	Subcortical brain structures, e.g., hippocampal formation and amygdale	250–400	5.0–20
Contingent negative variation (CNV)	DC wave	Association area of the cerebral cortex	>300	10–30

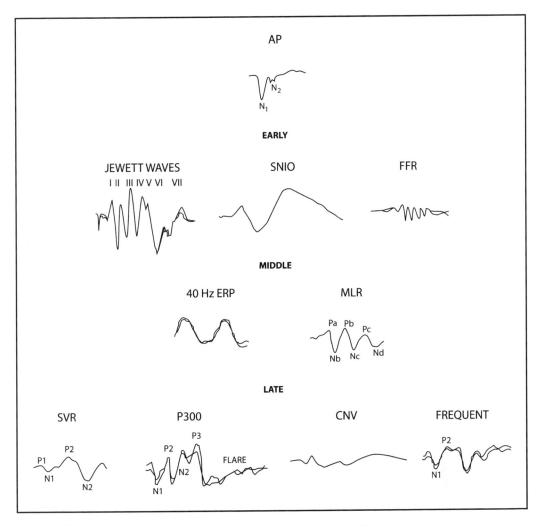

Figure 9–26. Auditory evoked potentials along the auditory pathway.

regarding the accuracy of hearing loss prediction in this population. This question has not arisen with ASSR (see section on ASSR to follow).

STIMULI USED IN AUDITORY EVOKED POTENTIALS (ABR)

Click Stimulus

A click is produced by rapidly switching on a voltage pulse of 100 μsec duration, and then rapidly switching the pulse off (Figures 9–27A and B).

Toneburst

A limitation of using a click stimulus is related to its broad spectrum, which precludes frequency specificity. A compromise was made between a signal with a broad-band spectrum, for example, click that is effective in obtaining auditory evoked potentials, and a signal with a narrow spectrum such as a pure tone that is ineffective in obtaining auditory evoked potentials. This compromise is a toneburst (Figure 9–28).

Log On

The logon is another type of toneburst (Figure 9–29), which is often used as the

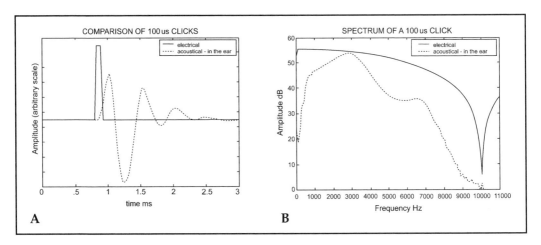

Figure 9–27. *A. Waveform of acoustic click. B. Spectrum of acoustic click.*

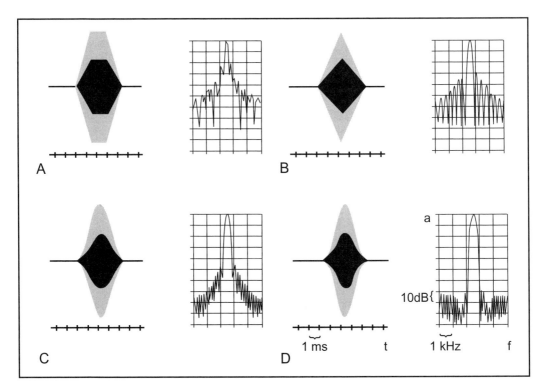

Figure 9–28. *Comparison of spectra among tonebursts of different envelopes. (A) Trapezoid. (B) Triangular. (C) Cosine squared. (D) Blackman. With permission from J. D. Durrant and J. R. Boston in Burkard et al. (2007).*

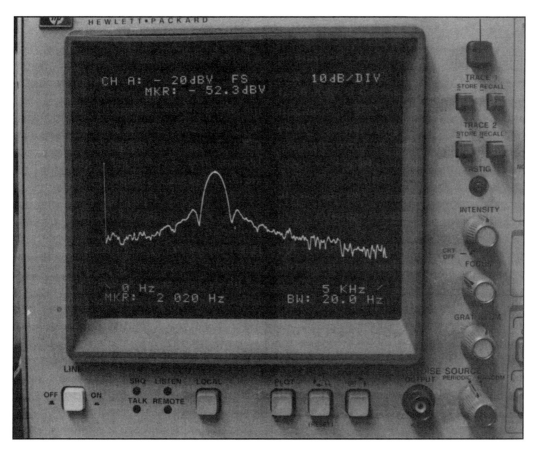

Figure 9–29. *The electrical spectrum for a 2000-Hz toneburst/log on with a rise-fall time of 2 ms and a plateau of 1 ms.*

stimulus in auditory evoked potentials for measurement of hearing in children.

Figure 9–30 shows a schematic drawing of instrumentation for auditory evoked potentials. The acoustic signal, that is, click or toneburst, its sensitivity, amplitude, and repetition rate are first converted from digital to analog and introduced to the ear of the subject.

Three electrodes placed on the skull when testing one channel using the International 10-20 system measure the evoked potentials (Figure 9–31). Four electrodes are used when testing two channels in order to observe the contralateral response. As you will see below, two channels are often desirable.

The first electrode (+) is placed on the vertex of the skull and is the noninverting electrode. The noninverting electrode picks up the potential from the vertex. The reason for the + or noninverted term is because this electrode receives the first wave, because the polarity is customarily positive. This electrode is also referred to as the "active" electrode. The second electrode in the inverted electrode (–) meaning that there is a change in polarity of the waves from positive to negative. This electrode is also called the reference electrode. The potential in the inverted and noninverted electrodes is compared or referenced to the neutral electrode. The neutral electrode is called the ground. The

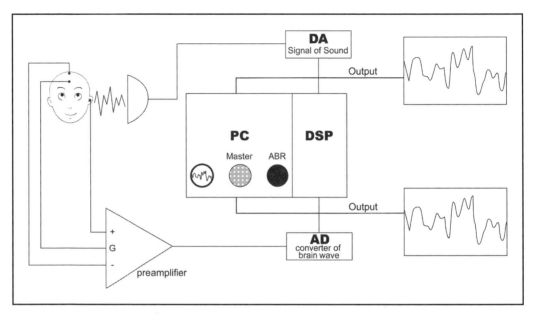

Figure 9–30. *Sketch of instrumentation for auditory evoked potentials.*

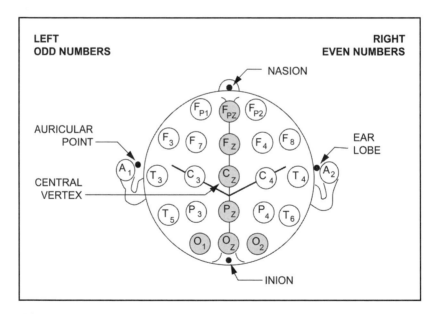

Figure 9–31. *The International 10-20 system for electrode placement.*

question to be asked is why we need an inverted electrode as this electrode, via its opposite polarity, will decrease electrical potential. Before we attempt to answer this question it is important to describe the electrodes best suited to carry the tiny potentials to be measured.

Brain activity of an individual can only be picked up through a conducting gel or paste placed on the electrodes.

The most common electrodes are colored gold, silver, or tin. When an electrode is attached to skin, it may generate contact potentials (Thornton, in Burkard et al., 2007), a type of noise artifact. The contact potentials may add to the noise generated by electrophysiologic or environmental noise. To avoid contact potential, the proper electrode must be selected. Silver has low contact potential. According to Thornton, to further reduce noise, the silver electrode should be coated with silver chloride. This author also stressed that the noise generated by an electrode is low-frequency noise. It therefore is crucial to eliminate low-frequency noise when we wish to measure low-frequency potentials, for example, middle- and cortical-latency potentials. The low-frequency noise might mask the potentials. Durrant and Boston in Burkhard et al. (2007) suggest a high-pass filter with a very low cutoff frequency, that is, down to several cycles per second. The output from the above-mentioned electrodes will be fed into the differential amplifier (Figure 9–32). The action of the differential amplifier will be described below.

The impedance between the skin and electrode should be minimal. The way in which we reduce Ω impedance is by rubbing the skin with alcohol before applying conductive gel or paste. Although it is ideal to have impedance between 2000 and 3000 Ω, it should never exceed 5000 Ω. The impedance difference between electrodes is of pivotal importance in that imbalance between electrodes may negatively affect the common mode reduction ratio. The common mode rejection ratio (CMRR) of a differential amplifier measures the ability of the device to reject input signals that are common to both the inverted and noninverted electrodes, such as a 60-Hz hum coming from electrical appliances. For example, a CMRR of 80 dB means that the input into the common electrodes is attenuated by a factor of 80,000 relative to the differential input. An impedance imbalance between electrodes decreases the effect of the CMRR thereby masking the evoked potential. As Figure 9–32 shows, the 60-Hz hum is equal in amplitude at both the inverted and noninverted electrodes but they are 180 degrees out-of-phase, thereby canceling each other. When an auditory evoked potential is measured, the noninverted electrode has more potential than the inverted because it is located at the vertex where the potential is strongest.

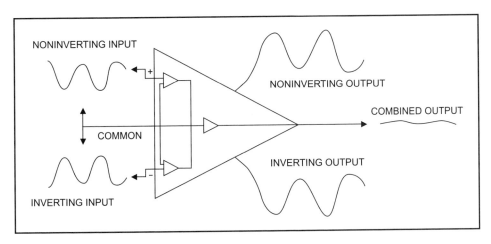

Figure 9–32. *Differential amplifier.*

Other aperiodic noise, whether biological or environmental, may affect auditory evoked potential measurements. There are several techniques used to reduce the noise. The techniques include filtering, A to D conversion, averaging, and others. Digital filtering, as mentioned in the chapter on digital signal processing (Chapter 8) is an algorithm that performs a mathematical calculation on a digitized sample of a waveform to attenuate or enhance certain aspects of that waveform. It is important to use digital filtering when measuring auditory evoked potentials because digital as opposed to analog filtering prevents phase distortion of the waveforms. If phase distortion is introduced, it might distort the latency of a certain wave relative to other waves. This will result in a misleading result. Some recent instrumentation used for the measurement of auditory potentials is adding FFT to identify the region of the best waveform as well as the surrounding noise (see Chapter 8 for FFT). This is helpful in filtering out the noise. In addition to increasing the signal-to-noise ratio, the waveform and its latency will be preserved and accurately displayed. A digital filter can be easily adjusted to locate the best evoked-potential response (see Chapter 5 on filtering). To illustrate the role that a digital filter plays, as well as its importance, see Figure 9–33. This recording is taken from six normal-hearing individuals. It was made through a band-pass filter of 1000 to 3000 Hz. The waveforms were digitally high-pass filtered at various cutoff frequencies from 1 to 1000 Hz. These waveforms were repeated for different cutoff frequencies.

Figure 9–34 shows the effect of a high-pass filter on the amplitude of the ABR waveform. When the waveform is filtered

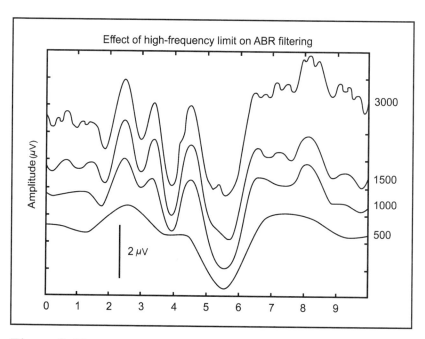

Figure 9–33. *Effect of various recording bandwidths on the ABR. Source: A. R. Thornton in Burkard et al. (2007).*

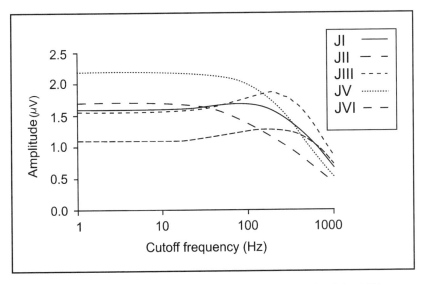

Figure 9–34. *Effect of a high-pass filter on the amplitude of the ABR waveform. Source: A. R. Thornton in Burkard et al. (2007).*

at 12 dB/octave, with a cutoff frequency ranging from 1 to 1000 Hz, it appears that no specific cutoff will highlight a specific waveform.

Averaging is another method by which the noise can be reduced. Noise is a random signal that is composed of positive and negative potentials. Averaging over time will have the effect of canceling the potentials, thereby reducing the noise. The response will have the same polarity over time. Signal-to-noise ratio (SNR) improves in proportion to the square root of the number of sweeps. Although this is the acceptable rule, the number of sweeps, in many instances, is dependent on the magnitude of the response, the type of stimulus (click or toneburst), and the purpose of the test, (threshold or diagnosis). For example, for threshold testing, the SNR can be close to 2 dB, whereas determining peak latency and amplitude requires a better SNR.

The digitized response, after being digitally shaped, filtered, and amplified, is converted to an analog signal and displayed on the monitor, and then printed.

Repetition Rate

In many instances, stimulus rate plays an important role in the interpretation of auditory evoked potentials. For example, Hall (1992) noted that for every ten stimulus increment changes in rate in the measurement of ABR, wave *V* latency is prolonged an average of 0.7 ms in adults, 150 microseconds for full-term infants and 225 microseconds for premature infants. Hall warns that the rate used in a particular clinic must be based on the rate used to obtain normative data in that clinic. The rate error can occur when a screener with a fixed rate is used. Hall (1992) recommended the use of ≥30.1 clicks/sec for detection of wave *V* and 11.1 clicks/sec for diagnostic purposes. There is no agreed upon rate for toneburst. However, we recommend using the same principle used for click rate. Therefore, it is very important to calibrate stimulus rate, particularly for a low rate (Figure 9–35).

The repetition rate can be calibrated using the oscilloscope. This can be achieved by routing the AC output from the sound-level meter (SLM) to an oscilloscope whose time window is set to 300 to 400 ms, and then presenting the clicks at the desired repetition rate. Inspect the oscilloscope to determine the interval in ms between two successive clicks, and then divide 1000 ms by that interval to yield the repetition rate (e.g., 1000 ms divided by 80 ms yields a repetition rate of 12.5 clicks/s).

An alternative approach to measurement of the click repetition rate is based on routing the AC output from the sound-level meter to the differential amplifier of the auditory evoked potentials device. Present 16 to 20 clicks from the auditory evoked potentials device with the time window set to 300 to 400 ms as before, and the click intensity at 80 to 90 dB nHL. Adjust the sensitivity of the auditory evoked potentials at the maximum or near maximum setting (whichever optimizes waveform morphology). Obtain the averaged waveform based on the 16 to 20 clicks. Determine the interval in ms between successive clicks on the monitor of the auditory evoked potentials device using the cursors. When using the oscilloscope, divide 1000 ms by the interval between successive clicks to yield the repetition rate. Figure 9–35 illustrates the determination of the interval between two successive clicks on the monitor of the auditory-evoked potentials device.

Polarity

We learn that the displacement of the basilar membrane toward the scala vestibuli is considered depolarization that causes the excitation phase of the auditory system. This process comes about from the outward movement of the stapes in the oval window. This is the negative going part of the wave. Conversely, the movement of the stapes inward is considered the polarizing phase, that is, the positive going part of the wave. Logically, therefore, the stimulus should begin with the negative phase as this represents excitation. You will expect to have large amplitude for the auditory evoked potential. However current research does not support a polarity effect on the click and toneburst.

Plotting the wave polarity varies according to the geographical location of the test site. In the United States, the positive voltage is plotted upward and the negative voltage is plotted downward. This arrangement was patterned after the somatosensory evoked potentials. Various countries plot negative voltage upward and positive voltage downward. It is therefore critical to monitor the polarity of the waves as part of ones general calibration.

An acoustic waveform displays amplitude as a function of time for an acoustic stimulus. It is important to use the same acoustic stimulus for calibration of the acoustic waveform that is used in the evaluation of brainstem auditory-evoked

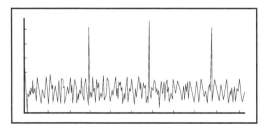

Figure 9–35. *Stimulus rate.*

potentials. For example, if clicks are used in brainstem auditory-evoked potentials evaluation, then the acoustic waveform of the click should be acquired.

In our lab, we obtain an acoustic waveform by routing the appropriate stimulus from the signal generator of the brainstem auditory-evoked potentials system through an earphone coupled to a 6-cm³ coupler which itself is coupled to a sound-level meter (the filter must be in off position). The AC output from the sound-level meter is then routed to an oscilloscope where we observe the acoustic waveform of the stimulus.

Rather than routing the AC output of the sound-level meter to the oscilloscope, we can route the AC output to the differential amplifier of the averager of the brainstem auditory-evoked potentials instrumentation. In this scenario, the sound-level meter mimics a patient in terms of hook-up. The stimulus from the signal generator of the brainstem auditory-evoked potentials device triggers the averager. The time window should be 2 rather than 10 ms. Sensitivity should be set near or at maximum; the clinician experiments with the sensitivity in order to acquire the sensitivity yielding the optimal waveform on the monitor. Our lab has determined that 16 to 20 samples and an intensity of 80 to 90 dB nHL will yield a superior waveform on the monitor. The waveform of the acoustic stimulus should be stored for comparison during future calibration. Figure 9–36 shows an example of the acoustic waveform for a click routed through TDH-49 earphones obtained by using the method previously described.

A change in the acoustic waveform can take place if the acoustic spectrum of the stimulus changes. Variation in the acoustic spectrum of the stimulus can

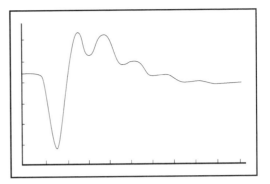

Figure 9–36. *Acoustic waveform for a click routed through TDH-49 earphones.*

result from damage to the earphones, for example, dropping the earphones. It therefore is important for periodic calibration of the acoustic waveform of the stimulus to take place, particularly when the earphones are dropped.

We prefer using both contralateral and ipsilateral recording of ABR waveforms. In some instances it is difficult to separate waves IV and V using ipsilateral recording whereas the contralateral recording clearly separates these waves (Figure 9–37).

According to Thornton, in Burkard (2007) we are living under the illusion that a toneburst of short duration can give us information regarding the hearing status of newborns and young children. For example, according to Thornton, it is thought that using a toneburst, even a Blackman toneburst, which has a rise and fall of 2 ms, and is known to have small side lobes and a high central peak, can be used for assessment of hearing loss in children. Although the spectrum of such a stimulus does not change with increased intensity level, the physiologic stimulation shows a wider range of frequencies than the range of the stimulus spectrum. This phenomenon is demonstrated in Figure 9–38.

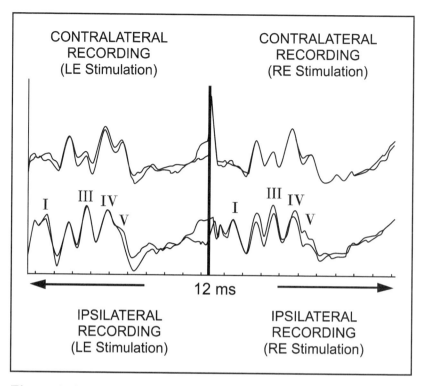

Figure 9–37. *Two-channel, contralateral and ipsilateral recordings for two patients.*

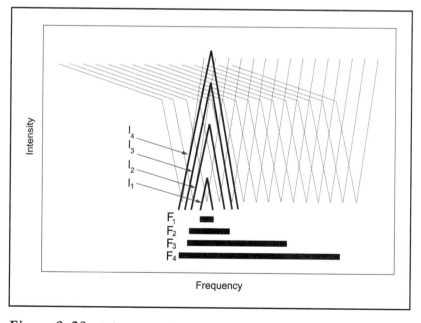

Figure 9–38. *A diagrammatic representation of the 8th nerve: The eighth nerve tuning curves and a frequency-specific stimulus at various intensity levels.*

As we can see from the figure, numbers I_1, I_2, I_3, and I_4 are the intensity levels and F_1, F_2, F_3, and F_4 are the tuning curves for the 8th nerve. Note that at low intensities, the tuning curves are narrow and at I_3 and I_4, the tuning curve broadens into the high frequencies. We can infer that it is possible to measure hearing at low intensity levels using a toneburst stimulus, but it becomes difficult to predict the true magnitude of the hearing loss at higher intensities. It is also possible, in subjects with damage to the outer hair cells and a broad tuning curve, even near threshold, that there will be less frequency specificity using a toneburst.

A promising technology has recently appeared in the literature. This new approach may improve the sensitivity of the test instrument used for universal newborn hearing screenings. As we know, the pass/fail criteria for screening a newborn using ALGO is 35–40 dB nHL. This range was selected because wave V is well defined at these levels. However, we are aware that a "pass" does not necessarily indicate normal hearing; an infant who passes at this level can still have a mild loss. Interacoustics® has introduced the CE-Chirp® (Figure 9–39). This stimulus is programmed so that the low frequencies of the Chirp appear at the apical end of the cochlea at the same time as the high frequencies of the Chirp arrive at the basal end of the cochlea. This results in a cumulative energy effect that enhances wave V. As we can see in Figure 9–40, wave V is clearly noted at 10 dB nHL when using the CE-Chirp® stimulus, whereas wave V is not clearly defined until 40 dB nHL when using the Click stimulus. Given the fact that an infant who passes a traditional screening may have a mild hearing loss, it seems incumbent on professionals in our field to use the most sensitive technology for screening newborn infants.

AUDITORY STEADY-STATE RESPONSE (ASSR)

ASSR and ABR are used in clinical audiology to evaluate hearing sensitivity. Although both ASSR and ABR involve the brainstem, there are technical differences such as differences in stimuli, data

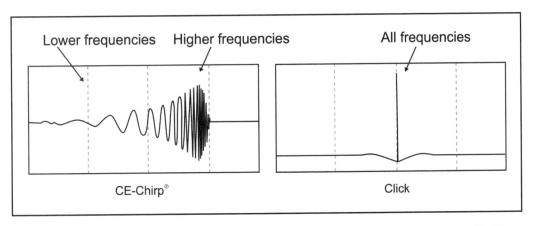

Figure 9–39. *Waveforms for CE-Chirp® and Click, with permission of Interacoustics®. CE are Claus Elberling's initials (inventor of the Chirp).*

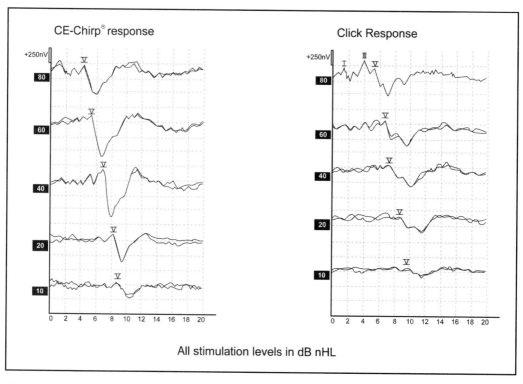

Figure 9–40. CE-Chirp® versus Click Responses, with permission of Interacoustics®.

collection, and interpretation. There are also clinical outcome differences. Let's first look at technical differences between ASSR and ABR. The ABR waveform is often subjectively determined by the examiner; for this reason it is important that the examiner be experienced in interpretation of the waveforms. On the other hand, ASSR is determined by objective statistical techniques. Another difference between ABR and ASSR lies with the characteristics of the stimulus and the response. In the case of ABR, where the stimulus is a click or toneburst, each click or toneburst will elicit a response and each stimulus and its response (a cycle) is independent of the previous and subsequent stimuli and responses. Ideally, During ASSR, both the stimulus and the response are continuous in a steady-state

pattern and are connected to each other. Both the stimuli and responses reach their peak and baseline simultaneously. Furthermore, the response of the ABR is measured in μV whereas the response of ASSR is measured in nV. At the present time, ABR is used more frequently than ASSR in measuring hearing sensitivity, as the latter is still in its infancy and to date there are less data on this instrumentation and procedure.

With respect to clinical-outcome differences, ASSR is unique because: (1) there is more frequency specificity when testing hearing; and (2) whereas ABR has a restricted range (hearing loss up to 80 dB), ASSR can test an individual with a loss as significant as 120 dB HTL (this is important when testing a patient with a profound loss, when determining cochlear-implant candidacy, and for hearing-aid evaluation for an individual with a profound loss). Furthermore, two ears and eight carrier signals can be tested simultaneously, which saves time.

Let us clarify the meaning of amplitude modulation (AM) and frequency modulation (FM) before speaking about ASSR, because ASSR incorporates AM and FM signals. AM signals are present in your own home. AM is used for transmitting signals such as speech, music, and so forth from a source to a radio station. In order for the desired signal to be transmitted to the radio in your home, it must be carried, that is, propagated, by another signal called the carrier signal. The amplitude of the carrier is modulated by the amplitude of the signal, that is, by the speech or music, and so forth). This modulation moves the signal from place to place. To clarify further, the amplitude of the carrier signal is changed in accordance with the instantaneous change of the modulator (Figure 9–41).

Unlike AM, where amplitude is modulated over time and frequency is constant, the converse is true for FM where

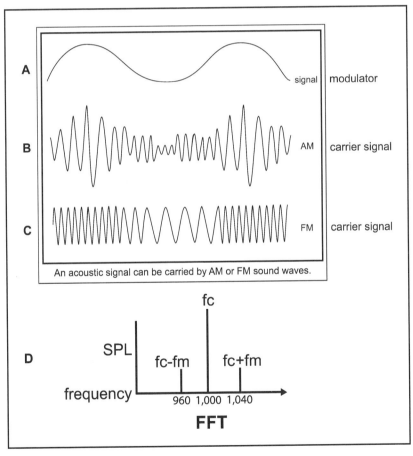

Figure 9–41. A is the low-frequency signal (modulator). B is an AM carrier signal modulated by a low-frequency modulator. C is an FM carrier signal. D is the spectrum of the carrier (AM signal).

frequency is modulated by the carrier over time while amplitude is constant (Figure 9–41C). AM and FM are used to elicit an electrophysiologic response.

As AM is more frequently used than either FM or AM/FM to detect hearing loss with ASSR, and provides reasonable data, we will concentrate on AM. However, the AM and FM used to elicit auditory evoked potentials, are slightly different from AM and FM on our radios in terms of how they are generated. We describe these differences shortly. There are several techniques added to the ASSR AM to enhance the magnitude of the response, for example, exponential stimuli. This technique provides shorter rise and fall times for the carrier signals because of its steeper slope. According to John, Brown, Muir, and Picton (2004), the steeper rise and fall time of an exponential stimulus will prolong the silent interval between the peaks of the carrier signal. This will enhance the amplitude because of the increased synchrony of the neural response. Increased synchrony will augment the ASSR amplitude for 500-Hz and 4000-Hz carrier signals in particular. To increase amplitude of the ASSR for 1000-Hz and 2000-Hz carrier signals, mixed modulation (MM) is added. When the MM stimuli are selected, the default parameters are as follows: (1) AM is fixed at 100%; (2) each of the carrier signals has its own AM frequency between 80 Hz and 100 Hz; (3) the modulations are increased with increased frequency of the carrier tone; and (4) FM is fixed at 20%, that is, the carrier signal used to elicit auditory evoked potentials is frequency modulated by 20% (10% on each side of the carrier signal). For example, a carrier signal of 1000 Hz modulates 10% below (900Hz) and 10% above (1010 Hz) similar

to warbled tones. Figure 9–42 shows the MASTER setup display screen. This figure shows us the carrier signal for left and right ears for 500 Hz, 1000 Hz, 2000 Hz, and 4000 Hz in the middle of the screen, exponential amplitude and mixed (AM 100% and FM 20%), on the right-hand side of the screen.

As mentioned above, there is a difference between AM on your radio at home, and the AM used to elicit auditory evoked potentials. An AM signal (the modulator) for evoked potentials doesn't really exist in ASSR. Instead, there are simulated techniques that provide a similar effect. There is software in the ASSR system that modulates the amplitude of the carrier signal. To simplify, let's consider an example. Many of you are familiar with or have heard of Békésy audiometry. In Békésy audiometry, the patient must push a button until he hears a sound. Upon hearing the sound, he releases the button. The subject modulates the amplitude around the threshold. This is similar to AM for ASSR where the amplitude of the carrier signal is modulated by computer software that serves as the modulator. Of course, the process in ASSR is much faster than that used for Békésy audiometry where the patient is modulating the amplitude of the signal to reach threshold. For example, the modulating frequency at the brainstem level is between 70 to 100 times per second. Let's assume that the modulating frequency is 80 Hz. This means that you are modulating the amplitude of the carrier 80 times/sec from 0 baseline to maximum, and back again. The AM frequency determines the shape of the envelope of the carrier frequency (Figure 9–43A).

Notice in Figure 9–43A that the duration of each modulating tone is 10 ms: 5-ms rise time and 5-ms fall (you can see

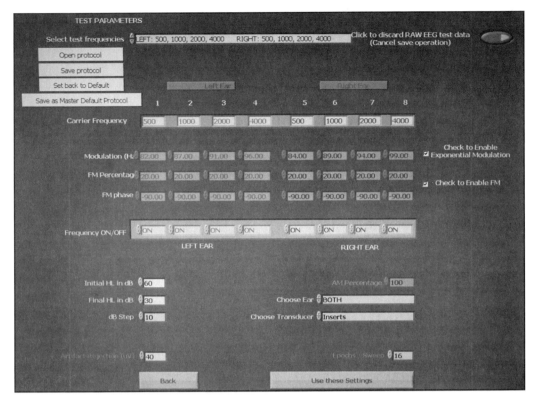

Figure 9–42. Setup for ASSR MASTER.

that there is no plateau). The ASSR carrier spectrum (the test signal) has a spectrum similar to Figure 9–41D (compare to Figure 9–43B). As you can see, most of the energy is concentrated at the modulated signal (carrier), in this case 1000 Hz. The frequencies of the sidebands are ± the modulating frequency, that is, 40 cycles on the right and 40 cycles on the left. As you see in Figure 9–40B, the lobes, fc − fm and fc + fm are significantly lower than fc. This is very important in achieving frequency specificity. You might expect the spectrum of the response of the ASSR to be similar to the spectrum of the carrier frequency. However, most of the energy's response is concentrated at the frequency close to the modulation frequency. This separation between

the two spectra (the carrier frequency and the response) prevents the introduction of artifacts resulting from the spectra's proximity. This is a very important aspect of measuring ASSR (Figure 9–43C). The envelope of the ASSR follows the envelope of the carrier, which is determined by the envelope of the modulator tone.

The frequency of the modulator (the signal) determines which part of the auditory system is evoked. The frequency modulator used in auditory evoked potentials ranges from approximately 70 to 100 cycles/sec to approximately 10 cycles/sec. The highest frequencies elicit potentials from the lower brainstem (ASSR) whereas the lower frequencies elicit potentials from the cortex.

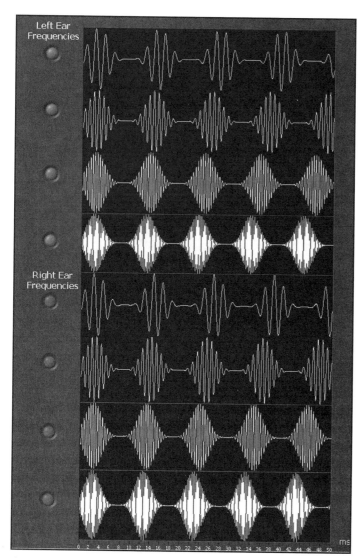

Left Ear
Frequencies

Right Ear
Frequencies

0 2 4 6 8 10 12 14 16 18 20 22 24 26 28 30 32 34 36 38 40 42 44 46 48 50 ms

A

Figure 9–43. **A** *is the ASSR carrier waveform for 500 Hz, 1000 Hz, 2000 Hz, and 4000 Hz for the left ear* (upper) *and right ear* (lower). **B** *is a schematic drawing of the spectrum of the carrier (stimulus).* continues

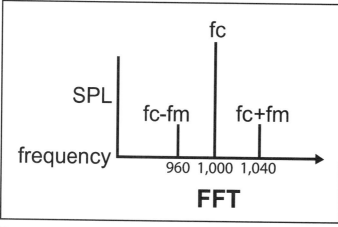

fc

SPL

fc-fm   fc+fm

frequency

960 1,000 1,040

FFT

B

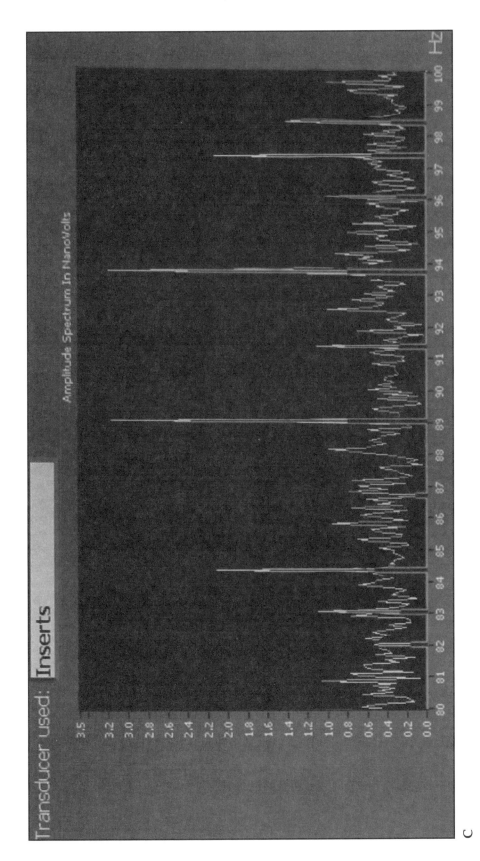

Figure 9–43. continued *C is a spectrum of the response.*

191

Figure 9–44 provides a summary of the principles of ASSR, its data collection and presentation. The upper part of the figure shows four stages of ASSR: (A) the stimulus presented to the patient's ear, (B) the location of the stimulus along the basilar membrane, (C) the stimulus in the auditory cortex, and (D) the recording of brain activity. The lower part of the figure shows how the data are collected, statistically evaluated, and presented. The frequencies are presented individually, sequentially, or simultaneously. Each carrier frequency has a different modulating frequency (from low to high as noted above). For example, a carrier frequency of 500 Hz might have a modulator of 81 Hz and a carrier frequency of 4000 Hz might have a modulator of 88 Hz.

As is the case for other digitally operated equipment such as other auditory evoked potentials, OAE, and some audiometers, the stimuli for ASSR are converted from digital to analog form. The EEG response, which is a voltage from the upper nervous system (cortex) is converted from analog to digital format and then stored in the computer's data buffer. Each carrier signal occupies a place along the basilar membrane with high-frequency carrier signals at the basilar end and low-frequency carrier frequencies at the apical end (Figure 9–44B). The signal will travel to the cortical area. When the modulator signal is below 70 Hz, it will travel to both hemispheres of the cortex. The ASSR response is recorded and amplified 50,000 times. The response is then filtered using a high-pass filter of 10 Hz to eliminate low-frequency noise and using a low-pass filter of 300 Hz to prevent aliasing. These filters are analog filters (see Chapter 5 on Filtering). The filtering for ASSR, as for other signals converted from analog to digital, is done prior to the conversion from analog to digital format. The response is digitized and displayed in its analog form as EEG activity on the computer monitor, as a time-series voltage signal (Figure 9–41D upper part of figure). The response at this stage will include ASSR and other brain activities and is stored in the computer's memory in segments labeled as epochs on the monitor with durations of approximately 1 second/epoch. Several of these epochs (up to 14) are termed "sweeps." This technique will yield an increase in sample size before it is subjected to an FFT algorithm, and will bring about enhanced frequency resolution, down to a fraction of a cycle. This process increases the signal-to-noise ratio allowing us to measure amplitude even in nV. The recommended number of sweeps is approximately 32, taking about 7 minutes at each intensity level. The proposed level at which to begin is about 60 dB IL. If a response is obtained at 60 dB IL, that is, statistical significance is achieved, then the tester lowers the intensity level in 10 dB increments. If there is no response at a particular level, the tester raises the intensity. Of course, if statistical significance is achieved at a particular level, one need not complete all 32 sweeps. A word of caution: patients may experience acoustic trauma at higher intensity levels. Therefore, it is advised that the tester observe the patient and inquire as to his comfort at the higher intensities.

Quantification of ASSR

Quantification of amplitude is the most commonly used procedure for the measurement of ASSR. When measuring the amplitude of ASSR, both amplitude and phase contribute to the final quantification of the amplitude. In this approach,

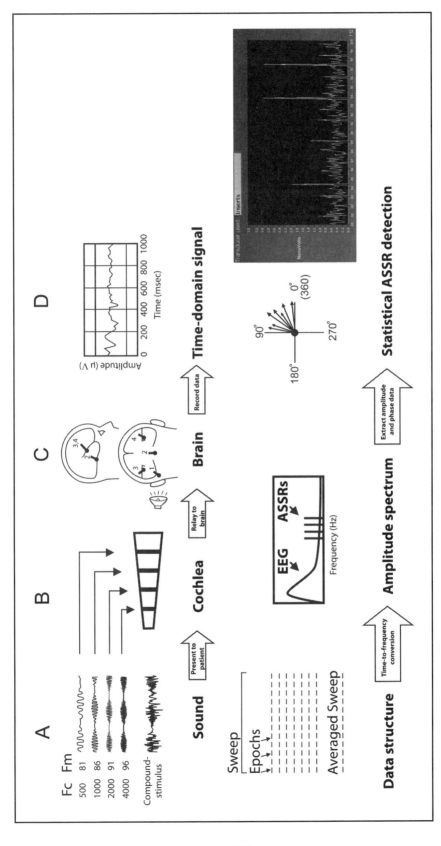

Figure 9–44. Summary of the principles, data collection, and presentation of ASSR. Modified from M. S. John and D. W. Purcell in G. Rance (2008). With permission from Plural Publishing, Inc.

the amplitude of ASSR is measured in comparison to the quantity of noise using F-ratio statistics. Large variability in the phase of the response usually accompanies small amplitude of response whereas large amplitude is always associated with small phase variability. Therefore, the amplitude of the response is a product of its phase and the magnitude. There are two factors that cause variability of the phase and the magnitude: noise and a low level of stimulation.

In order for an ASSR response to be considered valid, the F-ratio of significance must have a $p = <.05$ or better. This level of significance is achieved when the SNR is about 1.75 dB. In order to achieve an F-ratio of .005 level of significance, the SNR must be approximately 2.35 dB. There are essentially two statistical approaches to the analysis of the FFT spectrum. One method considers the variance of repeated measurements of the response. For example, a clinician can record 16 separate responses, each for a duration of 1.024 sec. A second approach measures the variance of the different amplitudes in a single spectrum. For example, one can join 16 responses into a single 16.384-second sweep and perform FFT that results in an amplitude spectrum (Picton et al., 2003).

It should be mentioned that statistical significance is not always obtained at levels up to 30 to 40 dB because of background noise. To improve SNR we must either increase the number of sweeps or the intensity of the carrier. As you are aware, an increased sweep will decrease the width of the bin and as a consequence increase SNR (see Chapter 8). A sample screen of a test in progress for MASTER is illustrated in Figure 9–45. We see that two ears can be measured simultaneously

for eight carrier frequencies. On the upper left-hand side (upper screen) we see that there is no response. Instead, there is noise. This outcome becomes clear when we observe the lack of significance throughout the carrier frequencies. On the upper right-hand side we see clear amplitude for FFT for the right ear as confirmed by the statistical significance of the results. This is achieved at 60 dB HL. Below the upper screen on the left side, we see 32 sweeps, 9 good epochs, and 7 artifacts.

Although several techniques have been proposed to enhance the magnitude of ASSR for the identification of normal hearing or mild hearing loss, our own experience has not always supported the successful use of these techniques. It is, in many cases, still difficult to identify normal hearing and a mild loss. To solve this problem, we propose the use of DPOAEs and ASSR as complementary techniques. Therefore, if an individual fails a DPOAE screening or test, we turn to ASSR, beginning at a level of 40 dB nHL.

The analog electrophysiologic data obtained from the human skull must be converted to digital form. The technique used to capture the ASSR spectrum employs a FFT computer algorithm requiring, as noted above, that the number of samples (N) taken for analysis must be a power of 2. The conversion is usually done using a rate performed at integer submultiples of 1 sec (e.g., there are 1024 samples collected at 1.04 sec, 2048 samples collected at 2.08 sec, and so forth).

Figure 9–46 describes an excellent hypothetical case (John & Purcell, 2008) in which the carrier frequency is modulated at 83 Hz/sec. The carrier frequency is used to evoke an 83-Hz ASSR. In this example, an estimation of ASSR was made

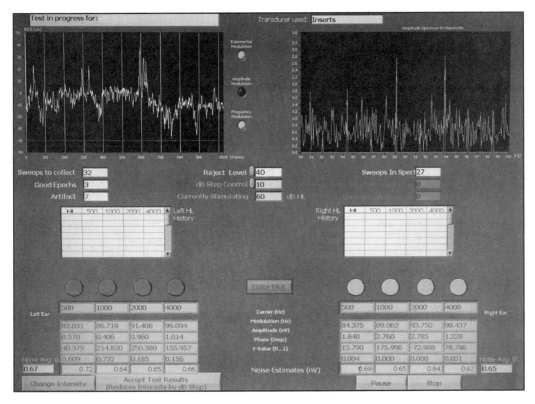

Figure 9–45. *A sample display of the screen for MASTER.*

after FFT was performed and a power spectrum obtained on averaged evoked potentials (averaged sweeps) for three durations: 1-sec FFT, 2-sec FFT, and 10-sec FFT. Recall that each sweep contains 12 epochs. For example, 1 sweep contains 12 averaged epochs, 2 sweeps contains 24 averaged epochs, 3 sweeps contains 36 averaged epochs, and 10 sweeps contains 120 averaged epochs.

The relationship between duration and spectral resolution can be further illustrated by the formula 1/time, where 1 is Hz and time is seconds. For example, if data of a 1-sec duration are submitted for FFT analysis, amplitude resolution (bin width) will be 0.2 Hz. If data of a 10 sec duration are submitted for FFT analysis, amplitude resolution (bin width) will be 0.1 Hz.

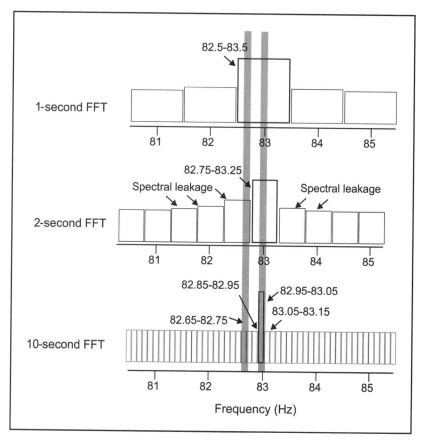

Figure 9–46. *The influence of spectral resolution on the estimation of ASSR energy. Amplitude spectra for simulated ASSR sweeps of 1, 2, and 10 sec generate spectral estimates with resolution 1.0, 0.5, and 0.1 Hz, respectively. Note that ASSR energy at 83 Hz and a noise peak at 82.7 Hz are clearly defined at a sweep duration of 10 sec, seen in the bottom spectra where we have a smaller bin. However, ASSR energy and noise cannot be separated at 1- and 2-sec sweep durations. The two vertical bars illustrate bin width for 1, 2, and 10 sec data sweeps. With permission from Plural Publishing, Inc.*

REFERENCES

Durrant, J. D., & Boston J. R. (2007). In R. F. Burkard, M. Don, & J. J Eggermont (Eds.), *Auditory evoked potentials: Basic principles and clinical application* (pp. 42–72). New York, NY: Lippincott Williams & Wilkins.

Fletcher, H., & Munson, W. A. (1937). Relation between loudness and masking. *Journal of Acoustical Society of America, 9*, 1–10.

Gorga, M. P., Neely, S. T., Johnson, T. A., Dierking, D. M., & Garner, C. A. (2007). In M. S. Robinette & T. J. Glattke (Eds.), *Otoacoustic emissions: Clinical applications* (pp. 197–226). New York, NY: Thieme.

Hall, J. W. (1992). *Handbook of auditory evoked responses.* Boston, MA: Allyn & Bacon.

John, S. M., Brown, D., Muir, P., & Picton, T. (2004). Recording auditory steady-state responses in young infants. *Ear and Hearing, 25*, 539–553.

John, M. S., & Purcell, D. W. (2008). In G. Rance (Ed.), *Auditory steady-state response: Generation, recording, and clinical applications* (pp. 11–53). San Diego, CA: Plural Publishing.

Lonsbury-Martin, B. L., & Martin, G. K. (2007). In M. S. Robinette & T. J. Glattke (Eds.), *Otoacoustic emissions: Clinical applications* (pp. 107–130). New York, NY: Thieme.

Margolis, R. H., Van Camp, K. J., Wilson, R. H., & Creten, W. L. (1985). Multifrequency tympanometry in normal ears. *Audiology, 24,* 44–53.

Picton, T. W., Sasha, J. M., Dimitrijevic, A., & Purcell, D. (2003). Human auditory steady-state responses. *International Journal of Audiology, 42,* 177–219.

Ren, T. (2004). Reverse propagation of sound in the gerbil cochlea. *Natural Neuroscience, 7,* 333–334.

Robinette, M. S., & Glattke, T. J. (2007). *Otoacoustic emissions: Clinical applications.* New York, NY: Thieme.

Silman, S., & Gelfand, S. A. (1981). The relationship between magnitude of hearing loss and acoustic reflex threshold levels. *Journal of Speech and Hearing Disorders, 46,* 312–316.

Silman, S., & Silverman, C. A. (1991). *Auditory diagnosis: Principles and applications.* New York, NY: Academic Press.

Sklare, D. A., & Denenberg, L. J. (1987). Technical note: Interaural attenuation for tubephone insert earphones. *Ear and Hearing, 8,* 298–300.

Thornton, A. R. (2007). In R. F. Burkard, M. Don, & J. J. Eggermont (Eds.), *Auditory evoked potentials: Basic principles and clinical application* (pp. 73–101). New York, NY: Lippincott Williams & Wilkins.

Van Camp, K. J., Margolis, R. H., Wilson, R. H., Creten, W. L., & Shanks, J. E. (1986). *Principles of tympanometry.* ASHA Monograph No. 24. Rockville, MD: American Speech-Language-Hearing Association.

10

Instrumentation for Calibration and Calibration of Test Stimuli

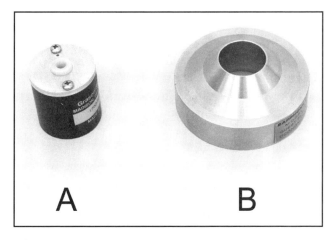

Figure 10–1. *HA-1 coupler and NBS 9A 6-cc coupler.*

In order to make a diagnosis, whether in medicine, psychology, audiology, or other similar discipline, we must first generate normative data. We use these data to determine whether results for an individual fall within or outside of our norms; the results allow the practitioner to draw the proper conclusions. Norms are established by using rigorous crite- ria based on a number of well-controlled studies. For example, investigators collect data for individuals who, based on cer- tain standards, are judged to have hearing within normal limits. Because we depend on the integrity of the instrumentation we use to evaluate our patients' results, it is essential that the clinician periodi- cally evaluate the internal consistency of the equipment, that is, to be sure that the equipment is calibrated. Instrumentation is subject to both internal and external factors that can cause a malfunction, for example, mechanical, environmental, electrical problems. Therefore, we must be sure that the output of the earphone or speaker will be the same as that described by normative guidelines or industry standards when guidelines are unavailable.

Test instrumentation used in the profession of Audiology has evolved from simple analog to sophisticated digital technology. Similarly, the devices we use to calibrate and maintain our instrumentation have evolved from analog to sophisticated digital technology including FFT. American National Standards Institute (ANSI) guidelines describe the standards pertaining primarily to analog equipment. Newer digital and hybrid devices have incorporated these standards in digital form. The first specification by ANSI was described in 1969. These standards were updated and revised in 1989, 1996, 2004, and 2010. Audiometric specifications include: (a) types of transducers; (b) signals and their sources, (c) reference threshold levels; and (d) calibration procedures.

We describe various instruments used to calibrate acoustic signals as well as the techniques employed to calibrate pure tones, speech, noise, click, and tone burst. These stimuli are generally used in audiometers, OAE devices, and auditory evoked potentials. Our students present various types of calibration procedures for several devices in Appendix A.

The most fundamental requirement for calibration of instrumentation used in Audiology and Hearing Science is a device that either resembles outer ear mechanical impedance (the enclosure between the earphone and tympanic membrane

when an earphone is being calibrated or from the insert receiver to the eardrum when the insert receiver is being used to calibrate) or to find a device that will have the same mechanical characteristics of the mastoid when calibrating the bone oscillator. These devices are addressed when we describe calibration for air conduction and bone conduction.

EQUIPMENT USED FOR CALIBRATION

Equipment for Calibration of Air Conduction

Equipment for calibration of air conduction includes the following: artificial ear, oscilloscope, real-time analyzer, and sound-level meter. These devices are described in detail below.

Artificial Ear

Artificial ears include the 2-cc coupler HA-2 or 1 (Figure 10–1A) 6-cc coupler (Model NBS 9A in Figure 10–1B), and 6-cc coupler (Model IEC 60318-3 with Type 1 adapter in Figure 10–2).

The NBS 9A 6-cc coupler is used to calibrate TDH 39, 49/50 earphones. The HA-2 and HA-1 couplers are used to calibrate insert receivers. Both HA-1 and HA-2 couplers are 2-cc. The type used may differ with manufacturer. IEC 60318-3 is used to calibrate HAD-200 high-frequency earphones.

Oscilloscope

An oscilloscope (Figure 10–3) is an electronic device with a fluorescent monitor displaying the instantaneous voltage of an

Figure 10–2. *IEC 60318-3.*

electrical signal as a function of time. The display is produced by a moving dot on the screen of a cathode-ray tube. There are two electrical circuits, one horizontal (to control the time domain) and one vertical (for control of the amplitude domain). The horizontal deflecting circuit moves the dot from left to right in a continuous cycle, and then, swiftly, back to the starting position to begin again. When the vertical deflecting circuits move the dot up and down in response to voltage changes in the signal, a wavelike image of the signal will be seen on the screen. An oscilloscope is used in medicine, science, engineering, telecommunication and hearing science (including Audiology). When the oscilloscope is connected to a SLM which

itself is connected to an acoustic signal, the monitor displays the electrical analog to a sound wave.

There are analog and digital oscilloscopes. A digital oscilloscope converts voltage into digital form (refer to section on analog to digital conversion in Chapter 8). In some modern digital oscilloscopes, LCD (Liquid Crystal Display) is used. An LCD oscilloscope uses two plates of opposing polarity. When the signal (in its electrical form) travels through the liquid produced by the plus and minus poles, the liquid turns black, that is, it crystallizes. The crystals return to their original liquid form when the current is switched off. Recently, Tektronix introduced a digital oscilloscope with FFT (Figure 10–3B).

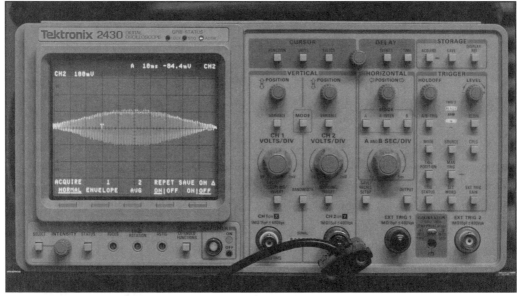

A

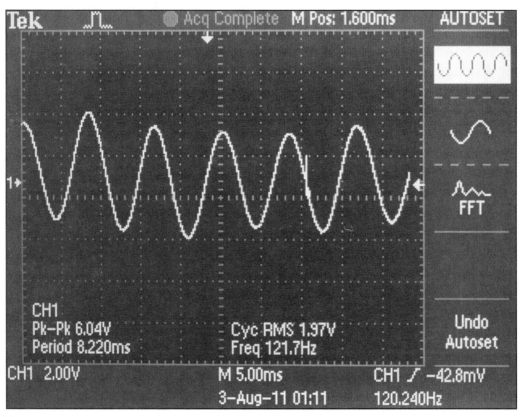

B

Figure 10–3. **A.** *2-channel storage oscilloscope showing rise and fall for a 100-Hz signal.* **B.** *Digital oscilloscope with FFT. We see the discrete waveform on the left-hand side of the figure (grid) and the FFT on the right-hand side.*

Real-Time Analyzer

The real-time analyzer (RTA) is an analog or digital device that breaks, measures, and displays the frequency spectrum of an acoustic signal (Figure 10–4). An analog system uses a complex network of capacitors and resistors, similar to those described in the chapter on filtering, to break the acoustic stimuli into their component frequencies. This is done through low-pass, high-pass, and band-pass filters. In contrast, a digital system does not employ capacitors and resistors to break down the signal. Rather, it uses digital sampling and a microprocessor that employs digital signal processing such as

FFT to derive the required measurement. Recall from Chapter 8 that at the present time digital-signal processing (DSP) is used more often than analog systems. Therefore, DSP is used more frequently than analog in various devices such as cell-phones, satellite, radar, television, and so forth. By breaking the signal, the unwanted components of the sound signal such as noise, are eliminated.

Sound Level Meter (SLM)

Before conducting calibration of acoustic stimuli using a SLM, one must verify the accuracy of the SLM itself. This is accomplished by using a calibration piston (sound

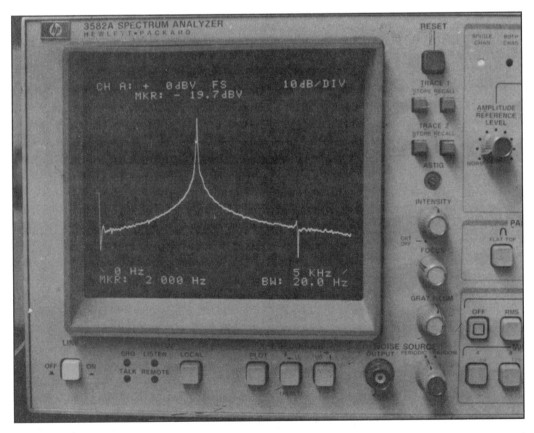

Figure 10–4. Real-time analyzer showing the electrical spectrum for a 2000-Hz pure-tone signal with a rise/fall time of 25 ms and a plateau of 950 ms.

calibrator). The piston generates one or two pure tones (usually 250 Hz and/or 1000 Hz) with a predetermined intensity choice of 94 or 114 dB SPL. Both can be used for 250 or 1000 Hz. The calibration piston consists of an oscillator that provides pure tones, an amplifier, transducers, and microphone coupler. The coupler of the piston usually accepts a standard microphone. The sound from the calibrator is fed to the SLM through the microphone of the meter. The SPL is read on the SLM. A deviation over 2 dB requires adjustment of the SLM. This is accomplished by rotation of a small screw on the side of the device either to the right, for upward adjustment, or to the left, for downward adjustment. Figure 10–5 shows the calibration assembly. Figure 10–6 shows the same assembly with an HA-2 cc coupler.

An SLM is generally composed of the following components: a microphone, amplifier, standard frequency weight-ing, and filters. The microphone is omni-directional in order to collect responses from all directions.

For each type of SLM, ANSI 1983 (R 2006) standard requires three types of frequency-weighting scales, A, B, and C, and two exponential-time-averaging characteristics: slow and fast. The standard has other features such as peak measurement and different approaches for displaying SPL in dB such as digital display, recording display, or analog display. Impulse sound level in dB is measured by using an impulse of 35-ms exponential-time-average for the rise-time of the signal and 1500 ms for the fall-time of the acoustic stimulus.

The frequency-weighting signals represent the average over time (exponential time-average) and are described as slow (S), fast (F), and impulse (I). SPL measurement can be presented in four scales: Linear, A, B, and C. The Linear scale is an absolute measurement with the lowest reading at 0 dB SPL. The A scale resem-

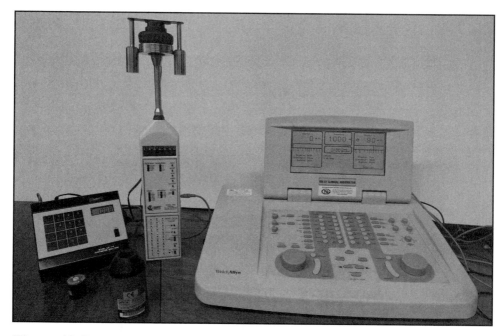

Figure 10–5. Calibration assembly with TDH-50 earphone.

bles the reverse of the 40 phon curve (Figure 10–7) and excludes sounds that are not essential for hearing.

The B scale is the reverse of the 100 phon curve. The C scale is similar to the Linear scale and is rarely used. The SLM also includes filters for pure tones, broadband noise, and narrowband noise (octave and third-octave band filters). The microphone used for the SLM is a condenser microphone (Chapter 6).

Audiologists sometimes need to conduct measurements using various scales. Table 10–1 presents details of intensity levels for nominal frequencies for A, B, and C weighting scales.

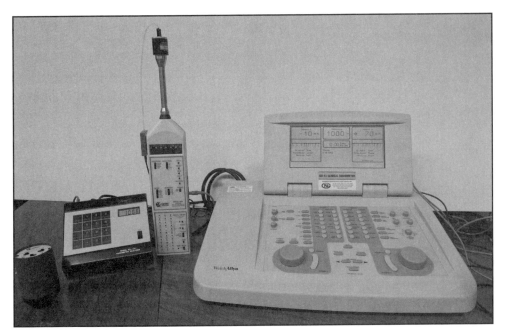

Figure 10–6. *Calibration assembly with 2-cc coupler.*

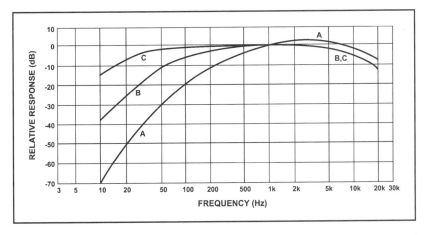

Figure 10–7. *Frequency-weighting scales for an SLM with permission of Grason-Stadler, Inc.*

Table 10–1. Intensity Levels for Nominal Frequencies for A, B, and C Weighting Scales

Nominal Frequency Hz	Exact Frequency In	A Weighting dB	B Weighting dB	C Weighting dB
10	10.00	−70.4	−38.2	−14.3
12.5	12.59	−63.4	−33.2	−11.2
16.0	15.85	−56.7	−28.5	−8.5
20	19.95	−50.5	−24.2	−6.2
25	25.12	−44.7	−20.4	−4.4
31.5	31.62	−39.4	−17.1	−3.0
40	39.81	−34.6	−14.2	−2.0
50	50.12	−30.2	−11.6	−1.3
63	63.10	−26.2	−9.3	−0.8
80	79.43	−22.5	−7.4	−0.5
100	100.0	−19.1	−5.6	−0.3
125	125.9	−16.1	−4.2	−0.2
160	158.5	−13.4	−3.0	−0.1
200	199.5	−10.9	−2.0	0
250	251.2	−8.6	−1.3	0
315	316.2	−6.6	−0.8	0
400	398.1	−4.8	−0.5	0
500	501.2	−3.2	−0.3	0
630	631.0	−1.9	−0.1	0
800	794.3	−0.8	0	0
1000	1000	0	0	0
1250	1259	+0.6	0	0
1600	1585	+1.0	0	−0.1
2000	1995	+1.2	−0.1	−0.2
2500	2512	+1.3	−0.2	−0.3
3150	3162	+1.2	−0.4	−0.5
4000	3981	+1.0	−0.7	−0.8
5000	5012	+0.5	−1.2	−1.3
6300	6310	−0.1	−1.9	−2.0
8000	7943	−1.1	−2.9	−3.0
10000	10000	−2.5	−4.3	−4.4
12500	12590	−4.3	−6.1	−6.2
16000	15850	−6.6	−8.4	−8.5
20000	19950	−9.3	−11.1	−11.2

Source: Reprinted from ANSI S1.4-1983 (R 2006) with permission of the Acoustical Society of America.

There are several current systems for calibration of a clinical audiometer. We can, for example, use the analog Quest calibration system (See Figures 10–5 and 10–6) that includes an analog SLM to calibrate the output for various earphones, and a system that measures rise and fall, frequency accuracy, and distortion.

A hybrid system, the SoundPro, also manufactured by Quest, includes a digital filter system to measure the output SPL and distortion of the frequency components. However, in order to measure rise and fall, frequency accuracy, and distortion, we need the Quest Audiometer Analyzer (Model AA-175). This device follows the same analog principle as the previous system. The digitized signals will be converted into analog signals and measured by the Quest Analyzer. Figure 10–8 shows the hybrid Quest system connected for calibration.

Recently, Larson Davis introduced a completely digital system with FFT to measure all variables. The calibration results can be displayed on either the SLM or a computer monitor (Figures 10–9, 10–10, and 10–11).

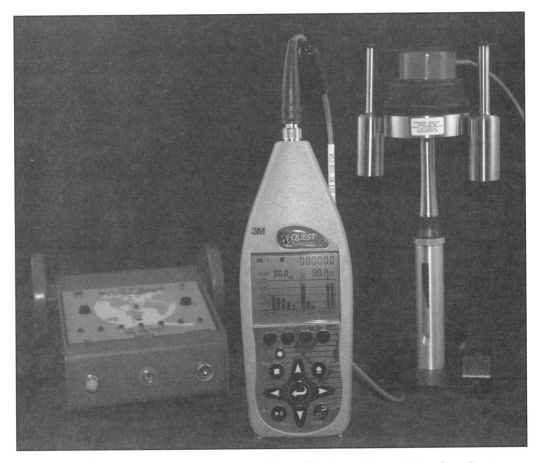

Figure 10–8. Hybrid Quest system connected for calibration with permission from Quest.

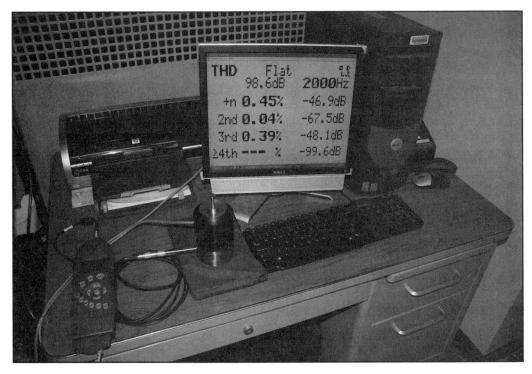

Figure 10–9. Larson Davis calibration system assembly.

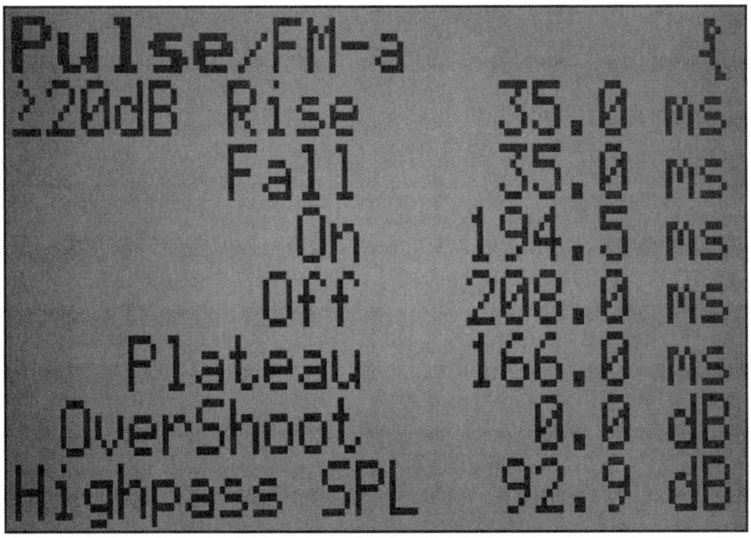

Figure 10–10. Rise, Fall, Plateau, Overshoot, and Intensity level details for Larson Davis system.

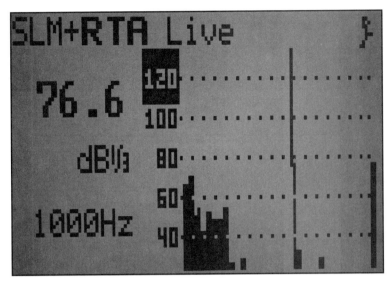

Figure 10–11. *FFT analysis of 1000-Hz signal with an intensity of 76.6 dB SPL.*

ANSI (2010) REQUIREMENTS FOR CALIBRATION OF AUDIOMETRIC SIGNALS

Thus far, we have described various equipment (analog, digital, and hybrid) used for the calibration of audiometric signals. Before we proceed to a description of calibration procedures, we must present reference equivalent threshold sound pressure levels (dB re 20 µPa) requirements for calibration.

Table 10–2 shows the reference equivalent threshold sound pressure levels for supra-aural earphones in common use and for two types of artificial ears (NBS 9A and IEC 60318-3). Table 10–3 shows the reference equivalent threshold sound pressure levels for insert receivers.

You may notice that in addition to the NBS 9A coupler (a 6-cc coupler approximating the impedance of the ear canal between the earphone and the tympanic membrane) there is another coupler, IEC (International Electrotechnical Commission) 60318-3. The IEC assumes that the NBS 9A coupler doesn't match the impedance characteristics of the ear. Therefore, the Commission constructed the IEC 60318-3 assuming this coupler represents the true impedance of the outer ear. However, a debate is ongoing as to whether the IEC 60318-3 truly represents the impedance of the outer ear. ANSI/ASA therefore has included the IEC 60318-3 coupler in its standards.

Table 10–4 shows reference equivalent threshold sound pressure levels (RETSPLs) (dB re 20 µPa) for high frequency circumaural earphones that include frequencies 125 Hz up to 16,000 Hz.

Table 10–2. Reference Equivalent Threshold SPLs (RETSPLs) (dB re 20 micro Pa) for Supra-Aural Earphones in Common Use and Two Types of Artificial Ears

Frequency Hz	TDH Type[a] IEC 60318-3	TDH 39 NBS 9A	TDH 49/50 NBS 9A
	Supra-Aural Earphone		
125	45.0	45.0	47.5
160	38.5		
200	32.5		
250	27.0	25.5	26.5
315	22.0		
400	17.0		
500	13.5	11.5	13.5
630	10.5		
750	9.0	8.0	8.5
800	8.5		
1000	7.5	7.0	7.5
1250	7.5		
1500	7.5	6.5	7.5
1600	8.0		
2000	9.0	9.0	11.0
2500	10.5		
3000	11.5	10.0	9.5
3150	11.5		
4000	12.0	9.5	10.5
5000	11.0		
6000	16.0	15.5	13.5
6300	21.0		
8000	15.5	13.0	13.0
Speech	20.0	19.5	20.0

[a]TDH Type or any supra-aural earphone having the characteristics described in clause 9.1.1 or ISO 389 Part 1.

Source: Reprinted from ANSI/ASA S3.6-2010 with permission of the American Acoustical Society.

Table 10–3. Reference Equivalent Threshold Sound Pressure Levels (RETSPLs) (dB re 20 µPa) for Insert Earphones

Frequency (Hz)	Coupler Type		
	Occluded Ear Simulator[a]	HA-2 with Rigid Tube[a]	HA-1[b]
125	28.0	26.0	26.5
160	24.5	22.0	22.0
200	21.5	18.0	19.5
250	17.5	14.0	14.5
315	15.5	12.0	15.0
400	13.0	9.0	10.5
500	9.5	5.5	6.0
630	7.5	4.0	4.5
750	6.0	2.0	2.0
800	5.5	1.5	1.5
1000	5.5	0.0	0.0
1250	8.5	2.0	1.0
1500	9.5	2.0	0.0
1600	9.5	2.0	1.5
2000	11.5	3.0	2.5
2500	13.5	5.0	4.5
3000	13.0	3.5	2.5
3150	13.0	4.0	2.5
4000	15.0	5.5	0.0
5000	18.5	5.0	1.5
6000	16.0	2.0	−2.5
6300	16.0	2.0	−2.0
8000	15.5	0.0	−3.5
Speech	18.0	12.5	12.5

[a]RETSPL using an occluded ear simulator (ANSI/ASA S3.7, IEC 60318-4, IEC 60711) and HA-2 coupler with rigid tube attachment (ANSI/ASA S3.7) are from ISO 389-2.

[b]The above values are valid when the end of the foam eartip or other eartip is inserted to a depth of 12 or 15 mm from the entrance to the ear canal. These values are based on a foam eartip having the length of 12 mm.

Source: Reprinted from ANSI/ASA S3.6-2010 with permission of the Acoustical Society of America.

Table 10–4. RETSPLs in dB re 20 µPa for High-Frequency Circumaural Earphones

Frequency Hz	Sennheiser HDA 200 IEC 60318-2 with Type 1 adapter	KOSS HV/1A IEC 60318-2 with Type 2 adapter[a]
125	30.5	
250	18	
500	11	
750	6	
1000	5.5	16
1500	5.5	
2000	4.5	
3000	2.5	
4000	9.5	8
5000	14	
6000	17	
8000	17.5	15.5
9000	19	19.5
10000	22	24
11200	23	23
12500	27.5	25
14000	35	34.5
16000	56	52
Speech	19	
RETSPLs	Reference ISO 389-5 (8 kHz–16 kHz) and ISO 389-8 (125 Hz–8 kHz)	

[a]Although this earphone is no longer in production, some users still need the RETSPL values. They are therefore given.

Source: Reprinted from ANSI/ASA S3.6-2010 with permission of the American Acoustical Society.

CALIBRATION

Frequency Accuracy

Each frequency generated by Type 1, Type 2, and extended high-frequency audiometers must be within a tolerance of ± 1% of the test frequency and ± 2% for Types 3 and 4 audiometers (Chapter 9).

Total Harmonic Distortion (THD)

Harmonic distortion refers to the amount of power present in the second, third (and so forth) harmonics based on the test tone. Harmonic distortion occurs in either a non-linear system that is overdriven by high-intensity sound or is generated by a brief sound such as a click. This type of distortion can be reported either in power dB or in percent.

In order to determine THD for each pure-tone frequency, one of the following procedures should be followed: reporting THD as a percentage (Table 10–5) of the output of the fundamental frequency (F0) or in dB HL. It is a simple process to report THD in dB HL. Let us assume that you are interested in the THD (in dB HL) for a 1000-Hz signal. Adjust the filter of the SLM to 1000 Hz and the output of the audiometer to maximum for 1000 Hz. Next, while keeping 1000 Hz as the signal, change the filter to 2000 Hz (2nd harmonic), 3000 Hz (3rd harmonic), and then 4000 Hz (4th harmonic). The level should be at least 50 dB from the fundamental frequency (in this case, 1000 Hz).

Repeat for all test frequencies. If we wish to report THD as a percentage value, we use the following formula:

$$\%THD = \frac{\sqrt{H_2^2 + H_3^2 + ... + H_N^2}}{\sqrt{H_1^2 + H_2^2 + H_3^2 + ... + H_N^2}} \times 100$$

(Eqn. 10.1)

The total harmonic distortion of a loudspeaker cannot exceed 3%. Distortion is measured using pure-tone input at 250, 500, and 1000 Hz. At an output SPL of 80 dB, THD must be less than 3%. At 100 dB SPL the THD must be less than 10%.

During measurement of harmonic distortion in soundfield, the SLM is placed in the position of the patient.

Rise and Fall

The rise time of a signal is the time required for the amplitude of the signal

Table 10–5. ANSI S3.6-2010 Maximum Permissible Harmonic Distortion, Expressed in Percent

Frequency (Hz)	Air Conduction				Bone Conduction		
	125	250	500 to 4000	6000 to 16000	250	500 to 750	1000 to 5000
Hearing level (dB HL)[a]	75.0	90.0	110.0	90.0	20.0	50.0	60.0
Second harmonic	2.0	2.0	2.0	2.0	5.0	5.0	5.0
Third harmonic	2.0	2.0	2.0		2.0	2.0	2.0
Fourth and each higher harmonic	0.3	0.3	0.3		2.0	2.0	2.0
All subharmonics		0.3	0.3	0.3			
Total harmonics	2.5	2.5	2.5	2.5	5.5	5.5	5.5

[a]Or maximum output level of the audiometer, whichever is lower. For circumaural and insert earphones the hearing level shall be 10 dB less than the levels specified in the table.

Source: Reprinted from ANSI/ASA S3.6-2010 with permission of the Acoustical Society of America.

to increase from 10% to 90% of its steady-state value. The fall time of a signal is the time required for the amplitude of the signal to decrease from 90% to 10% of its steady-state value. Rise-time for an audiometric pure-tone test signal for both air- and bone-conduction, should not be less than 20 ms. Fall-time for pure tones should not exceed 200 ms. Rise-time for a pulsed tone should not be less than 20 ms; the fall should not be more than 50 msec.

Linearity

When measuring output levels between two increments, assuming that they are in 5-dB increments, the deviation from 5 dB should not exceed ± 1 dB. Please see experiment by students in Appendix A.

SOUND-FIELD TESTING

Not all hearing tests are performed under earphones or using insert receivers. Some testing takes place in a soundproof booth without earphones. The signal is routed through a speaker (Chapter 6). Recall that when we discussed audiometric stimuli we also described warbled tones that are used in the booth to prevent the generation of standing waves. Sound-field testing is used for various purposes, for example, pediatric testing, hearing-aid evaluation, and evaluation of difficult-to-test populations. Table 10–6 specifies ANSI/ASA S3.6-2010 reference equivalent threshold SPL in the free-field and diffuse-field. Free-field exists in an anechoic chamber generally used to test hearing-aid characteristics and also for some other calibration, for example, calibration of the microphone for OAE, and frequency responses of hearing aids. The diffuse field (semi-free-field) exists in the test booth.

We previously have described calibration of audiometric stimuli using instrumentation that will, for the most part, give us direct numerical readings. If one wishes a visual representation of the process by which these numbers are obtained, one can use straightforward mathematics and a SLM, storage oscilloscope, and frequency counter. For example, we see the rise and fall of a 100-Hz signal in Figure 10–3. The time domain has been adjusted so that each division is equivalent to 10 ms. Figure 10–3 shows a total duration equal to 10 divisions. Three divisions equal 30 ms, representing the rise-time of the signal, 40 ms (four divisions) represents the plateau, and we again have three divisions (30 ms) representing the fall. We selected 10 ms per div in order to compress the cycles/div for clarity of visualization of rise and fall.

We need to make some modifications in measurement technique to compute rise, fall, and duration of longer lasting signals such as pure tones whose durations are 1 to 2 sec with rise and fall of 30 ms and plateau of at least 900 ms. This requires that rise and fall encompass approximately six divisions (3 for rise and 3 for fall). We selected 10 ms/div in order to compress an adequate number of cycles so that we can clearly see rise and fall. Generally, it is very difficult to observe rise, fall, and duration for a 1- to 2-sec signal. However, when we compress the cycles, as described above, and trigger the oscilloscope for a single capture, we are able to determine at least the rise and part of the plateau. We assume that rise and fall are symmetrical but if you wish to be certain, set the oscilloscope to "normal" run and you may capture both rise and fall as well as the plateau.

Table 10–6. Reference Equivalent Threshold Sound Pressure Levels (RETSPLs) (dB re 20 µPa) for Sound-Field Testing

Frequency (Hz)	Binaural Listening[a] in Free Field			Diffuse-Field Listening[a]		
	0-Degree Incidence	45-Degree Incidence	90-Degree Incidence	0-Degree Incidence	45-Degree Incidence	90-Degree Incidence
125	22.1	21.6	21.1	22.1	21.6	21.1
160	17.9	16.9	16.4	17.9	16.9	16.4
200	14.4	13.4	12.9	14.4	13.3	12.9
250	11.4	10.4	9.4	11.4	10.4	9.4
315	8.6	7.1	6.1	8.4	6.9	5.9
400	6.2	3.7	2.7	5.8	3.3	2.3
500	4.4	1.4	−0.1	3.8	0.8	0.8
630	3	−0.5	−2	2.1	−1.4	−2.9
750	2.4	−1.1	−2.6	1.2	−2.3	−3.8
800	2.2	−1.3	−2.8	1	−2.5	−4
1000	2.4	−1.6	−3.1	0.8	−3.2	−3.2
1250	3.5	−0.5	−2.5	1.9	−2.1	−4.1
1500	2.4	1.1	−2.6	1	−2.5	−4
1600	1.7	−1.8	−2.8	0.5	−3	−4
2000	−1.3	−4.3	−3.3	−1.5	−4.5	−3.5
2500	−4.2	−7.7	−6.2	−3.1	−6.6	−5.1
3000	−5.8	−10.5	−8.3	−4	−9	−6.5
3150	−6	−11	−8	−4	−9	−6
4000	−5.4	−9.4	−4.9	−3.8	−7.8	−3.3
5000	−1.5	−7.5	−5.5	−1.8	−7.8	−5.8
6000	4.3	−3.2	−5.2	1.4	−6.1	−8.1
6300	6	−1.5	−4	2.5	−5	−7.5
8000	12.6	−7.1	4.1	6.8	1.3	−1.7
9000	13.8	8.8	6.8	8.4	3.4	1.4
10000	13.9	9.4	7.9	9.8	5.3	3.8
11200	13	9	6	11.5	7.5	4.5
12500	12.3	10.8	4.3	14.4	12.9	6.4
14000	18.4			23.2		
16000	40.2			43.7		
18000	73.2					
Speech	14.5	12.5	11			

[a]ISO 389-7 Acoustics—Reference zero for the calibration of audiometric equipment, Part 7: Reference threshold of hearing under free field and diffuse field listening conditions.

Source: With permission of the Acoustical Society of America.

To determine frequency accuracy, one can easily observe the signal on the storage oscilloscope. For example, if one adjusts the time/div (given proper calibration) to 100 ms/div and a 2000-Hz tone is presented through a SLM, you will see that one cycle of 360° occupies five divisions (Figure 9–8 in Chapter 9). Another approach to frequency verification involves routing the output of the SLM into a frequency counter. Alternatively, a clinician can use a frequency counter from an electronics store such as Radio Shack. Although within this chapter we describe calibration techniques, please see Appendix A for actual student reports depicting their own work in carrying out these procedures.

Regarding measurement of harmonic distortion, one can use the second approach described in the section on total harmonic distortion, that is, measurement of the second, third, and so forth, harmonics by keeping the fundamental constant and changing the filters.

BONE CONDUCTION CALIBRATION

Artificial Mastoid

We rely on sound pressure developed between the transducer (earphone or insert receiver) and the tympanic membrane for calibration of pure-tone air-conducted signals. The sound pressure in the ear canal can be measured using a microphone. Recall that the microphone converts sound pressure into an electrical signal that can be measured. In measuring bone conduction we place the bone oscillator on either the mastoid or the forehead in order to directly test the integrity of the cochlea. In this case, we do not have a cavity in which to measure sound pressure

for purposes of calibration. In the case of bone–conduction measurement, there is no analogous cavity, that is, there is only bone throughout which the sound travels to the inner ear. Therefore, we must construct a device that simulates the mastoid in order to calibrate the bone oscillator. An artificial mastoid, having the impedance characteristics of this structure, is used to calibrate the bone conduction oscillator. As we do not have a cavity, we must measure force instead of pressure. However, as we will see below, the force level of the new artificial mastoid (Larson Davis AMC 493A) is converted into SLP.

Type 4930

The Artificial Mastoid Type 4930 is used for calibration of the bone conduction vibrator in clinical testing as well as for the calibration of bone conduction hearing aids. The calibrator consists of inertial mass that simulates the human head. The Artificial Mastoid has a force transducer that monitors the output of the device to be calibrated, that is, the bone conduction oscillator or bone conduction hearing aid. The Artificial Mastoid is constructed in accordance with International Electrotechnical Commission publication IEC R 373 (1971) and meets the specifications of the British Standard BS 4009 (1975) and ANSI S3.26-1981 (Table 10–7 presents reference equivalent threshold force levels for bone vibrators). The table shows the force level when the bone vibrator is placed on the mastoid or forehead and the difference between the two placements. Although forehead placement is less often used for hearing measurement it has significant clinical value in assisting in the diagnosis of sensorineural versus conductive hearing loss.

Table 10–7. Reference Equivalent Threshold Force Levels (RETFLs) for Bone Vibrators

Frequency (Hz)	Mastoid (dB re 1 μN)	Forehead (dB re 1 μN)	Forehead Minus Mastoid
250	67.0	79.0	12.0
315	64.0	76.5	12.5
400	61.0	74.5	13.5
500	58.0	72.0	14.0
630	52.5	66.0	13.5
750	48.5	61.5	13.0
800	47.0	59.0	12.0
1000	42.5	51.0	8.5
1250	39.0	49.0	10.0
1500	36.5	47.5	11.0
1600	35.5	46.5	11.0
2000	31.0	42.5	11.5
2500	29.5	41.5	12.0
3000	30.0	42.0	12.0
3150	31.0	42.5	11.5
4000	35.5	43.5	8.0
5000	40.0	51.0	11.0
6000	40.0	51.0	11.0
6300	40.0	50.0	10.0
8000	40.0	50.0	10.0
Speech	55.0	63.5	8.5

Source: With permission of Acoustical Society of America.

When the electrical output of the Artificial Mastoid is connected to the appropriate instrumentation such as a SLM or a system designed to be sensitive to vibration (force), the characteristics of bone vibration can be determined (Figures 10–12 and 10–13 show calibration arrangement). Figure 10–12 shows the arrangement prior to calibration. The upper part of the device shown on the right side of the figure is the 400-g weight representing the weight of the bone oscillator on the skull. The lower part of the device is the artificial mastoid. The output voltage (force) from the artificial mastoid is connected directly into the SLM and the force, which is then converted into voltage, is read in dB. Figure 10–13 shows placement of the

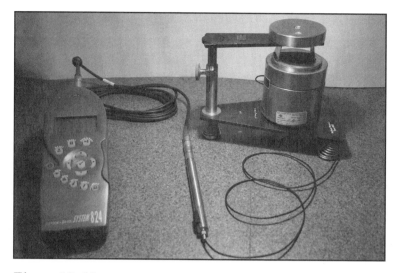

Figure 10–12. *Arrangement of artificial mastoid (Bruel & Kjaer Type 4930) prior to calibration. On the left of the figure we see the SLM connected to the artificial mastoid on the right. We see the 400-g weight above the artificial mastoid.*

Figure 10–13. *Placement of the bone oscillator between the 400-g weight and the artificial mastoid.*

bone oscillator during calibration. The force level is read in dB. The output measured in dB by the SLM is proportional to the force (voltage).

Larson Davis AMC 493A

A new artificial mastoid has been introduced to the market, the Larson Davis AMC 493A (Figure 10–14). According to the manufacturer, the impedance of this device meets the impedance characteristics of the human head and meets the impedance characteristics as specified by ANSI S3.13, ANSI S326, and IEC 60318-6. The AMC 493A is much smaller than the traditional artificial mastoid seen in Figure 10–12. Therefore, it has less mass and much less thermal inertia. Thermal

Figure 10–14. *Larson Davis Artificial Mastoid (AMC 493A) held by a student prior to calibration.*

Figure 10–15. *Artificial mastoid placed on 6-cc coupler and microphone. On the right of the figure, we see the 400-g force.*

inertia is the ability to store heat energy in a given material during a diurnal cycle. You may have learned in a basic physics course that a diurnal cycle is a complete rotation of the earth around its axis in a 24-hour period.

Calibration of the AMC 493A is accomplished in two stages by the integration of the artificial mastoid with a microphone (Figure 10–15). First, the artificial mastoid is placed on a 6-cc coupler and microphone.

The second step requires that we place the bone oscillator on the artificial mastoid. The black retaining ring is placed on the bone oscillator, artificial mastoid, 6 cc coupler and microphone. Next we place the 400-g weight into the cylinder (see Figure 10–15). Note that the entire unit is placed on a pad to prevent vibrations.

The bone oscillator creates a force on the artificial mastoid. The artificial mastoid then creates sound pressure within the artificial ear. The bone conduction oscillator is calibrated in Pa/N (pascal per newton). The microphone senses the sound pressure and converts this pressure into voltage read by the SLM which is cali-

brated in mV/Pa (millivolts per pascal). The values of SPL generated by the microphone are listed in Table 10–8. For example, see data for 1000 Hz. The HL of the audiometer is set at 40 dB HL for a force level (expressed in dB relative to 1 µN) of 42.5 N, which yields the HL noted in column 8. These levels are obtained after subtracting the values in column 4. Bruel and Kjaer (B & K) provides a chart showing the Force Sensitivity (135 mV/N) referenced to 0 dB at 1 kHz. The chart also shows the response for the other frequencies for which you need to correct. The Larson-Davis artificial mastoid provides a force sensitivity value for each frequency individually, rather than just for 1 kHz, to correct the frequency response against values initially produced by the manufacturer under very rigorous conditions.

Our students participate in the calibration process. Sometimes this involves an assignment in an Instrumentation course (Appendix A) and sometimes this entails participation in the decision-making process for purchase of new equipment (Figures 10–16 and 10–17).

Table 10–8. Sample Manual Calculation of Bone Conduction Calibration Using Larson-Davis Artificial Mastoid (AMC 493A)

1 Frequency	2 Input Level HL	3 Reference Force Level	4 AMC493A Response	5 Model 2575 Response	6 Temp. Response	7 Humidity Response	8 Target Levels	9 Target Levels	10 Deviation
250.0	20.0	67.0	−10.6	0.0	0.9	0.0	77.3	79.3	2.0
500.0	40.0	58.0	−12.8	0.0	1.0	0.0	86.2	84.6	−1.6
750.0	40.0	48.5	−14.0	0.0	1.1	0.0	75.6	76.0	0.4
1000.0	40.0	42.5	−14.4	0.0	1.1	0.0	69.2	68.8	−0.4
1500.0	40.0	36.5	−13.8	0.0	1.2	0.0	63.9	63.8	−0.1
2000.0	40.0	31.0	−13.2	0.1	1.1	0.0	59.0	58.9	−0.1
3000.0	40.0	30.0	−12.9	0.5	0.5	0.0	58.1	58.1	0.0
4000.0	40.0	35.5	−15.5	0.7	−0.6	0.0	60.1	61.9	1.8
6000.0	40.0	40.0	−19.2	−2.3	−0.2	0.0	58.3	59.1	0.8

Figure 10–16. *Representative of Northeastern Technologies, Inc. demonstrating the difference between the traditional artificial mastoid and the Larson Davis Artificial Mastoid (AMC 493A) prior to purchase of the Larson Davis device.*

Figure 10–17. *Students calibrating with traditional artificial mastoid and Larson Davis Artificial Mastoid for purposes of comparison prior to purchase of Larson Davis device. It is important to include students in the decision-making process.*

CALIBRATION OF THE ACOUSTIC ADMITTANCE DEVICE

Calibration of Admittance Unit of Measurement

The acoustic admittance of a volume of air enclosed in a cavity can be determined if the volume of the cavity and the atmospheric conditions are known. The acoustic admittance of a volume of air enclosed in a hard-walled cavity is specified in polar notation by the formula:

$$YA = fV/k \qquad \text{(Eqn. 10.2)}$$

Where f is the probe-tone frequency, V is the volume of the hard-walled cavity, and k is a constant obtained from the formula:

$$k = (Qc^2)/2\pi \qquad \text{(Eqn. 10.3)}$$

where Q is the ambient density of the air in kg/m^3 and c is the velocity of sound in m/s. The k value under standard atmospheric conditions (P_o of 776.0 mm Hg.,

temperature of 22°C, and relative humidity of 50%) is 227,840.858. Table 10–9 gives the k value for different cities (which differ in P). Using the formula $YA=fV/k$, the acoustic admittance of 1 cm^3 of air (air in a hard-walled cavity has no conductance so the admittance is composed only of susceptance) is equivalent to 1 acoustic mmho for the 226-Hz probe tone and 3 mmhos for the 678-Hz probe tone. Therefore, when the acoustic-admittance device is calibrated with a hard-walled cavity, 1 cm^3 of air should be equivalent to 1 acoustic mmho. Similarly, the commonly used 2-cm^3 hard-walled cavity should yield an acoustic admittance or susceptance of 2 acoustic mmho and acoustic conductance of 0 mmho.

Calibration of Probe Signal Intensity

According to ANSI 1987 and 2002, the frequency of the probe signal shall be within ± 3% of the nominal frequency. Harmonic distortion of the probe should not exceed

Table 10–9. The K Values for Washington, DC, Syracuse, New York, Iowa City, Iowa, and Denver, Colorado[a]

City	Elevation[b] (m)	Temperature[b] (°C)	Relative Humidity[b] (%)	K Value[c]
Washington, D.C.	34	22	50	225,076
Syracuse	182	22	50	220,608
Iowa City	224	20	50	219,812
Denver	1613	22	50	184,750

[a]Adapted from Lilly (1970).
[b]The elevation (m), temperature (°C), and relative humidity (5) are shown for these cities.
[c]Converted for cgs units.

5% of the fundamental frequency for all probe signals when they are measured in a 2-cm³ acoustic coupler. Measurement of the probe-tone characteristics of the immittance device follows the same procedure used for audiometric calibration. Current instrumentation has from 1 to 3 probe signals: 226 Hz, 676 Hz, and 1000 Hz.

Calibration of the Activating Stimuli

In Chapter 9 (section on instrumentation for acoustic immittance) we reported upper limits for various stimuli for three probe tones as indicated by the manufacturer (Grason-Stadler) for the Tympstar Middle Ear Analyzer. The calibration procedure is the same as that used to calibrate audiometric pure tones (ANSI, 2001). As mentioned in that chapter, manufacturers may report different upper limit values for different instrumentation or different transducers. In order to obtain zero HL for the Tympstar Middle Ear Analyzer, we must first establish the upper limit in SPL as reported in Chapter 9. We next subtract total SPL from the upper limit HL to derive zero HL. ANSI (2002) also specified maximum total harmonic distortion for pure-tone activating signals. These values are essentially the same as those for audiometric pure tones.

Calibration of the Pneumatic System

Although ANSI (2002) specified the pressure limit of a pneumatic system to be within −800 to +600 daPa, many instruments specify a range between −600 and +400. The accuracy of a pneumatic system should be measured in a .5-cc cavity. According to ANSI (2002) measured pressure in the cavity should not exceed ± 10 daPa.

CALIBRATION OF THE OTOACOUSTIC EMISSIONS PROBE SIGNAL

Although calibration of most equipment used in clinical audiology and hearing science/research has been standardized, a standard for calibration of the otoacoustic emission probe signal remains unresolved at this time. One of the major problems rests with standing waves at or near the probe. This is of particular concern when calibrating for distortion products. There are no standing waves at the tympanic membrane because the incident and reflected waves are in phase. As you move away from the tympanic membrane, the reflected and incident waves will be out of phase. The greatest impact will be closest to the probe where there can be as much as a 20-dB reduction in intensity.

To date we do not have a uniform approach or method for calibrating OAE probe signals. Therefore, some clinics are restricted to a "check probe" option on the device. This requires that the clinician insert the probe into a 1-cc coupler to determine whether the sound generated in the coupler is similar to levels provided by the manufacturer. The manufacturer also indicates tolerance levels of approximately ± 3 dB. The intensity of the probe signal must be within a predetermined intensity level of three reference frequencies. This applies to stimuli for both DPOAEs and TEOAEs. If a deviation is noted beyond the standard tolerance recommended by the manufacturer, one should first check for a loose connection and then check the probe for debris such as cerumen. If there is no interfering debris the clinician should contact the manufacturer to resolve the problem. In reality, the above process is not "calibration" as the profession understands the term; it is a simple check of the probe output.

Another approach involves the use of a sound level meter (SLM) and a 2-cc cavity. This technique can be used for both transient and distortion product probe signals. In the case of calibration for TEOAEs, the probe is coupled to the 2-cc cavity which in turn is coupled to the SLM. The weighting network of the SLM is set "peak-hold" for TEOAEs and

DPOAEs. These measurements are carried out before the equipment is used for clinical or research purposes.

Siegel (2007) suggested an interesting method for calibration of DPOAE and TEOAE stimuli. This method is similar to the method by which group norms are established for behavioral threshold. Siegel suggested generating normative data for all signals by establishing their behavioral thresholds and corresponding voltage levels (Figure 10–18).

The initial normative data for voltage levels will provide the basis for future calibration of OAE stimuli when using this

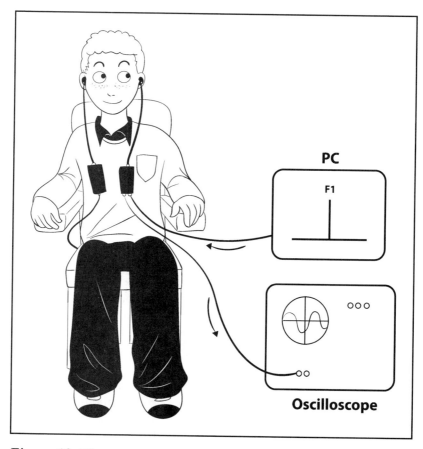

Figure 10–18. Setup for Siegel (2007) calibration of the stimuli (TEOAEs and DPOAEs).

method. Calibration entails the following: (a) a cavity that is used to calibrate insert receivers is coupled to a SLM; (b) the emissions probe is inserted into the coupler and into the oscilloscope; (c) a signal whose level has been established during initial determination of behavioral threshold is introduced into the coupler; and (d) the output voltage is read on the oscilloscope and corrected for any deviation from the initial normative data.

Although Siegel's approach is novel, it demands that OAE devices have the ability to measure behavioral thresholds at very low levels. Not all current devices have this capability. However, it may be possible for a manufacturer to lower the minimum level of the stimuli.

The proper approach to the measurement of OAES requires confidence in the approximate input level reaching the inner ear. This said, only approximate calibration methods exist, as one cannot measure the pressure level attained in the cochlear partition. Therefore, only the sound pressure level reaching the tympanic membrane (TM) can be calibrated with relative certainty.

One calibration technique uses a head and torso simulator known as KEMAR, which stands for Knowles Electronic Manikin for Acoustic Research (see Appendix A for a complete description of calibration using KEMAR).

CALIBRATION FOR AUDITORY EVOKED POTENTIALS

Silman and Silverman (1997) emphasized the limitation of using a SLM for the measurement of a click. Generally, intensity in dB SPL of any stimulus is determined by the following formula as mentioned in the first chapter:

$$dB\ SPL = 20\ log\ P_1/P_2$$

where P_1 is the SPL in micropascal (µPa) of the stimulus we wish to measure, and P_2 is the reference SPL (20 µPa). In order to obtain the value for P_1, the root-mean square (rms) for the instantaneous amplitudes of several sine waveforms is calculated. In order to calculate the rms value of amplitude we use the following formula:

$$rms = \{\Sigma(P^2)/N\}^{1/2}$$

where P is the instantaneous pressure amplitude and N is the number of instantaneous amplitudes. go back to first chapter to explain rms. Recall from Chapter 1 that the rms value for intensity is the average sound pressure over time. When the fast mode of the SLM is used, the time period for the rms average is usually calculated over a period of 250 msec. Therefore, the rms for a click, as measured by a SLM, is not an accurate measure of its average SPL because the average measured over a 250-msec period is calculated over silent off-times as well as on-times (Burkard, 1984).

For calibration of a brief stimulus such as a click, tone burst, or ASSR carrier frequency you need to use both scientific and behavioral approaches to devise the best method. One popular method is the calculation of instantaneous peak SPL (pSPL). The formula used to calculate pSPL is:

$$pSPL = 20\ log\ (P_{max}/P_{ref})$$

where P_{max} is equivalent to the maximum instantaneous pressure in µPa and P_{ref} is equivalent to 20 µPa. Many SLMs can measure pSPL based on the formula noted above. In addition to standard calibration capability, these instruments will have peak detectors that measure maximum peak for very short durations, durations as small as 50 µs (below the 100 µs duration for a click). The SLMs have a peak-hold capability. When a SLM with a peak detector is unavailable, or if you want to determine the accuracy of a SLM with a peak detector in its measurement of a click, the click intensity can be quantified by using the peak equivalent SPL (peSPL) method. The click that has been generated by an auditory evoked potential device is routed through an earphone or insert received coupled to a 6-cc or a 2-cc coupler into an SLM. The AC output of the SLM will be fed into an oscilloscope (see Figure 10–18). The peak-to-peak or baseline-to-peak voltage is measured. A pure tone instead of a click is delivered through the same earphone or insert receiver, couplers, SLM, and oscilloscope. The rms intensity value of the pure tone in dB SPL can be read from the SLM. This rms value is the peSPL of the click.

Silman and Silverman (1997) describe the oft used behavioral approach as an alternative to the physical measurement of click intensity. The behavioral threshold for the click stimulus is established for a group of 10 normal-hearing (pure-tone thresholds must not exceed 20 dB HL) young adults. The mean of the behavioral threshold for the click will be assigned a value of 0 dB nHL. For example, if an ABR response is recorded at 50 dB above the 0 (mean behavioral threshold) then the response is considered to be at 50 dB nHL. Gorga, Abbas, and Worthington (1985) suggested a click repetition rate of 50 per second for measuring threshold of the click. Their rationale was that a click

rate of 50/sec represents a compromise between low repetition rates required to obtain a clear BAEP waveform and high repetition rates needed to obtain a low behavioral click threshold.

Click intensity customarily is specified in dB nHL, we recommend that the initial calibration of click intensity be made using the behavioral method and using the pSPL method providing an SLM with a peak detector and peak-hold capacity is available. We also recommend follow-up calibrations at regular intervals using the pSPL method. These follow-up results are compared with those of the initial calibration. If there is no access to an SLM with a peak-detector and peak-hold capacity, one should consider the clinically-based method of physical measurement described by Weber, Seitz, and McCutcheon (1981) for initial and follow-up calibrations.

The most recent recommended ISO standard recommends the use of peak-to-peak equivalent for calibration of click stimuli. In this standard, the behavioral threshold for the click is expected to be around 35 dB. This value will be considered as 0 nHL This level may not be consistent with behavioral threshold obtained in various clinics or appear in manuals of various ABR systems. According to Durrant and Boston (2007) the threshold hearing level observed in various clinics is significantly less than the 35 dB nHL that will appear in the ISO draft standard. Therefore, these investigators suggest that each clinic generate its own reference nHL. For example, in our clinic, nHL is somewhat lower than 35 dB nHL. We suggest that calibration be done for peak-to-peak equivalent SPL in the following manner: each clinic will use the value of 0 nHL to which 30 dB is added. Peak-to-peak is then measured. For example, if 0 nHL is equivalent to 20 dB, add 30 dB and measure peak-to-peak. Maintain this value as the basis for your calibration in the future.

Calibration for ASSR stimuli (carrier frequency) is straightforward because the stimuli resemble warbled tones. Therefore, calibration for ASSR stimuli is similar to calibration for pure tones.

CALIBRATION FOR MASKING NOISE

Let us return to Chapter 5 where we describe a band-pass filter. Figure 5–11 in Chapter 5 shows the electrical spectrum of a narrow-band noise signal with a center frequency of 2000 Hz routed from a GSI-10 audiometer through a real-time analyzer. The frequencies to which the arrows point represent the half-power points (3 dB down) from the peak sound-pressure level of the noise. Note the narrowness of the frequency range encompassed by these half-power points. The sound-pressure level for the band determined by the half-power points should be equivalent to that of a pure tone at the center frequency of the band. Commercially available audiometers do not generate NBN bandwidths as narrow as the critical bands; they employ wider bandwidths based on, for example, third-octave bandwidths or BBN bandwidths.

A pure-tone signal (maskee) at a given intensity and frequency will be masked by a masking noise (masker) whose energy in the frequency range corresponding to the critical band for the maskee is equivalent to the energy of the maskee. The intensity of the maskee can be referred to as the effective masking level (EML) of the masker. The difference between the intensity of the masker which just masks a given tone and the EML is the minimum

effective masking (MEM). For example, if a 2000-Hz pure tone is presented at 60 dB HL, the EML is 60 dB HL and the intensity of NBN centered at 2000 Hz that just masks the tone is 70 dB HL, the MEM is 10 dB HL (70 dB HL masker intensity minus 60 dB HL EML). Therefore, with electroacoustic calibration, the masker levels corresponding to various EMLs can be established for NBN and BBN maskers.

For biological calibration, MEM can be established for NBN and BBN maskers. For biologic calibration, data from a group of at least 10 normal-hearing, otologically normal young adults should be obtained. In establishing the MEM of the NBN and BBN maskers, subjects should be randomly selected, and only one ear from each subject should be evaluated. The masker should be introduced at 50 dB HL (continuously on) and the intensity of the tone (maskee) presented in the same ear should be increased in 5-dB steps (pulsed tones) until the tone becomes barely audible. Then the maskee (test tone) is decreased in 5-dB steps until it just becomes inaudible. The decibel difference between the intensity of the masker and the intensity of the maskee when it just becomes inaudible (EML) is the MEM. The mean MEM should be calculated for the group, based on the mean of three trials for each person.

For clinical purposes, the MEM is the mean MEM calculated for the group plus a 10-dB safety factor to sufficiently account for intersubject variability. Table 10–10 shows the dB differences between the masker levels that just mask the test tone and the EML of the masker; the MEMs with the safety factor added are also shown. The values reported in Table 10–10 are based on a GSI-10 audiometer from a particular clinic. Each center must establish its own MEM values.

Table 10–10. Differences Between the Masker Level (dB HL) Which Just Masks the Test Tone (EM) and the EML of the Masker (dB HL) with a Center Frequency at the Nominal Frequency of the Test Tone

Frequency (Hz)	MEM Rt Channel	MEM Lft Channel	MEM + 10-dB Safety Factor[a] Rt Channel	MEM + 10-dB Safety Factor[a] Lft Channel
250	0	0	+10	+10
500	+5	0	+15	+10
1000	+5	+5	+15	+15
2000	0	0	+10	+10
3000	0	+10	+10	+20
4000	+5	+5	+15	+15
6000	0	0	+10	+10
8000	0	0	+10	+10

[a]These decibel differences (MEMs) added to a safety factor as a function of test-tone frequency are also shown. These values, rounded off to the nearest 5-dB step, were obtained for a GSI-10 audiometer. These values were obtained using TDH-50 earphones. Normative data should be established for each center and for each transducers used, for example, insert earphones.

The electroacoustic method for establishing masker levels for various EMLs was described by Sanders (1972). For the electroacoustic method, the intensity level (energy) per cycle for the masker must be determined as described in Chapter 9. That is, the bandwidth of the masker is converted into decibels and the dB SPL of the masker is divided by the dB of the bandwidth. This resultant quantity is the intensity level (energy) per cycle of the masker. The critical bandwidth is then converted into dB of bandwidth. Normative data should be established for each center and for each transducers used, for example, insert earphones.

In order to obtain the total energy of the critical band (in dB SPL), the level per cycle of the masker is multiplied by the dB of the critical bandwidth. The EML of the masker is determined by subtracting the audiometric zero level (expressed in dB SPL) from the total energy of the critical band. The EML should be derived for masker levels ranging from 20 dB SPL to the maximum output of the audiometer. In pure-tone clinical masking situations, the intensity of the masker needed is based on an EML equivalent to the air-conduction threshold of the non-test ear at the test frequency. In speech clinical masking situations, the intensity of the masker needed is based on the average of the air-conduction thresholds at 500, 1000, and 2000 Hz in the nontest ear. To employ the electroacoustic approach to masking, equipment is needed to determine the overall SPL of the masker and the frequency response of the transducer (which affects the number of cycles of the masker).

The purpose of introducing the concepts of masking, effective masking, and so forth was to allow us to find an easy way to calibrate masking noise. By establishing minimum effective masking for pure tones and speech you will be able to use minimum effective masking as a basis for calibration of the masking noise. After establishing normative data for effective masking, you can measure at a predetermined level, for example, 70 dB HL for BBN, NBN, and speech noise and measure the equivalent SPL by using an SLM; record this level for future use. When you return to calibrate effective masking, you will have a reference point for a decision as to whether or not you need new normative data. If the output level of the instrument for NBN, BBN, and speech noise is the same the following year, one does not need to establish normative data again. If the output level deviates, a correction factor can be included.

NOISE LEVELS IN THE TEST ENVIRONMENT

Thus far, we have described in detail how to calibrate various equipment. In order to increase accuracy of calibration, we need to have a quiet environment, one almost free of noise. Table 10–11 describes maximum permissible ambient noise. It is important to measure noise levels in the booth before beginning the calibration

Table 10–11. Maximum Permissible Sound-Pressure Levels for Ambient Noise during Audiometric Testing[a]

| Frequency (Hz) | Ears Uncovered | | Ears Covered | |
	Octave Band	1/3-Octave Band	Octave Band	1/3-Octave Band
125	28.0	23.0	34.5	29.5
250	18.5	13.5	23.0	18.0
500	14.5	9.5	21.5	16.0
750	12.5	7.5	22.5	17.5
1000	14.0	9.0	29.5	24.5
1500	10.5	5.5	29.0	24.0
2000	8.5	3.5	34.5	29.5
3000	8.5	3.5	39.0	34.0
4000	9.0	4.0	42.0	37.0
6000	14.0	9.0	41.0	36.0
8000	20.5	15.5	45.0	40.0

Source: Adapted from ANSI (1978).

[a]Values for ears not covered apply to bone-conduction and sound-field testing. Values for ears covered apply to air-conduction testing.

process. Table 10–11 is only pertinent to the audiomtric booth. However, audiologists may be called upon to conduct hearing screenings in small health centers or in the school system. As the screening level is usually at the upper level of normal hearing, more noise is permitted in the test environment. This noise should be measured using one-third-octave-band center frequency of the test tone and its level should not interfere at the level of screening. The screening level should always be slightly above the noise level in the environment. The attenuation of the earphone should be subtracted from the noise level in the room.

REFERENCES

American National Standards Institute. (1987). *American National Standard specification for instruments to measure aural acoustic impedance and admittance* (ANSI S3.39-1987). New York, NY: Author.

American National Standards Institute. (2006). *American National Standard specification for sound level meters* (ANSI S1.4-1983 – R2006). New York, NY: Author.

American National Standards Institute. (2010). *American National Standard specification for audiometers* (ANSI S3.6-2010). New York, NY: Author.

Burkard, R. (1984). Sound pressure level measurement and spectral analysis of brief acoustic transients. *Electroencephalography and Clinical Neurophysiology, 32,* 83–91.

Durrant, J. D., & Boston, J. R. (2007). Stimuli for auditory evoked potential assessement. In R. F. Burkard, M. Don, & J. J. Eggermont (Eds.), *Auditory evoked potentials: Basic principles and clinical application* (pp. 42–72). New York, NY: Lippincott Williams & Wilkins.

Gorga, M. P., Abbas, P. J., & Worthington, D. W. (1985). Stimulus calibration in ABR measurements. In J. T. Jacobson (Ed.), *Auditory brainstem response* (pp. 49–62). San Diego, CA: College-Hill Press.

Sanders, J. W. (1972). Masking. In J. Katz (Ed.), *Handbook of clinical audiology* (pp. 111–142). Baltimore, MD: Williams & Wilkins.

Siegel, J. (2007). Calibrating otoacoustic emission probes. In M. S. Robinette & T. J. Glattke (Eds.), *Otoacoustic emissions: Clinical applications* (pp. 403–428). New York, NY: Thieme.

Silman, S., & Silverman, C. A. (1997). *Auditory diagnosis: Principles and applications.* New York, NY: Academic Press.

Weber, B., Seitz, M., & McCutcheon, M. (1981). Quantifying click stimuli in auditory brainstem response audiometry. *Ear and Hearing, 2,* 215–219.

APPENDIX

Students' Experiments

SIMON HENIN, PhD STUDENT IN SPEECH-LANGUAGE-HEARING PROGRAM AT THE GRADUATE CENTER/ CITY UNIVERSITY OF NEW YORK (OTOACOUSTIC EMISSIONS LAB)

As mentioned in Chapter 10, KEMAR is one technique used for the calibration of stimuli for OAEs. KEMAR is outfitted with an ER-11 (Etymotic Research, Elk Grove Village, IL) microphone and pre-amplifier system connected to KEMAR's built-in DB-100 2-cc Zwislocki coupler (Figure A–1). This configuration allows for the measurement of the sound pressure level in the "average" ear and, more specifically, the sound pressure level reaching the tympanic membrane in an average ear.

Calibration requires a high-quality measurement microphone (ER11) with a flat frequency response (as given in the manufacturer's specifications) and a certified calibrator like a pistonphone, for example, B&K type 4231. Complete calibration requires acquisition of the signal from the measurement microphone. In addition, the sensitivity of the measurement system (measurement microphone, amplifier, and A/D) must be measured. The sensitivity of the system is acquired using the a 1-kHz reference signal from the pistonphone. Given the sensitivity of the measurement microphone the overall sensitivity of the system can be calculated as the microphone sensitivity is multiplied by the reference level and divided by the peak-to-peak amplitude of the recorded signal.

Once the sensitivity is known, calibration of the probe microphone's speakers can be conducted by placing the probe microphone into KEMAR ear, playing white noise through each probe microphone, and recording the response from the ER-11 measurement microphone. Using the known sensitivity, an FFT then can be used to plot the response as a function of frequency. An example of this measurement is shown in Figure A–2 (black lines, ER-11). In this measurement white noise at 65 dB SPL was played via ER2 tube phones connected to an ER10A probe assembly.

Following calibration of the probe stimuli, an in-the-ear calibration can be

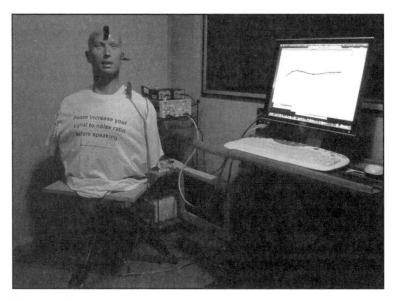

Figure A–1. *KEMAR setup for calibration in a real ear provided by Simon Henin, PhD.*

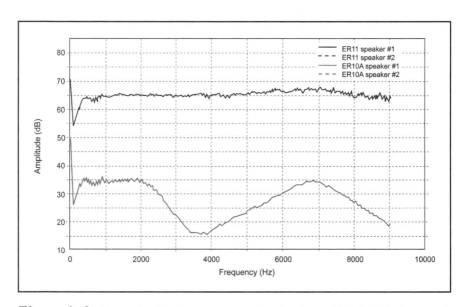

Figure A–2. *Example of probe measurement using KEMAR. Note that although four lines are described, the broken and solid lines for each speaker are superimposed.*

made using the probe microphone. If possible, several re-insertions of the probe should be made and verified as having a flat frequency spectrum at the eardrum. Using the same insertions, in-the-ear calibrations should be made using the probe microphone and used as a reference for in situ in-ear calibrations (see Figure A–2) gray lines and ER10A). The null exhibited in this frequency response is a result of ear canal resonance in which standing waves cancel one another at the probe microphone. The in-ear calibrations shown in Figure A–2 (gray lines) are not plotted as a function of the probe microphone's sensitivity, and, therefore, exhibit a low overall level. However, if desired, the probe microphone sensitivity may be determined in the same manner as described for the measurement microphone.

Using the technique noted above, the in-ear calibrations can serve as a guide for real in-ear calibrations. If the same in-ear calibration is achieved, one can assume a flat frequency spectrum at the subject's eardrum.

The following experiments were performed by AuD students past and present as part of their work for a course in Instrumention.

ILANA CELLUM, AUD (CUNY), FINAL LAB, FALL, 2005

Purpose

The following experiments expose and familiarize us to the most common instrumentation used in audiologic testing, among other disciplines. To appropriately use this instrumentation in a clinical setting, we must show that we can correctly calibrate it, and be aware of when results may be suspect due to improperly calibrated equipment. As audiologists and clinicians, we must recognize the difference between properly and improperly calibrated equipment, know which modifications to make, and when test results are valid and invalid.

Methodology

Experiment I

Calibration of at least one frequency of:

I. Intensity
II. Frequency
III. Rise and Fall
IV. Distortion

and validate on the oscilloscope.

Instrumentation

1. Quest Technologies Acoustic Calibrator Model QC-10/QC-20
2. Quest Technologies Model 1800/ Model OB-300 1/3 to 1/1 Octave Filter Set
   Precision Impulse Integrating Sound Level Meter (SLM)
3. Microphone element to probe QE-4170 S/N N010462
4. Welch Allyn Audiometer
5. Quest Model AA-175 Audiometer Analyzer
6. Telephonics Headphones Model TDH-49P
7. Oscilloscope
8. Various connecting cables
9. 400-g weight

Procedure

Calibrating the SLM

1. Turn on Acoustic Calibrator, making sure low battery indicator is not on
2. Set positions to <u>1-kHz</u>, <u>114 dB</u>
3. Power on SLM
   a. Check battery (must be at least 60% or greater)
4. Power on Filter Set to <u>Manual</u> position, Time Mode <u>1/3</u>, Filter <u>1 kHz</u>

5. Carefully inserting 4-pins from probe into the body of the SLM, tighten probe
6. Attach microphone element to probe by removing it from its box, removing it from its protective plastic covering, and carefully threading element to probe
7. Place calibrator over probe of SLM
   a. Press "reset," "run" on SLM
8. Record level <u>114.9 dB</u>

Note: If level not approximately 114 dB, check batteries of both units

Checking intensity and frequency from audiometer to SLM

1. Select frequency on audiometer at fixed output level— Select 1-kHz @ 70 dB HL, which corresponds to 77.5 dB SPL

2. Connect one-ear headphone output (using 1/4" phone plug and cable) from audiometer to SLM:
   a. Place black collar, 6-cc coupler on SLM
   b. Place headphone on top of that (Figure A–3)
   c. Place weight firmly on headphone
3. Verify intensity at SLM by pressing "reset," "run" and read value: <u>76.7 dB SPL</u>, which is within acceptable range
4. Connect output of SLM to audiometer analyzer using mono-mini-phone— mono-mini-phone cable
5. Reset audiometer output level to 100 dB HL @ 1 Khz, verify level on SML by "reset," "run": <u>107.2 dB SPL</u>, in the acceptable range
6. Turn on analyzer, press "reset," "rep," and "level"—<u>107.9 dB SPL</u>
7. Measure frequency by pressing: "reset," "rep," and "freq"—<u>1001 Hz</u>

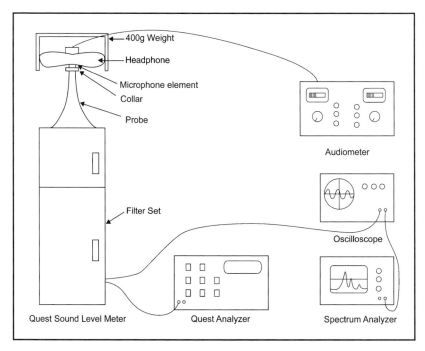

400g Weight
Headphone
Microphone element
Collar
Probe

Audiometer

Filter Set

Oscilloscope

Quest Sound Level Meter   Quest Analyzer   Spectrum Analyzer

Figure A–3. *Composite equipment for calibration of intensity and frequency.*

8. Confirm frequency on oscilloscope by connecting output of analyzer to input of 'scope using mono-mini to double-banana cable, adjusting time (msec)/div to .5. We observed a full cycle at 2 divisions, which corresponds to a frequency of 1-kHz (1/T msec = f)
9. Reconnect SLM to analyzer
10. To measure rise and fall of the signal we did the following on the analyzer:
    a. Press "reset," press "Range," Input "90," and press "Range" again
    b. Press "Cal," input "108," press "Cal" again
    c. Press "level," for verification—result <u>107.9 dB SPL</u>
    d. Press "Fall," then interrupt signal from audiometer and record value: <u>34 microseconds</u> (acceptable range)
    e. Press "Rise," then defeat "interrupt" of audiometer, and record value: <u>36 microseconds</u>, also within acceptable limits

Measuring Distortion

Continuing with the above setup:

1. Press "Dist" on analyzer, record value: −L54.4 (Value okay until −57 dB)
2. Adjust filter on SLM to 2-kHz to record second harmonic distortion, repeat Step 1. Result: LO.

I repeated the frequency, intensity, rise and fall, and distortion testing for 250 Hz. The measured values are shown in Table A–1.

Conclusions

All measurements complied with ANSI standards S3.6-1989 and these standards were referred to to ensure that the calibration was in limits.

Experiment II

Calibration of the bandwidth of NBN using the Real-Time Analyzer (RTA) and biological testing (250, 500, 1000, 1500, 2000, 3000, 4000, 6000 Hz).

Purpose

Narrowband noise is centered about a pure tone. Using a center frequency of

Table A–1. Frequency, Intensity, Fall, Rise, and Distortion for 250 Hz

Frequency (Hz)	Intensity (dB SPL)	Fall (Microseconds)	Rise (Microseconds)	Distortion (dB SPL)
250	100 dB HL audiometer → 129.8 dB SPL SLM *required range change 70 dB HL → 95.9 dB SPL	34	36	−55.8—filter at 250 Hz LO—filter at 500 Hz

1000 Hz, and an RTA, we determined the critical band (half-power point of high and low range of the band). We also measured the masking level needed to render the pure-tone frequency inaudible for a range of frequencies, with NBN in one ear and PT also in that ear. (Subject was R. Strom, normal hearing, young (22-y), and female).

Instrumentation

1. Real-Time Analyzer
2. Audiometer
3. Sound Level Meter
4. Oscilloscope
5. Headphones
6. Various cables

Procedure

1. Connect audiometer to SLM (see Procedure for Experiment I)
2. Connect SLM to Oscilloscope (see Procedure for Experiment I)
3. Using double-banana-to-double-banana cables, with grounds in correct orientation, connect scope to RTA
4. The spectrum should appear on the RTA
   a. Set range of frequency for abscissa of spectrum. To see more clearly, adjust trigger dial
   b. Press "restart" and "ARM"
   c. Using position marker, go to peak level to verify frequency (1001 Hz)
   d. Note −3 dB point on either side of peak (961 Hz and 1041 Hz), which is in acceptable range for CB.
5. Place subject in booth with headphones and ask her to raise her hand when she no longer hears the PT. NBN and PT are ipsilateral. Vary the center frequency of the NBN on the audiometer (Table A–2).

Conclusion

Subject required more masking in the low end than in mid to high frequency ranges due to basilar membrane characteristics. Results were in normal range.

Experiment III

Calibration of the immitance device for the following:

1. Y value
2. B value

This will be done for both 226 Hz and 660 Hz

Purpose

Measuring the admittance and susceptance of the middle ear as a function of frequency should show that at low frequencies Y and B are similar in value, and G is negligible. We expect to see a

Table A–2. Amount of Masking Required for NBN and PT, Ipsilaterally

NBN@ 50 dB HL	250 Hz	500 Hz	1000 Hz	1500 Hz	2000 Hz	3000 Hz	4000 Hz	6000 Hz
PT dB HL	55	55	55	40	45	50	50	45

linear relationship: as frequency triples, so should admittance (as measured in mmhos. We also measure the middle ear volume (or its proxy, the cavity) using this equipment. We derive the admittance from the volume velocity incoming from the special cables connected to the coupler. Air in a hard-walled cavity has no conductance so the admittance is only composed of susceptance. Therefore, the acoustic immitance of 1 cm^3 is equivalent to 1 acoustic mmho.

Instrumentation

1. GSI TympStar Middle Ear Analyzer
2. 2.0-cc cavity
3. Multitubed probe

Procedure

1. Connect the analyzer to the 2.0-cc cavity using the probe
2. To find Y Press "Y" to 226 Hz
3. Press "Tymp," then "Start." The value of the cavity was shown to be 1.9 cm^3, which shows the unit to be in an acceptably calibrated range.
4. To find B, press "B," press "Start." The result was 1.8 mmhos, approximating our Y result, and what we should expect to see.
5. We next vary the frequency to 667 Hz, first by pressing "Admittance," then "Y," and then "Start." The result: <u>5.8 mmho</u>
6. To measure B, press B, then "Start." The result at 667 Hz is <u>5.4 mmhos</u>

Conclusion

The results exhibited the linear response expected where Y = 2∏f/S (S for stiffness, f for frequency). Tripling the frequency

tripled the admittance. At the low frequency (226 Hz) B approximated Y.

Experiment IV

Conduct an experiment to identify the additive and subtractive artifacts for the immitance device.

Purpose

To see if there are artifacts using the middle ear analyzer, we compare the results of using a 2.0-cc cavity, and repeat the same test with a human ear. One would expect to see an acoustic reflex in the tympanogram of the person; however, if one is present testing the cavity, it may be surmised to be an additive artifact.

Instrumentation

Same as Experiment III

Procedure

1. Set level and frequency to 500 Hz @ 85 dB, and connect probe to 2.0-cc cavity
2. Press "Ipsi" and "Start"
3. ml vs. daPa should show a horizontal straight line, or else there is a problem
4. Repeat above steps; however, place probe in subject's EAM
5. Press "Ipsi" and "Start"
6. Should see the expected acoustic reflex, which is an indication of no artifact.

Conclusion

A properly calibrated middle ear analyzer should show no acoustic reflex-like artifacts when using a hard-walled cavity. The acoustic reflex should only be exhibited when the tympanic membrane is impinged upon.

Experiment V

Sound-field calibration (warbled tones and NBN)

Purpose

To calibrate warble tones and narrow-band noise in a sound field. Warble tones are used to prevent standing waves and beats. Narrowband noise shows a continuous spectrum for a range of frequencies at equal energies. In a sound booth these sources are considered to be in a "free field," so reflective waves are considered insignificant.

Instrumentation

1. SLM
2. Audiometer
3. Sound booth with speakers

Procedure

1. Calibrate SLM to 70 dBHL (from audiometer) with 1 kHz, as in Procedure for Experiment I. Confirm intensity measure is correct.
2. Present "Warble Tone" to left speaker in booth
3. Place SLM 3 feet from speaker at an angle of 45° azimuth
4. Measure intensity: <u>67 dB</u>
5. Repeat for NBN, by changing warble tone to NBN originating from audiometer, and presented to left speaker.
6. Measure intensity: <u>70.8 dB</u>

Conclusions

To calibrate both the warble tones and the NBN in a we saw a 3-dB drop for the warble tones, which should be expected

for a monoaural source, but because of the more diffuse nature of the NBN, we saw no intensity decline.

Experiment VI

Calibration of speech in sound field and under phones

Purpose

To calibrate speech in a sound field with no reflections.

Instrumentation

1. SLM
2. Audiometer
3. Sound booth with speakers
4. Headphones
5. Calibration CD for to determine Speech Recognition Threshold and Phonetically Balanced.

Procedure

1. Calibrate the output from the CD to the input to the audiometer. 0 VU @ 1 kHz = 20 dB, press external A on audiometer, so 70 dB audiometer = 90 dB on SLM
2. The speech noise was measured 70 dB on phones, and 93.7 dB in the sound field, measured at 45° azimuth, and at a distance of 3 feet from the speaker.

Conclusion

No ANSI specifications have been for calibration of sound-field testing; however, the volume recorded showed a +3.7 dB increase, and this correction factor can be used across the board for the speech measurements in this scenario.

JESSICA GORDON, AUD (CUNY), 12/22/05

I. Frequency Calibration

Purpose

To make sure that the output frequency of an audiometer is the true frequency.

Methodology

The following instruments were used:

1. GSI 61 audiometer
2. Quest model 1800 sound level meter
3. Calibration piston
4. 6-cc coupler.
5. Probe
6. Sound level meter microphone
7. Left earphone model TDH-49P
8. Earphone weight
9. Mono-mini-cable
10. Quest system model AA-175

The following procedure was performed:

A. To calibrate the sound level meter:

1. Attach the probe to sound level meter.
2. Attach the microphone to the top of the probe.
3. Place the calibration piston on the microphone.
4. Turn the piston on 114 dB SPL at 1000 Hz.
5. Put the sound level meter at a 1000 Hz filter manually and between the intensities of 60 dB SPL and 60 dB SPL.
6. Make sure the sound level meter is on "linear" and "slow."
7. Press "reset" and then "run."
8. Find the intensity reading.

B. To calibrate intensity:

1. Attach the probe to the sound level meter and the microphone to the probe.
2. Place the "black collar" on the microphone.
3. Place the 6-cc coupler on the "black collar."
4. Put the left earphone on the coupler.
5. Hold down the earphone with the weight.
6. Turn the audiometer on a pure tone of 2000 Hz at 70 dB HL.
7. Make sure the sound level meter is on a filter of 2000 Hz and between the intensities of 60 dB SPL and 60 dB SPL.
8. Press "reset" and "run."
9. Find the intensity reading.

C. To calibrate frequency:

1. Attach the probe to the sound level meter and the microphone to the probe.
2. Place the "black collar" on the microphone.
3. Place the 6-cc coupler on the "black collar."
4. Put the left earphone on the coupler.
5. Hold down the earphone with the weight.
6. Turn the audiometer on a pure tone of 2000 Hz at 100 dB HL.
7. Attach the output of the sound level meter to the input of the Quest system via the mono-mini-cable.
8. Turn on Quest system.
9. Press "reset" and then "run" on the sound level meter.
10. Press "Rep" and then "Freq" on the Quest system.
11. Find the frequency reading.

D. To calibrate Rise and Fall:

1. Attach the probe to the sound level meter and the microphone to the probe.
2. Place the "black collar" on the microphone.
3. Place the 6-cc coupler on the "black collar."
4. Put the left earphone on the coupler.
5. Hold down the earphone with the weight.
6. Turn the audiometer on a pure tone of 2000 Hz at 100 dB HL.
7. Attach the output of the sound level meter to the input of the Quest system via the mono-mini-cable.
8. Turn on Quest system.
9. Press "reset" and then "run" on the sound level meter.
10. On Quest system press "range," type in "90," press "range" again, press "cal," type in the number that is on the sound level meter, press "cal" again, press "level," press "fall."
11. Turn off the audiometer to get fall reading on Quest system.
12. Press "rise" and turn on audiometer to get rise reading on Quest system.

E. To calibrate distortion:

1. Attach the probe to the sound level meter and the microphone to the probe.
2. Place the "black collar" on the microphone.
3. Place the 6-cc coupler on the "black collar."
4. Put the left earphone on the coupler.
5. Hold down the earphone with the weight.
6. Turn the audiometer on a pure tone of 2000 Hz at 100 dB HL.
7. Attach the output of the sound level meter to the input of the Quest system via the mono-mini-cable.
8. Turn on Quest system.
9. Press "reset" and then "run" on the sound level meter.
10. Press "rep" and then "dist" on Quest system.
11. Find the reading.
12. Change the filter on the sound level meter to the next harmonic, 4000 Hz.
13. Find the distortion reading of the second harmonic.

F. I checked the validity of the frequency by measuring the frequency on the oscilloscope as well as on the Quest meter.

The following instruments were used:

1. GSI 61 audiometer
2. Quest model 1800 sound level meter
3. Probe
4. Sound level meter microphone
5. Left earphone
6. Earphone weight
7. Double-banana cable
8. Mono-mini-cable
9. Oscilloscope

The following procedure was performed:

1. Attach the audiometer to the sound level meter via the left earphone.
2. Attach the output of the sound level meter to the input of the oscilloscope via the mono-mini-cable.
3. Connect the double-banana cable to channel A of the oscilloscope and attach the mono-mini-cable to the double-banana cable.
4. Turn on the oscilloscope.
5. Adjust the intensity of the sound wave so it is clearly shown in the frame.

6. Use the "trig level" dial to stop the motion of the sound wave.
7. Set 1 ms to equal one division square in the frame.
8. Determine if one cycle is equal to one division square.

Results

A. When calibrating the sound level meter, I put in a 1000-Hz tone at 114 dB SPL. The meter read 114.7 dB SPL.
B. When calibrating the intensity of the audiometer, I put 2000 Hz in the sound level meter at 70 dB HL. The meter read 80.2 dB SPL.
C. When calibrating the frequency of the audiometer, I put 2000 Hz in the Quest system via the sound level meter at 100 dB. The frequency read 1983 Hz.
D. When calibrating the rise and fall of the 2000-Hz tone at 100 dB HL, the Quest system read 33.0 ms for the fall and 36.0 ms for the rise.
E. When calibrating the distortion of the 2000-Hz tone at 100 dB HL, the Quest system read −L 39.0 with the filter at 2000 Hz. For the second harmonic distortion, the Quest system read "Lo" with the filter on 4000 Hz.
F. One cycle does fit in one division square on the oscilloscope for 1000 Hz.

Conclusions

A. The sound level meter had a deviation of only 0.7 dB SPL so the calibration was within normal limits.
B. The calibration of the intensity of the audiometer was within normal limits. The sound level meter read dB SPL and the audiometer reads dB HL so the difference between them for 2000 Hz should have been 11 dB. The measured difference was 10.2 dB which is within the allowable deviation of 2 dB.

C. The calibration of the frequency of the audiometer was within normal limits. The measured frequency deviated from 2000 Hz by 17 Hz, which is within the allowable deviation amount of 5%.
D. The rise and fall time for the 2000-Hz tone was around 30 ms which is normal for a tone.
E. The calibrated distortion for 2000 Hz was within normal limits. The ideal deviation is 43% which is higher than what was measured.
F. Since one cycle of the 1000 Hz tone fit in one division square on the oscilloscope which was equal to 1 ms, the results were normal.

II. Narrowband Noise Bandwidth Calibration

Purpose

To make sure the narrowband noise has an appropriate bandwidth for a specific frequency.

Methodology

A. Using the real-time analyzer

The following instruments were used:

1. Real-Time analyzer
2. GSI 61 audiometer
3. Quest model 1800 sound level meter
4. Probe
5. Sound-level meter microphone
6. Black "collar"
7. 6-cc coupler
8. Left earphone
9. Earphone weight
10. Oscilloscope
11. Mono-mini-cable
12. Double-banana cable

The following procedure was performed:

1. Attach the probe to the sound level meter and the microphone to the probe.
2. Place the black "collar" on the microphone.
3. Place the 6-cc coupler on the "black collar."
4. Put the left earphone on the coupler.
5. Hold down the earphone with the weight.
6. Turn the audiometer on a pure tone of 1000 Hz at 70 dB HL.
7. Connect the sound level meter to the real-time analyzer via a mono-mini-cable.
8. Attach the double-banana cable to the input port.
5. Get the narrowband noise on the real time analyzer by pressing button "restart" and then "arm."
6. Use the position trigger dial to find frequencies 3 dB below and above the frequency in question, 1000 Hz.
7. Subtract the lower frequency from the higher frequency to get the bandwidth.

B. Using biological testing

The following instruments were used:

1. Audiometer
2. Headphones
3. 5 voluntary subjects
4. Sound-proof booth

The following procedure was performed:

1. Place the subject in a sound-proof booth.
2. Place headphones on the subject.
3. Turn the audiometer on at a narrow-band noise of 1000 Hz at 30 dB in channel one and a 1000-Hz pure-tone in channel two at 50 dB.
4. Present both sounds in one ear.

5. Raise the narrowband noise 5 dB until the subject does not hear a tone.
6. Repeat this procedure for the following frequencies: 250 Hz, 500 Hz, 1500 Hz, 2000 Hz, 3000 Hz, 4000 Hz, and 6000 Hz.
7. Repeat steps 1 to 6 for four more subjects.

Results

A. When a 1000-Hz tone was placed in the real-time analyzer, a bandwidth of 80 Hz was found. The range was 961 Hz to 1041 Hz.
B. Due to time constraints, only one subject was tested. She was tested at all frequencies. Her results are as follows in Figure A–4.

Conclusion

A. The results were within normal limits because the bandwidth was within 100 Hz.
B. The results were within normal limits because the tone was masked around the level of the narrowband noise. This means the width of the narrowband noise did not exceed too far.

III. Middle Ear Analyzer Calibration

Purpose

To make sure immitance readings are accurate.

Methodology

The following instruments were used:

1. GSI Test calibration cavity
2. GSI TympStart middle ear analyzer

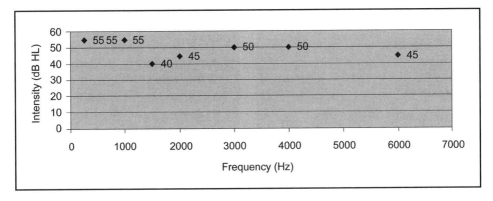

Figure A–4. *Effective masking for single subject.*

The following procedure was performed:

1. Attach the middle ear analyzer probes to the 2-cc cavity.
2. Turn on middle ear analyzer.
3. Press "tymp" to get the middle ear analyzers in "Y" mode at 226 Hz.
4. Press "start."
5. Find the ear canal volume Y.
6. Press "admittance" and then press "B."
7. Press "start."
8. Find the ear canal volume for B.
9. Change the frequency to 660 Hz by pressing "probe" and change the admittance to "Y"
10. Press "start" to find ear canal volume.
11. Press "admittance" and then press "B."
12. Press "start" to find ear canal volume.

Results

When finding the ear canal volume of Y at 226 Hz, the volume was 1.9 mmhos. For B, it was the same value, 1.9 mmhos.

When finding the ear canal volume of Y at 660 Hz, the volume was 5.5 mmhos. For B, the value was 5.4 mmhos.

Conclusions

As Y = immittance, G = acoustic conductance, and B = acoustic susceptance, at low frequencies such as 220 Hz, Y and B will have the same measurement because G is very low. When frequencies increase to 660 Hz, G gets bigger and so the values of Y and B will be different.

IV. Reflex Calibration Experiment

Purpose

To make sure there are no positive or negative artifacts in the immittance device.

Methodology

The following instruments were used:

1. GSI Test calibration cavity
2. GSI TympStart middle ear analyzer

The following procedure was performed:

1. Place tubes in 2-cc cavity.
2. Turn on middle ear analyzer.
3. Press "reflex."
4. Press "stimulus ear" and then press "ipsilateral."
5. Change the stimulus to a tone of 1000 Hz at 95 dB.
6. Press "start."
7. Press "present."

Results

A flat reflex response was created.

Conclusions

A flat response means that no artifacts were in the closed cavity. This is the intended and expected result. The GSI TympStart middle ear analyzer is a multiplex system, which means the stimulus and probe are presented at different times to prevent a distortion of the two tones. This creates an artifact-free system.

In a normal situation, only the probe will go through the filter. If the stimulus goes through the filter with it, the additional tone will boost the probe's intensity and the response will be additive. The will make the analyzer look like a reflex was present, when it really was not. If the two tones are put through the filter together and there is intermodulation distortion $(2f_1-f_2)$, a subtract artifact will be present.

V. Sound-Field Calibrations

Purpose

To make sure the warbled tones and narrowband noise are reaching the patient at accurate intensities.

Methodology

The following instruments were used:

1. GSI 61 audiometer
2. Sound-proof booth
3. Chair
4. Quest model 1800 sound-level meter
5. Probe
6. Sound level meter microphone

The following procedure was performed:

1. Turn the audiometer on a warbled FM tone of 1000 Hz at 70 dB.
2. Attach the probe to the sound level meter and the microphone to the probe.
3. Place the sound level meter on a chair angled at 45 degrees 3 feet from the speaker in the sound-proof booth.
4. Make sure the sound level meter is on a filter of 1000 Hz, between the intensities of 60 dB SPL and 120 dB SPL.
5. Press "reset" and then "run."
6. Measure the sound level meter reading.
7. Repeat the procedure with the audiometer outputting narrowband noise.

Results

The measured reading on the sound level meter for the warbled tone was 69 dB SPL. The measured reading for the narrowband noise was 70.8 dB SPL.

Conclusions

The calibrations of the warbled tone and the narrowband noise were both within normal limits. The measured intensity for both was just about equal to the audiometer ouput.

VI. Speech Calibration

Purpose

To make sure speech sounds are produced at the accurate intensity for research and clinical use.

Methodology

The following instruments were used:

1. GSI 61 audiometer

2. Headphones
3. CD of speech sounds
4. CD player
5. Sound-proof booth
6. Quest model 1800 sound-level meter
7. 6-cc coupler
8. Sound-level meter microphone
9. Probe
10. Headphone weight
11. Black "collar"

The following procedure was performed:

1. Put the speech CD in the CD player and attach the CD player to the audiometer.
2. Turn on the CD player.
3. Put the audiometer at 1000 Hz in External A so the input comes from the CD player.
3. When the tone begins, adjust the audiometer so the reference level reads 0. This will make the speech phonetically balanced.
4. Connect the audiometer headphones to the sound level meter by placing the probe on the meter, the microphone on the probe, the black "collar" on the microphone, the 6-cc coupler on the "collar," the headphones on the coupler, and the weight on the headphones.
5. Make sure the sound level meter is at 1000 Hz at 70 Hz.
6. Press "reset" and then press "run."
7. Read the measurement on the meter.
8. To calibrate speech noise in the sound-proof booth, adjust the output of the audiometer to speech noise of 70 dB HL. Place the sound-level meter in the sound-proof booth on a chair angled 45 degrees 3 feet from the speaker. Measure the reading of speech noise tone by pressing "reset" and "run" on the sound-level meter.

Results

When calibrating the speech CD, the sound level meter reading was 93 dB SPL. The speech noise was determined to be 85 dB in the sound-proof booth.

Conclusions

The reading should have a deviation of about 19.5 from the intensity on the audiometer because the recorded speech was at 20 dB SPL. As the deviation was 23 dB, then 5 dB must be added to the client's threshold as a correction factor. There was no deviation for the speech noise in the sound proof booth because a 15 dB difference is allowable, and that is exactly what was measured.

JENNA HOLKE, LAUREN ROUSE, AND RENA LEVY, CURRENT AUD STUDENTS (CUNY), 07/11

Calibration of Click Stimulus

Purpose

The purpose of this experiment is to calibrate the output of a transient acoustic signal (click) used for auditory brainstem response testing. It is critical for clinical audiologists to calibrate all equipment to ensure valid test results. When equipment is out of calibration, audiologists must know how to make the correct adjustments.

An auditory brainstem response is electrical activity generated in the auditory nerve and brainstem in response to transient sounds. The measurement of auditory brainstem responses can be used to help identify retrocochlear pathologies (otoneurologic) or to measure hearing thresholds.

As the intensity of the auditory evoked potential response is measured in microvolts, we need a stimulus that is capable of recruiting as many neurons as possible in order to permit us to see a response. Therefore, we need a transient stimulus such as a click, with a very short duration, that is, approximately 100 microseconds. Calibration of a click is different from calibration of pure-tone stimuli used to measure behavioral threshold. Such a stimulus has duration greater than 1 second. To calibrate pure-tone stimuli, we obtain the rms value. This value for a pure tone is defined as average sound pressure (SPL) over time $rms = \{S(P^2)/N\}^{1/2}$ where P represents instantaneous sound-pressure value, N is the sum of the instantaneous values over time. In order to obtain SPL rms, SLM should be set to Fast mode.

Therefore, the method used to measure the intensity of a click stimulus is based on the calculation of instantaneous peak SPL (pSPL). The formula used to measure pSPL is $pSPL = 20 \ log \ (P_{max}/P_{ref})$ where P_{max} refers to the instantaneous peak in µPa and P_{ref} is equivalent to 20 µPa.

ISO 2010 recommends behavioral threshold testing and measurement of transient acoustic stimuli with a sound level meter using the "peak hold" function. This function essentially assesses the largest instantaneous pressure of the signal, locks onto this peak value and holds it. This gives the sound level meter sufficient time to make an accurate measure.

Equipment

Auditory Evoked Potentials System: Nicolet Spirit

Sound Level Meter: Quest 1800

Calibration Piston: Quest Technology QC-10/QC-20

6-cc Coupler: Quest Model EC-9A

2-cc Coupler: Grason Stradler

400-g Weight

Insert Earphones: Ear Tone 3A

Headphones: TDH 39

Procedures

Calibrate Sound Level Meter

Before using the sound-level meter to calibrate other devices, it is critical to calibrate the sound level meter itself to ensure accurate readings. The sound-level meter has a preamplifier, which increases the voltage from the microphone, and raises it up to a level that the unit can analyze. Once the preamplifier module and the microphone are added to the body of the sound-level meter, the meter can be calibrated using the Quest calibration piston. This ensures that the sound level meter has valid readings, before it is used to calibrate other devices.

1. Check battery level on piston and sound level meter.
2. Before calibrating, be sure that the sound level meter is at the correct settings:

   Mode: SPL

   Response: Fast

   Range: 60 to 120 dB

   Weighting: Linear

   Filter: 1000 Hz

   Manual

3. Turn the piston on to 114 dB at 1000 Hz and place on top of sound level meter microphone (can also be calibrated at 94 dB or 250 Hz).
4. Read output from sound level meter; should match input (Figure A–5).
5. During our study, the sound-level meter output measured 116.2 dB, so the meter was adjusted until it read 114 dB. The output of the sound-level meter can be adjusted using a small screwdriver to adjust a lever on the side of the meter. Turning counter-clockwise will decrease the output level; continue to turn until the output matches the designated input. After adjustments, the sound level meter read 114 dB, which matches the signal input (Figure A–6).

Determine 0 dB nHL

Auditory brainstem responses are measured in dB nHL, which represents an average normal hearing level. In order to establish the dB that will be represented by 0 dB nHL, it is necessary to obtain normative data.

When establishing norms it is important to control for age and gender, as both can affect auditory evoked potentials.

For our study, 10 adult females between 18 and 29 years of age, were tested to establish clinic norms for 0 dB nHL using TDH 39 headphones and 10 adult males between 18 and 29 years of age using Ear Tone 3A insert earphones. Participants were screened for behavioral thresholds of 15 dB HL at octave frequencies 250 to 8000 Hz, bilaterally. Participants were then tested for behavioral click thresholds. Remember that this was a learning experience intended to provide practice in performing a number of experiments. If we had truly designed the experiments to provide normative data for headphones and inserts, we would have included both younger and older females and younger and older males in both groups.

Set Up ABR Stimulus for Headphones

1. Open Nicolet Program
2. Select "Utility"
   a. Select *Phone* and nHL, click "ok"
3. Select on "AEP"

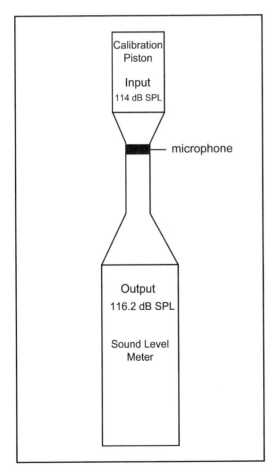

Figure A–5. *Calibration system coupled to SLM.*

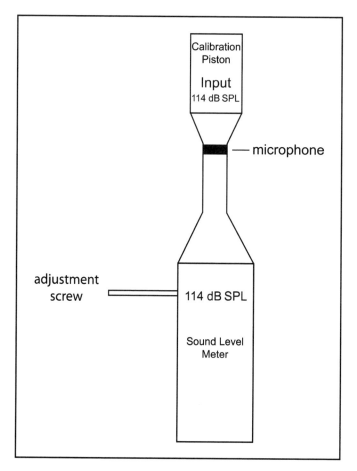

Figure A–6. *Adjustment of SLM to meet the calibration piston's levels.*

4. Select on "Setup" and "Load Protocol"
5. Select "ABR-AS" and click "Load"
6. Select "Stim" and highlight "Level" to adjust for threshold testing

Results

Data for females using TD39 headphones:

1. Participant #1: 20 dB
2. Participant #2: 25 dB
3. Participant #3: 25 dB
4. Participant #4: 25 dB
5. Participant #5: 25 dB
6. Participant #6: 25 dB

7. Participant #7: 20 dB
8. Participant #8: 20 dB
9. Participant #9: 20 dB
10. Participant #10: 25 dB

The average threshold response was 23 dB, which we then equated to 0 dB nHL using TD39 headphones.

Set Up ABR Stimulus for Insert Earphones:

1. Open Nicolet Program
2. Select "Utility"
   a. Select ***Insert*** and nHL, click "ok"

3. Select on "AEP"
4. Select on "Setup" and "Load Protocol"
5. Select "ABR-AS" and click "Load"
6. Select "Stim" and highlight "Level" to adjust for threshold testing

Results

Data for males using Ear Tone 3A earphones:

1. Participant #1: 5 dB
2. Participant #2: 10 dB
3. Participant #3: 10 dB
4. Participant #4: 5 dB
5. Participant #5: 15 dB
6. Participant #6: 5 dB
7. Participant #7: 10 dB
8. Participant #8: 0 dB
9. Participant #9: 10dB
10. Participant #10: 5 dB

The average threshold response was 7.5 dB, which we then equated to 0 dB nHL using Ear Tone 3A insert earphones.

Calibrating the Click with TDH 39 Headphones

The click stimulus was then measured at 30 dB nHL (Figure A–7).

1. Before calibrating, be sure that the sound level meter is in the correct settings:

   Mode: Maximum

   dB Range: 20 to 80 (lowest)

   Weighting: Linear

   Response: Peak

   Filter: Off

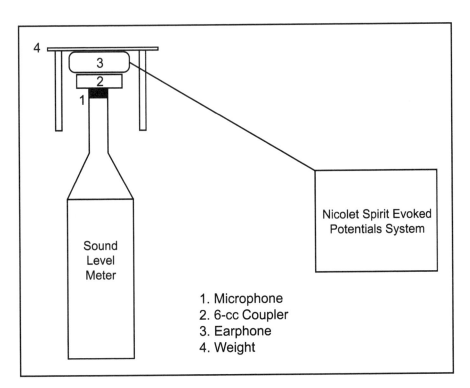

Figure A–7. Calibration assembly for click using TDH 39 headphones.

2. Add the pre-amplifier module to the body of the sound level meter
3. Add the microphone
4. Add the 6-cc coupler
5. Add the headphone
6. Add 400 grams
7. Present the click from the Nicolet system
8. Press "reset" and "run"

The click played at 30 dB nHL displayed a readout of 82.8 dB on the sound level meter. Thus, we equate 30 dB nHL into 82.8 dB for headphones.

Calibrating the Click with Ear Tone 3A Earphones

The click stimulus was then measured at 30 dB nHL (Figure A–8).

1. Before calibrating, be sure that the sound level meter is in the correct settings:

   Mode: Minimum

   dB Range: 20 to 80 (lowest)

   Weighting: Linear

   Response: Peak

   Filter: Off

2. Add the preamplifier module to the body of the sound-level meter
3. Add the microphone
4. Add the 2-cc coupler
5. Add the insert ear phone into the 2-cc coupler
6. Present the click from the Nicolet system
7. Press "reset" and "run"

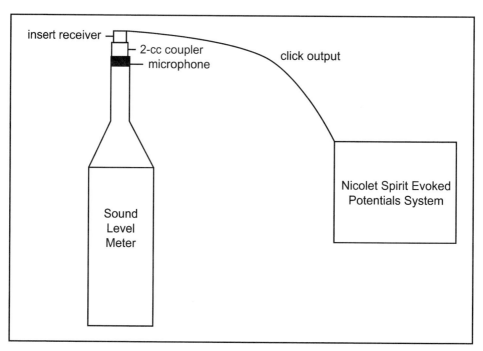

Figure A–8. Calibration of click using Ear Tone 3A Earphones.

The click played at 30 dB nHL displayed readout of 67.2 dB on the sound level meter. Thus, we equate 30 dB nHL into 67.2 dB for insert earphones.

Conclusions

The click stimulus was calibrated using behavioral threshold testing and the peak function of the sound level meter. By establishing and recording normative data, future clinicians need only compare the transient signal output to the current results. Based on our results, if a 30 dB nHL click reads 82.8 dB on the sound-level meter, future clinicians will know that the click is calibrated properly under headphones. Similarly, if a 30 dB nHL click is properly calibrated under insert earphones, the output of the sound-level meter should read 67.2 dB. It is imperative that audiologists are capable of properly calibrating equipment to obtain accurate results when testing patients.

Digital Integrated Circuits

In the first section of this appendix, the electromechanical concept of a digital integrated circuit was adapted and modified from *Getting Started in Electronics* by Forrest M. Mims III (2006). The simplest digital integrated circuit contains a power source and multiple gates, which can number in the hundreds of thousands. A gate is a pair of electronically controlled switches, each of which is either in the *open* position (switch is off) or in the *closed* position (switch is on). Before digital integrated circuits employed in digital instrumentation are discussed, the electromechanical concept of some gates will be presented. With the *Switch-AND* gate, the light bulb lights up only when switches A and B are both closed (switch on). The light bulb does not light up when switches A and B are both open (switch off, shown at the top of Figure B–1); when switch A is open (switch off) and switch B is closed (switch on); or when switch A is closed (switch on) and switch B is open (switch off). With the *Switch-OR* gate (see Figure B–1), the light bulb lights up when one of the two switches is closed (switch on). Thus, the light bulb lights up when switch A is closed (and switch B is either open or

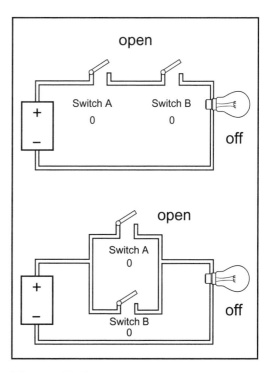

Figure B–1. *The top figure represents the* Switch-AND *gate (with switches* A *and* B *open and therefore off, representing the 00 inputs controlling the switching settings); and the bottom figure represents the* Switch-OR *gate (with switches* A *and* B *open and therefore off, representing the 00 inputs controlling the switch settings). The light bulb is not illuminated with either gate.*

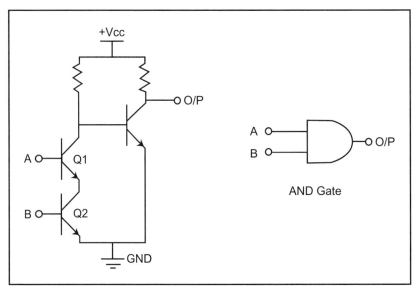

Figure B–2. *The left illustration represents the electrical circuit for an* AND *gate. The right illustration is the symbol for the electrical circuit for an* AND *gate.*

closed), or when switch *B* is closed (and switch *A* is either open or closed). The light bulb does not light up when both switches are open (as shown at the bottom of Figure B–1). The *Switch-AND* gate in Figure B–1 essentially functions like a DC circuit with in-series resistors (switches), whereas the *Switch-OR* gate in Figure B–1 functions like a DC circuit with in-parallel resistors (switches) (see Chapter 3).

In a digital integrated circuit such as that found in a computer, the binary number 0 inputs to an open switch (switch off) and the binary number 1 inputs to a closed switch (switch on). Table B–1 shows the output for the switch inputs with the *Switch-AND* gate and the *Switch-OR* gate.

The 0 and 1 combinations are inputs controlling the switch settings (on versus off), which lead to a gate output that is a binary number (see Chapter 8).

Computer components such as CPU chips, RAM memory chips, and other digital integrated circuits use more technologically advanced switches in the gates.

Many of these gates (such as the *Switch-AND* gate, which is more commonly referred to as an *AND* gate, and the *Switch-OR* gate, which is more commonly referred to as an *OR* gate) can be connected in a specific order to run more complex circuits that operate the various instrumentation. Figure B–2 shows a simplified circuit and symbol for a basic, two-input *AND* gate.

The binary inputs *A* and *B* are connected to the bases of transistors *Q1* and *Q2* (see Chapter 6), respectively; the transistors essentially represent advanced forms of the switches shown in Figure B–1. With an *AND* gate, when *A* = 1, transistor *Q1* turns on and enables current flow through it. When *A* = 0, transistor *Q1* turns off and stops the current flow (see Table B–1). Similarly, when *B* = 1, transistor *Q2* turns on, and when *B* = 0, *Q2* turns off (see Table B–1). With an in-series connection of transistors *Q1* and *Q2*, no current flows occur if either *Q1* is off (*A* = 0) or *Q2* is off (*B* = 0), or if both *Q1* and *Q2* are off (*A* = 0 and *B* = 0); all of these options result in a 0 output (*O/P*) (see Table B–1). The current will flow through the circuit only when both *Q1* and *Q2* are on (*A* = 1 and *B* = 1), yielding output *O/P* = 1 (see Table B–1).

Figure B–3 shows a simplified circuit and symbol for a basic, two-input *OR* gate. As for an *AND* gate, the binary inputs are connected to the bases of transistors *Q1* and *Q2*. Similar to the *AND* gate, the

Table B–1. Binary Inputs to the *Switch-AND* and *Switch-OR* Gates, Associated Switch Settings for These Inputs, Gate Outputs, and Impact on Current Flow

	Switch A		Switch B		
Gate/Input	*Off*	*On*	*Off*	*On*	*Output (O/P)*
Switch-AND					
00	✓		✓		0 (no current flow)
01	✓			✓	0 (no current flow)
10		✓	✓		0 (no current flow)
11		✓		✓	1 (current flow)
Switch-OR					
00	✓		✓		0 (no current flow)
01	✓			✓	1 (current flow)
10		✓	✓		1 (current flow)
11		✓		✓	1 (current flow)

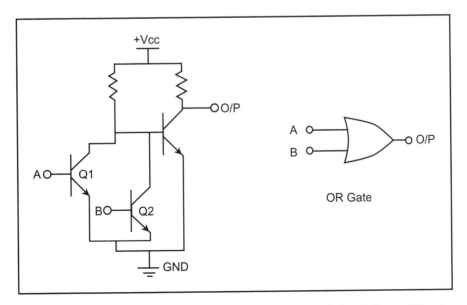

Figure B–3. *The left illustration represents the electrical circuit for an* OR *gate. The right illustration is the symbol for the electrical circuit for an* OR *gate.*

inputs *A* and *B* are connected to the inputs of *Q1* and *Q2*. However, the connection of transistors *Q1* and *Q2* is in-parallel rather than in-series. Thus, if either *Q1* is on (*A* = 1) or *Q2* is on (*B* = 1), the output *O/P* = 1 and current flows through the circuit (see Table B–1). The output *O/P* is also equal to 1 if both *Q1* and *Q2* are turned on (*A* = 1 and *B* = 1). If *Q1* is off (*A* = 0) and *Q2* is off (*B* = 0), the output *O/P* = 0 and no current flow occurs (see Table B–1).

REFERENCE

Mims, F. M., III. (2006). *Getting started in electronics*. Lincolnwood, IL: Master Publishing.

Index